AN INTRODUCTION TO
ASTRODYNAMICS

This volume is published in association with
the Academic Press serial publication
Advances in Space Science
edited by Frederick I. Ordway, III

AN INTRODUCTION TO

ASTRODYNAMICS

ROBERT M. L. BAKER, Jr. and MAUD W. MAKEMSON
Department of Astronomy, University of California, Los Angeles, California

1960 ACADEMIC PRESS · NEW YORK AND LONDON

ACADEMIC PRESS INC.
111 FIFTH AVENUE
NEW YORK 3, N. Y.

United Kingdom Edition
Published by
ACADEMIC PRESS INC. (LONDON) LTD.
BERKELEY SQUARE HOUSE, LONDON W. 1

Library of Congress Catalog Card Number: 60-14268

First Printing, 1960
Second Printing, 1962
Third Printing, 1963

PRINTED IN THE UNITED STATES OF AMERICA

To Samuel Herrick

This work represents, in part, research sponsored by the United States Air Force under contract AF 49(638)-498 monitored at UCLA by the Air Force Office of Scientific Research; the United States Army under contract DA-04-495-ORD-1389 monitored at Aeronutronic by the Army Ballistic Missile Agency; and by the National Aeronautics and Space Administration under contracts NAS-5-76 and NAS-1-204 monitored at Aeronutronic by the Langley Research Center.

PREFACE

The following text is partially an outgrowth of course notes for an intensive short summer course in astrodynamics presented annually by Dr. Baker at the University of California, Los Angeles. This course in turn is derived from a similar semester-long course initiated by Samuel Herrick in 1946. For this reason the text owes much of its organization and content to Dr. Herrick's pioneering efforts in astrodynamics. The historical roots of astrodynamics in celestial mechanics suggest a background discussion of minor planets and comets. These areas, especially, represent the researches of Dr. Makemson.

Astrodynamics is rapidly becoming an engineering subject and, consequently, the text is directed particularly toward the engineer or other non-astronomer. In this regard, this work is meant to serve both as a brief introduction to the history, nomenclature, and *practical* application of astrodynamics and as a key or handbook of specific astrodynamic techniques. The book is organized on the basis of two broad divisions: *Fundamentals* and *More Detailed Analyses.* The chapters included under fundamentals contain discussions of general laws, minor planets, comets, geometry, and the astrodynamic constants. A mastery of this division would allow for an approximate solution of most astrodynamic problems. Included in the more detailed analyses are chapters concerned with orbit-determination, n-body problem, orbit computation, nongravitational forces, observation theory, and applications to interplanetary orbits. Mastery of this division would provide for more definitive and sophisticated orbit analyses.

At present there exists no true introductory textbook in the field of astrodynamics that has been derived from or could be utilized in a college-level course. The present volume is meant to serve such a purpose and stresses clarity and the practical application of astrodynamics. In this same regard a completely general approach is sacrificed for more specific approaches that can be clearly identified with contemporary space-vehicle problems. This same philosophy has been applied to the question of exercises. Formal exercises are grouped at the end of the text on page 329. Also the division of the text concerned with *Fundamentals* has been illustrated by examples presented in Chapters 2 and 3. Nevertheless, the instructor has been given the latitude to further illustrate these basic principles by means of their application to whatever astronautical system is currently of interest during the period of the course presentation. Based on the modern demands of space science a different philosophy underlies the choice of exercises in the division of the text concerned with *More Detailed Analyses*. As the arts of computer technology and programming become more advanced it becomes less profitable to drill the potential astrodynamicist in hand numerical computation and such drills are not given emphasis. The true understanding and usefulness of these more detailed methods must ultimately lie in the practical application of them, via programs on high speed electronic digital computers, to actual problems. Consequently, the reader's time would probably be most efficiently spent in deriving those relationships whose origins are not obvious to him and postpone the formal application of the methods until the time when a high-speed computer is available.

The present volume is not intended to give the reader a complete theoretical background in celestial mechanics—a number of other texts in classical mechanics and celestial mechanics already serve this purpose. Furthermore, the more general and all-inclusive approach, which is of particular advantage in graduate study, has already been developed in Dr. Herrick's text. Because of this, and since practical applications of specific techniques are emphasized, the all-inclusive approach has been de-emphasized.

Most of the analyses are derived from first principles and the glossary of definitions provides a self-contained key to all of the astronomical nomenclature utilized in the text. Thus the reader is not expected to have had a prior background in classical mechanics or astronomy and, for that matter, a sufficient prerequisite for the book would be freshman and sophomore courses in physics or engineering and in mathematics (preferably through calculus). For the more advanced reader the rather comprehensive list of references should serve as a key to the literature (up to 1960) for the purpose of further research. Furthermore, portions of Chapters 6, 8, and 9 are specifically directed to the more advanced reader and should even be of interest to the graduate student.

Although this book is specifically designed for a short intensive summer course in astrodynamics, it could be utilized in an introductory semester-length junior or senior year university course. For such a purpose, half of the course could be drawn from Chapters 1 through 5 (excluding Section 4.5 on the more advanced selenographic transformations); a quarter of the course drawn from Chapters 7, 10, and 11; and the last quarter might concern applications taken from Chapter 12 (interplanetary) and perhaps Chapter 4 of reference 2 (lunar). A second semester course could be organized around Chapter 6 (one-half semester) and Chapters 8 and 9 for the second half of the semester.

The authors wish to acknowledge the extensive services of Jan Baker who typed the final manuscript and of Jean Swain who typed many of the rough drafts. Mary P. Francis aided us in the preparation of the list of references and, along with Bernard Cohlan, Lynn Averill, and Jeannine Arsenault, read through the manuscript and added many worthwhile suggestions. We are also indebted to George B. Westrom, Paul Koskela, C. G. Hilton, and Edward Pitkin who provided us with technical material for many of the subsections. A number of the formulas included in these subsections were extracted from *Astrodynamics*.

ROBERT M. L. BAKER, JR.
MAUD W. MAKEMSON

June, 1960

CONTENTS

ERRATA

Page	Line	Instead of:	Read:
xi	Following 1.5		1.6 Astrodynamic Units
4	4	on page 285,	on pages 285–312,
4	18	the planets	any two planets
6	18	Radar will undoubtedly change	Radar has now greatly changed
9; 10	15; 1, 2	vernal equinox . . . . A more detailed	vernal equinox, e.g., 1950.0, which is the beginning of the Besselian year (the annus fictus), determined by the rule that the right ascension of the fictitious mean sun is exactly 18^h40^m. A more detailed
16	Following Eq. (11)		1.6. Astrodynamic Units
16	11	there often arises	there may arise
17	Running head	1.5. EQUATIONS OF ABSOLUTE AND RELATIVE MOTION	1.6. ASTRODYNAMIC UNITS
20	2	the perturbative effect	the gravitational effect
30	5	triangle solution	triangle and straight-line solutions
32	20	$\tau \triangleq k_s(t - t_0)$, the	$\tau \triangleq k_s(t - t_0)$, as shown on page 13, the
34	23	$\dot{s}_1^2 = \frac{2}{1.05} - \frac{1}{2}$.	$\dot{s}_1^2 = \frac{2}{1.05} - \frac{1}{2.025}$, since $2a_T = 3 + 1.05 = 4.05$.
43	21	radii vectors	radii vectores
45	10	last section	last chapter,
46	12	circular satellite or	circular satellite speed at unit distance or
46	Last line	Nevertheless,	Consequently,
58	2	astronomical parlance:	astronomical practice:

Page	Line	Instead of:	Read:
67	Last line	$\dot{\varrho} = \dot{\varrho}\mathbf{L} = \dot{\mathbf{r}} + \dot{\mathbf{R}}$	$\dot{\varrho} = \dot{\varrho}\mathbf{L} + \rho\dot{\mathbf{L}} = \dot{\mathbf{r}} + \dot{\mathbf{R}}$
69	Eq. (30)	cosh cos$A$ (3 times) cos ϕ sinh (2 times) cosh sin$A$ (2 times) sin ϕ sinh (1 time)	cos h cos A cos ϕ sin h cos h sin A sin ϕ sin h
74	16	carried out.	carried out (see footnote on page 92).
93	29	masses	mass
93	30	were independently . . . prod-	was independently . . . prod-
93	31	ucts of the	uct of the
96	5, 6	semi-major axes	semi-axes
96	11	is given	are given
101	Table IX,	Rabe[c]	Rabe, W.[c]
	col. 2	Rabe	Rabe, W.
106	13	"scale height."	"scale height," H_{SH}.
106	17	$\rho_0 = \frac{P_0 m_0}{(T_m)_0} R^*.$	$\rho_0 = \frac{P_0 m_0}{(T_m)_0 R^*}.$
108	19	apsides,	nodes,
117	Eq. (90)	$k\sqrt{\mu}(t - T) = qD + D^3/6.$	$M_p = k\sqrt{\mu}(t - T) = qD + D^3/6.$
118	4	parabola $\tilde{M} \triangleq D$, and	parabola $\tilde{M} = M_p$, and
119	1	representations	ephemerides
119	1	orbit	ephemeris
129	34	$\Delta\rho = \frac{\partial\rho}{\partial(1/a)}\Delta(1/a) + \frac{\partial^2\rho}{\partial(1/a)^2}\Delta(1/a)^2 + \ldots$	$\Delta\rho = \frac{\partial\rho}{\partial(1/a)}\Delta(1/a) + \frac{1}{2!}\frac{\partial^2\rho}{\partial(1/a)^2}\Delta(1/a)^2 + \ldots$
139	15	determined.	determined (cf. page 134).
155	16	The equation of motion takes the form	The equation for the sum of forces acting on the satellite is:

Page	Line	Instead of:	Read:
157	Eq. (157)	$n = \dfrac{2\pi}{P_☾}.$	$n = \dfrac{2\pi}{P_☾}$ radians per mean solar minute.
157	Eq. (158)	$\dot{s} = \dfrac{\eta a_☾ n}{k_e} = \dfrac{\eta\sqrt{\mu}}{\sqrt{a_☾}}.$	$\dot{s} = \dfrac{\eta a_☾ n}{k_e} = \dfrac{\eta\sqrt{\mu}}{\sqrt{a_☾}}$ surface-circular-satellite speed.
162	Eq. (164)	$\dfrac{d^2x}{d\tau^2} = \ddot{x} + \dot{x}^{\backprime}.$	$\dfrac{d^2x}{d\tau^2} = \ddot{x} + \dot{x}^{\backprime}, \qquad x \to y, z.$
166	11	0.058,834,470	0.058,834,478,0
178	25	For any time	For any time on an osculating two-body orbit,
179	10	$\dot{H}^{\backprime} = \mathbf{r} \cdot \dot{\mathbf{r}}^{\backprime}$	$\dot{H} = \mathbf{r} \cdot \dot{\mathbf{r}}/r$
191	1	$\Delta\mathbf{U} = \Delta l\mathbf{V}$ and $\Delta\mathbf{U} = \Delta b\mathbf{W}$,	$\Delta\mathbf{U} = \Delta l\mathbf{V} + \Delta b\mathbf{W}$,
191	6	(see Fig. 32)	(see Fig. 21 and page 163)
195	22	indicated.	indicated (for $v < 1$).
228	1	speed v relative	speed v $(v \to \dot{s})$ relative
228	3	$x_1 = \alpha(x_2 - vt_2)$,	$x_1 = \alpha(x_2 - vt_2), \qquad v \to \dot{s}$,
229	1	$c^2\beta^2 - v^2\alpha^2 = c^2$,	$c^2\beta^2 - v^2\alpha^2 = c^2, \qquad v \to \dot{s}$,
229	6	$\beta^2 \triangleq 1/(1 - v^2/c^2)$ proves	$\beta^2 \triangleq 1/(1 - v^2/c^2),\ v \to \dot{s}$, proves
229	9	values of v.	values of v $(v \to \dot{s})$.
229	Eq. (269)	$L_2 = \sqrt{1 - \dfrac{v^2}{c^2}}\, L_1.$	$L_2 = \sqrt{1 - \dfrac{v^2}{c^2}}\, L_1, \qquad v \to \dot{s}.$
229	Eq. (270)	$\sqrt{1 - v^2/c^2}.$	$\sqrt{1 - v^2/c^2}, \qquad v \to \dot{s}.$
229	Eq. (271)	$m = \dfrac{m_0}{\sqrt{1 - v^2/c^2}},$	$m = \dfrac{m_0}{\sqrt{1 - v^2/c^2}}, \qquad v \to \dot{s},$
246	Last line	*Catadioptic.*	*Catadioptric.*
286	28	*Catadioptic:*	*Catadioptric:*
327	Ref. 147	Bain, W. A.	Baum, W. A.
341	18	Bain, W. A.,	Baum, W. A.,

FUNDAMENTALS AND BACKGROUND

1 INTRODUCTION

Astrodynamics is the engineering or practical application of celestial mechanics and other allied fields such as high-altitude aerodynamics; geophysics; and electromagnetic, optimization, observation, navigation, and propulsion theory to the contemporary problems of space vehicles. It is not meant to include conventional aerodynamics or booster propulsion theory.*

The following chapters introduce the reader to those aspects of astrodynamics that have found recent emphasis in the astrodynamicist's efforts to cope with the contemporary problems of space vehicle trajectories. The text is separated into two general sections: "Fundamentals and Background" and "More Detailed Analyses." Included in the first section are chapters concerned with the introduction, minor planet and comet background, geometry and coordinate systems, and astrodynamic constants. The second section includes chapters involving orbit determination; the n-body problem, special and general perturbations, nongravitational forces (including a brief discussion of low-density drag and sputtering, low-thrust forces, electromagnetic forces, and relativistic effects), observation theory, and concludes with a chapter on applications to interplanetary orbits. (The application of astrodynamics to lunar orbits is discussed by Baker[2].)

Because astrodynamics is primarily an applied science, the following development will not proceed along the lines of the often impractical, albeit sophisticated, techniques of Hamiltonian mechanics. Although Hamiltonian mechanics has been applied effectively by Smart[3], Vinti[4], and others, it has generally proven to be vastly too complex and cumbersome for most practical applications. In fine, astrodynamics, unlike quantum me-

* Astrodynamics often has a more comprehensive definition in which it is also taken to be concerned with minor planet, meteoritic, and cometary orbit theory and attitude dynamics.

chanics, does not find a clear and convenient formulation in terms of Hamiltonian mechanics.

The reader who is uninitiated into astronomical parlance will find that a frequent reference to the glossary, which is included on page 285, will be indispensable.

1.1. Historical Background

When the first spaceship leaves the Earth on an interplanetary flight bound for Mars or Venus, its voyage will be the logical outgrowth of theoretical celestial mechanics as applied to astronomical subjects during the 300 years since Newton discovered his epoch-making law of gravitation. With his newly invented calculus and fundamental laws of motion, Newton proved that Kepler's empirical laws of planetary motion (1609) follow as a necessary consequence of the law of gravitation. Kepler's laws are:

(i) Every planet moves on an ellipse with the Sun at one focus.

(ii) Every planet moves in such a way that its radius vector sweeps over equal areas in equal times.

(iii) The squares of the periods of revolution of the planets about the Sun are to each other as the cubes of their mean distances.

Newton extended these important laws to all conics and modified the third law to include the planetary masses. To Newton, therefore, we owe the foundation of theoretical celestial mechanics.

In spite of the difference in approach, there are striking parallels between the situations encountered in classical celestial mechanics and the current problems of space navigation. Lunar theory provides an important example. The great astronomers of the 18th century were deeply concerned with the problem of reducing to mathematical order the puzzling departures of the Moon from elliptic motion that had been observed since the time of Hipparchus (150 B.C.). Their work prepared the way for an understanding of the complexities of Earth satellite motions. The study of the Moon necessitated development of valuable methods of "general perturbations" (discussed in Chapter 9) in order to account for the disturbing action of the Sun. So elusive was the solution of the lunar enigma, in fact, that Clairaut (1749) was on the point of adding an r^{-3} term to Newton's inverse square law when he suddenly chanced upon the true explanation of the motion of the Moon's orbit. The great genius of Newton is indicated by the subsequent discovery in one of his unpublished manuscripts of a complete solution of this problem. Seventeenth century interest in lunar theory was stimulated by the demand of navigators for accurate tables of the Moon's position to be used in finding their longitude at sea, before the invention of accurate chronometers, and by the substantial prizes offered by the English government and some learned societies.

The revolutions of the moons of Jupiter have also contributed valuable data to modern satellite orbit determinations, especially those of the inner satellites, which are subject to large perturbations due to the oblateness of the "great planet" in the same way that Earth-satellites are affected by the Earth's departure from sphericity.

The first minor planet, Ceres, discovered January 1, 1801, ushered in a century of great activity in gravitational astronomy. The Moon's vagaries had made difficult demands upon the ingenuity of astronomers, but there had never been any danger of its disappearing from view. The first minor planet, however, was lost in the Sun's rays after only 41 days, and there was every reason to believe that it would never be recognized again. "Nowhere in the annals of astronomy," Gauss[5] wrote, "do we meet with so great an opportunity, and a greater one could hardly be imagined for showing most strikingly the value of this problem [of calculating the orbit of a newly discovered object] than in this crisis and urgent necessity when all hope of discovering in the heavens this planetary atom among innumerable small stars after nearly a year, rested upon a sufficient approximation to the orbit." Gauss met the challenge with the first crude method of determining an orbit without hypothesis as to the period or eccentricity of the elliptical orbit and Ceres was rediscovered on the last day of the year.

To meet the need for a definitive orbit determination, methods of both special and general perturbations to account for the attractions of the principal planets were developed by Gauss and others. Such methods are discussed in Chapters 8 and 9. The new members of the solar system provide an unlimited field for the application of Newtonian mechanics and the testing of new ideas and theories. Every minor planet was different from every other. Some results of these developments that are of inestimable value to astrodynamics today are the determination of more accurate values of the masses of the planets including the Earth–Moon system, the length of the "astronomical unit" or Earth's mean distance from the Sun, and the use of minor-planet orbit analysis as a test bed for various computational techniques. Furthermore, the discovery, from observations of the nearer astronomical bodies, of the variability of the Earth's rate of rotation has revolutionized our practice regarding "time."

As it happened, to the great benefit of astrodynamics, the extensive advances of celestial mechanics were brought to a high degree of perfection before the vast possibilities of another of Newton's discoveries—the dispersion of light in the spectrum—were realized, and the science of astrophysics diverted the attention of astronomers from the determination of orbital motions.

A study of the motions of meteors by such men as Whipple, Thomas, and Jacchia has contributed information pertinent to satellite orbits in regard to the temperature and density of the Earth's atmosphere and motion in a resisting medium. Comets have furnished much valuable data, especially in the effect of perturbations produced by a close approach to a major planet such as Jupiter (cf. Williams[6]). There are still, moreover, a few unsolved problems in the theory of comets and their motions that may or may not have a bearing on interplanetary travel.

One important difference between astronomical problems and those relating to man-made vehicles must be borne in mind. In observing positions of bodies in the solar system—minor planets, comets, and so on—there has been up to the present no possibility of measuring the *distance* directly. Radar will undoubtedly change this situation for bodies that approach within a few million miles, like Venus at its closest approach or *inferior conjunction*, Mars at its closest approach or *opposition*, and a few minor planets such as Eros and Icarus; but in general the determination of a heliocentric (Sun-centered) orbit from observations of a newly discovered object requires the derivation of its distances from the Earth and Sun by a laborious process (see Section 6.3).

In the case of an interplanetary flight of a spaceship, on the other hand, the problem is simplified. If the vehicle is bound for Venus, the design distances will be known near the Earth's orbit at injection and near Venus at arrival. The heliocentric distances at these points are thus predetermined, and from them the elements of the heliocentric orbit can be derived. In the observations of artificial satellites, the distances above the Earth's surface are found from range data, and can be converted to geocentric (Earth-centered) distances by a simple transformation of coordinates. Thus the laborious calculation of distance is avoided.

And so, when a payload is carried on a voyage to Mars, Venus, or the Moon, its trajectory will have been calculated with mathematical precision by the same formulas that astronomers have been developing for the past 300 years, now adapted to modern electronic computers. The transition from predicting the motions of the Moon to predicting those of artificial satellites, and from the determination of the orbits of small planets and eccentric comets to that of man-made vehicles through the vast reaches of the solar system, has been readily accomplished through adapting the well-tested laws of celestial mechanics to the engineering demands of the modern space age.

The remainder of this introductory section will endeavor to acquaint the engineer or nonastronomer with some of the jargon and fundamental principles of astronomy—a knowledge of which is indispensable to any serious study of astrodynamics. In this regard it is again noted that many perhaps unfamiliar terms may be found defined in the glossary and the reader is invited to make frequent reference to it.

1.2. Elements of a Two-Body Orbit

The paths traced out by most space vehicles closely approximate two-body orbits, and a brief discussion of such orbits provides a logical introduction to the discipline of astrodynamics.

Formulating Newton's universal law of gravitation (in relative coordinates) into its x, y, and z components, (see Section 1.4)

$$d^2x/dt^2 = -\mu k^2 x/r^3,$$

$$d^2y/dt^2 = -\mu k^2 y/r^3,$$

and

$$d^2z/dt^2 = -\mu k^2 z/r^3, \qquad (1)$$

where μ is the sum of the masses of the attracting bodies, k^2 is the gravitational constant, and $r^2 = x^2 + y^2 + z^2$, we find that there exist three second-order differential equations. Consequently, there are six arbitrary constants of integration. Conventionally these constants or *elements* are defined as the semimajor axis, a; the eccentricity, e; and the time of perifocal passage, T; the angle of inclination, i; the longitude of the ascending node, Ω; and the argument of perifocus, ω (see Fig. 1). These elements may be replaced by any other six quantities: these may be the three components of position and three components of velocity, or, as will be demonstrated in Chapter 6, certain vectorial parameters. The chief value of these vectorial parameters lies in two areas: (i) they allow simplification of the problem of representing observations and (ii) they can be effectively utilized as integrable quantities in the perturbative procedures to be discussed in Chapter 8 because such elements may change more slowly in response to "perturbative forces" (to be defined presently).

It is appropriate at this point to define the x, y, and z coordinate system that we are here considering, as well as some of the standard nomenclature of astronomy. In almost all orbit problems an *equatorial* coordinate system is preferred because one finds that the positions of the stars, planets, and the Moon are almost always tabulated in terms of such a system in almanacs, catalogs, and ephemerides. (This system along with others will be

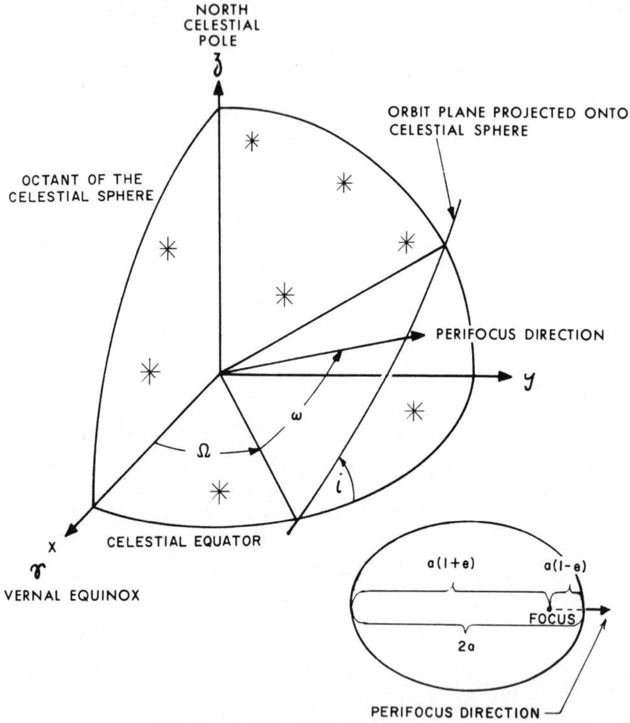

FIG. 1. Elements of the orbit.

defined in more detail in Chapter 4.) Such a coordinate system is defined by an x-axis directed towards the vernal equinox, a z-axis directed towards the north celestial pole, and a y-axis directed so as to form a right-handed orthogonal set (see Figs. 1 and 2). The *vernal equinox* (symbolized by ♈, the ram's horns) is defined as that point on the celestial sphere where the apparent orbit of the Sun crosses the celestial equator from the south to the north (at the time of equal days and nights—hence, the term equinox). The apparent orbit plane of the Sun or, equivalently, the Earth is termed the *ecliptic plane.* The *north celestial pole* is the point where the polar axis of the Earth intersects the celestial sphere on the Northern Hemisphere. The *celestial sphere* is simply an imaginary sphere at an infinite distance from us upon which the positions of the stars, planets, and other objects are projected. Hence, the *celestial equator* is the projection of the Earth's equator on the celestial sphere. This equatorial coordinate system is not a perfectly inertial system.* Because of the Earth's oblateness it precesses

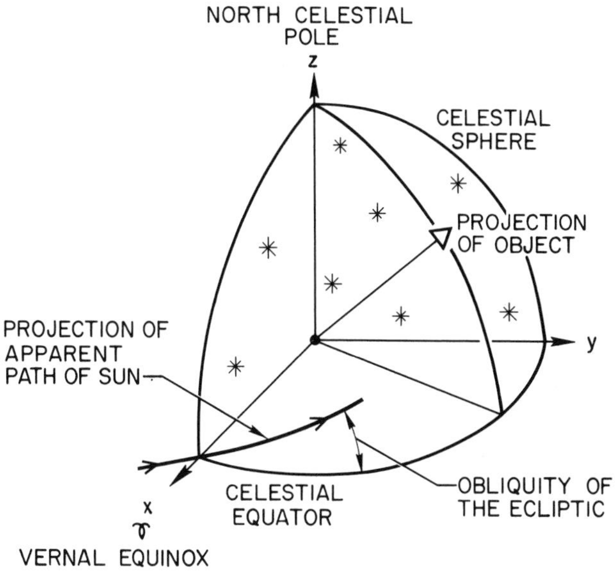

FIG. 2. Equatorial system.

like a top and its axis describes a cone in space with a semivertex angle equal to the angle between the polar axis and the normal to the ecliptic plane. (This angle is called the *obliquity of the ecliptic* and amounts to about $23\frac{1}{2}°$.) As the Earth's polar axis precesses, it carries the equator around with it so that the vernal equinox also moves. This westward motion amounts to about 50.27″ per year and consequently, when the coordinates are given in an equatorial system, they should be referred to a specific vernal equinox, e.g., 1950.0 (1950.0 means the equinox as of January 1.0

* For all problems of celestial mechanics a system of coordinates fixed relative to our galaxy represents an inertial system with sufficient accuracy. See the work of Benedikt[10] in this regard.

1950, i.e., midnight between December 31 and January 1, or in other words, New Year's Eve). A more detailed discussion of coordinate systems is to be found in Chapter 4; see also Herrick.[1]

1.3. Harmonic and *Vis-Viva* Laws

Newton developed Kepler's laws of motion on the basis of his more general law of universal gravitation. In particular he extended Kepler's first law, which stated that planets move about the Sun on elliptical orbits with one focus occupied by the Sun, to include any object moving about a central force on a conic section. Newton also modified Kepler's third or harmonic law by introducing the effect of the masses of the two bodies, i.e.,

$$P^2 = (2\pi/k)^2 a^3/(m_1 + m_2) \tag{2}$$

where P is the period of the orbit, m_1 and m_2 are the masses of the two bodies and a is again the semimajor axis of the orbit. In deriving and generalizing Kepler's laws, Newton found other integrals of the two-body problem. In particular he came upon the extremely important *vis-viva* or energy integral, which relates the speed at any point on a two-body orbit to the distance of the object from the force center, r; i.e.,

$$(ds/dt)^2 = k^2(m_1 + m_2)(2/r - 1/a) \tag{3}$$

where ds/dt is the speed of the object (see Fig. 3). This very important relation finds wide application in all areas of astrodynamics. In particular, consider the co-speed orbits shown in Fig. 4. Note that because at take-off both the initial values (denoted by the subscript 0) $(ds/dt)_0$ and r_0 are constant (only the angle at take-off is varied), all orbits exhibit the same semimajor axis. If, in particular, the speed at the point of take-off is equal to the circular-satellite speed at this point, then the orbits range from a circular orbit ($e = 0$) with horizontal injection, to a rectilinear orbit ($e = 1$) with vertical injection. At all angles between horizontal and vertical the semimajor axis remains the same while the eccentricity changes from 0 to 1.* (See Section 4.1.2 for an interpretation of the variation of the eccentricity e, and the Appendix for a derivation of the *vis-viva* integral.)

* The *vis-viva* integral can be thought of as a conservation-of-energy relation in which $(\frac{1}{2})(ds/dt)^2$ represents the kinetic energy per unit mass, $-k^2(m_1 + m_2)/r$ the potential energy per unit mass, and $-k^2(m_1 + m_2)/2a$ their constant sum.

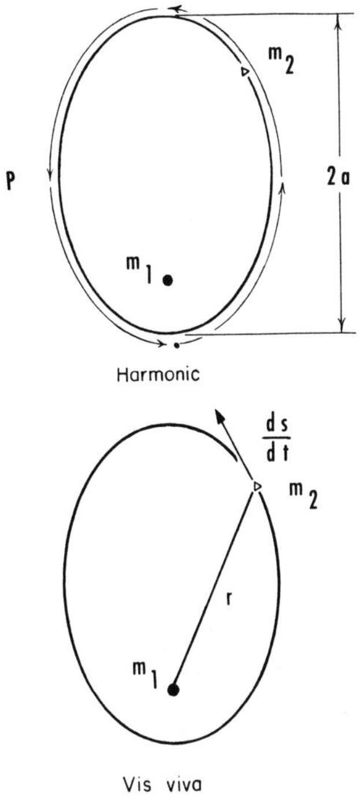

FIG. 3. Harmonic and *vis-viva* laws.

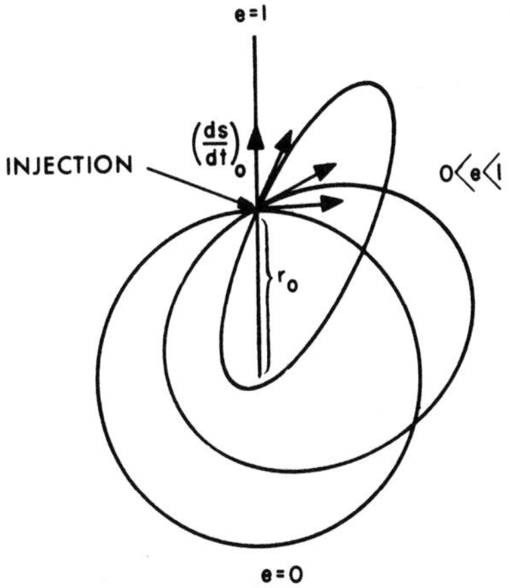

FIG. 4. Co-speed orbits.

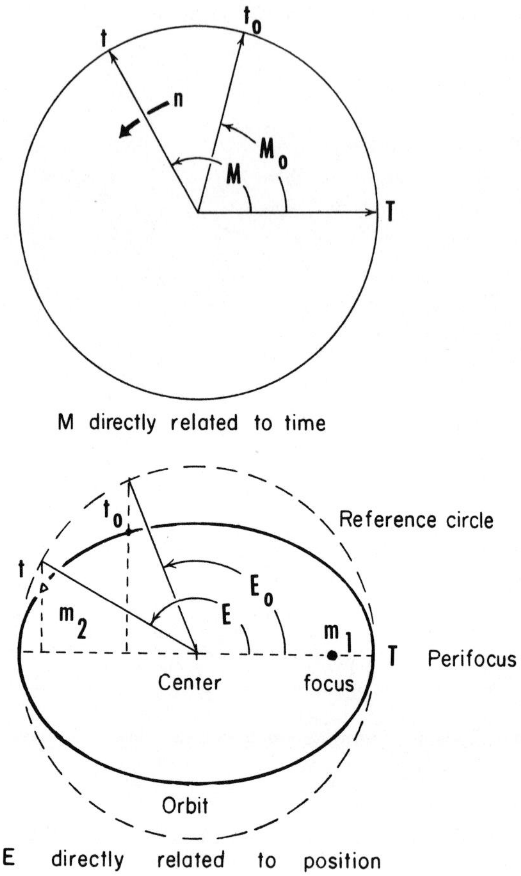

FIG. 5. Kepler's equation.

The derivation of Kepler's laws will be taken up at a later point in the text (in Section 6.1) after the reader has acquired a greater facility with astrodynamical notation. It is manifest that the simple practical application of these basic relations need not be preceded by their theoretical development in any event.

Kepler's equation (as differentiated from Kepler's laws) is given for elliptical orbits by

$$M = n(t - T) = M_0 + n(t - t_0) = E - e \sin E. \tag{4}$$

In this relationship several new terms have been introduced, namely, M, the mean anomaly, which is essentially defined by its equivalence to $n(t - T)$ where n is the mean motion and is equal to $k\sqrt{m_1 + m_2}\,a^{-3/2}$; M_0 is the value of M at some specified time t_0, the so-called epoch (see Fig. 5); and, E, the eccentric anomaly, which is defined in Section 4.2.2 by Fig. 14. Kepler's equation finds its great utility in relating position (through E) to time (directly proportional to M). Historically, it was the first transcendental equation to be investigated extensively by mathematicians. A logical consequence of Kepler's equation is Kepler's third law i.e., for one complete period of revolution of a planet from perihelion back to perihelion the angle E advances from 0 to 2π radians while $t - T$ progresses from 0 ($t = T$) to P; hence

$$nP = 2\pi - e \sin 2\pi = 2\pi$$

or

$$P = 2\pi/n = 2\pi a^{3/2}/\sqrt{m_1 + m_2}\,k$$

which upon squaring is identical to Eq. (2). The derivation of Kepler's equation is found in the Appendix.

1.4. Velocity Components

A brief discussion would now seem to be appropriate on the subject of velocity components. For reasons that will become apparent later it is advisable to change the time variable from t to τ and define a time derivative of some typical quantity x, with respect to τ, by the notation

$$\dot{x} \triangleq \frac{dx}{d\tau}.$$

The magnitude of the total vector velocity of a space vehicle, $\dot{\mathbf{r}}$, is then defined by $\dot{s}$, where s is a measure of the distance along an arc of the trajectory and was employed in Eq. (3). The velocity vector, $\dot{\mathbf{r}}$, has two components both in the orbit plane (co-planar orbital motion implies no velocity component normal to the plane). The first is the radial component termed $\dot{r}$. It is specifically *not* equal to $|\dot{\mathbf{r}}|$ since it is the time rate of change of the scalar r not the vector $\mathbf{r}$. The second is the transverse component termed $r\dot{v}$. The quantity v is the so-called *true anomaly* and is essentially defined by Fig. 6 as the angle between the line of symmetry of the conic

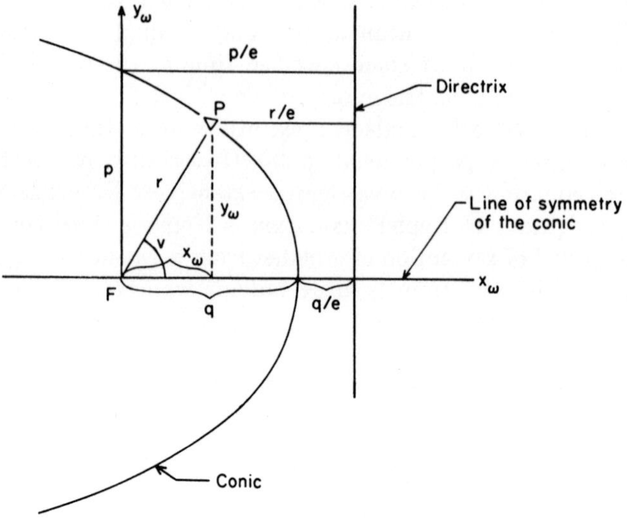

FIG. 6. Directrix definition of the conic.

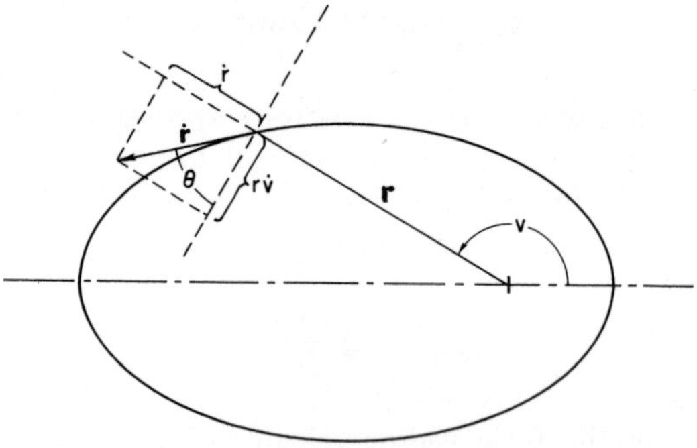

FIG. 7. Velocity components.

and **r**. Clearly, $\dot{r}$ is perpendicular to $r\dot{v}$ and if θ, the so-called *angle of elevation,* is measured from the transverse direction (normal to **r** in the orbit plane) to $\dot{\mathbf{r}}$, then

$$\dot{r} = \dot{s} \sin \theta \text{ and } r\dot{v} = \dot{s} \cos \theta, \tag{5}$$

see Fig. 7.

In terms of the equatorial coordinates discussed in Section 1.2, these speeds are given by vector *dot products* as

$$\dot{s}^2 = \dot{\mathbf{r}} \cdot \dot{\mathbf{r}} = \dot{x}^2 + \dot{y}^2 + \dot{z}^2 \tag{6}$$

$$r\dot{r} = \mathbf{r} \cdot \dot{\mathbf{r}} = x\dot{x} + y\dot{y} + z\dot{z}, \tag{7}$$

while

$$(r\dot{v})^2 = \dot{s}^2 - \dot{r}^2 \tag{8}$$

where the components of $\mathbf{r}$ are x, y, z and the components of $\dot{\mathbf{r}}$ are $\dot{x}$, $\dot{y}$, $\dot{z}$ in the equatorial coordinate system.

1.5. Equations of Absolute and Relative Motion

In the case of two-body motion, Newton's law of universal gravitation relating the force vector $\mathbf{f}_{12}$ acting on an object of "gravitational" mass m_1, in the presence of a second body of "gravitational" mass m_2 is

$$\mathbf{f}_{12} = \frac{k^2 m_1 m_2}{r_{12}^2} \frac{\mathbf{r}_{12}}{r_{12}} \tag{9}$$

where k^2 is a gravitational constant and $\mathbf{r}_{12}$ is the vector distance from m_1 to m_2. By Newton's third law

$$\mathbf{f}_{12} = -\mathbf{f}_{21}. \tag{10}$$

Introducing Newton's second or "inertial" mass law, and equating "inertial" mass to "gravitational" mass, we find that

$$\mathbf{f}_{12} = m_1 \frac{d^2\mathbf{r}_1}{dt^2} \text{ and } \mathbf{f}_{21} = m_2 \frac{d^2\mathbf{r}_2}{dt^2}.$$

Combining the foregoing relationships and considering only the x-component, we find the equations of *absolute motion* to be

$$\frac{d^2x_1}{dt^2} = k^2 m_2 \frac{x_{12}}{r_{12}^3} \text{ and } \frac{d^2x_2}{dt^2} = -k^2 m_1 \frac{x_{12}}{r_{12}^3}, \quad x \rightarrow y,z$$

where $x \rightarrow y, z$ signifies that x is replaced by y and then z to yield the other two components.

If we adopt $\mathbf{r}_{12} = \mathbf{r}_2 - \mathbf{r}_1 \triangleq \mathbf{r}$, and $x_{12} = x_2 - x_1 \triangleq x$, then

$$\frac{d^2x_{12}}{dt^2} = \frac{d^2x_2}{dt^2} - \frac{d^2x_1}{dt^2} = \frac{d^2x}{dt^2},$$

which results in the equation of *relative motion:*

$$\frac{d^2x}{dt^2} = -k^2(m_1 + m_2)\frac{x}{r^3} = -k^2\mu\frac{x}{r^3}, \text{ or } \ddot{x} \triangleq \frac{d^2x}{d\tau^2} = \frac{-\mu x}{r^3}$$
$$x \to y,z,$$

where $\mu = m_1 + m_2$, $\tau \triangleq k(t - t_0)$, and t_0 = some epoch or arbitrary initial time (see Fig. 8). The foregoing equations of relative motion can be expressed more concisely as one single *vector equation* of the form

$$\ddot{\mathbf{r}} = -\mu\frac{\mathbf{r}}{r^3}. \tag{11}$$

At this point there often arises confusion as to the units employed and the relationship of the cgs value of the universal constant of gravitation, G, to k^2. Although there exist alternative definitions, we will consistently employ as unit of mass the mass of the most ponderous body: i.e., the Sun, for heliocentric orbits and the Earth for geocentric orbits. Consequently, for a heliocentric orbit m_1 = one solar mass and for a geocentric orbit m_1 = one Earth mass, while m_2 is the mass of the second body in solar or Earth masses respectively.

In the cgs (or mks) system, the law of attraction is

$$\frac{d^2x}{dt^2} = -G(m_1 + m_2)x/r^3, \tag{12}$$

where m_1 and m_2 are measured in grams (or kilograms); hence, for heliocentric orbits,

$$k^2 \text{ (usually denoted as } k_s^2) = Gm_\odot$$

and for the geocentric orbits,

$$k^2 \text{ (usually denoted as } k_e^2) = Gm_\oplus,$$

where $m_\odot$ and $m_\oplus$ are the masses of the Sun and Earth respectively, as measured in grams (or kilograms).

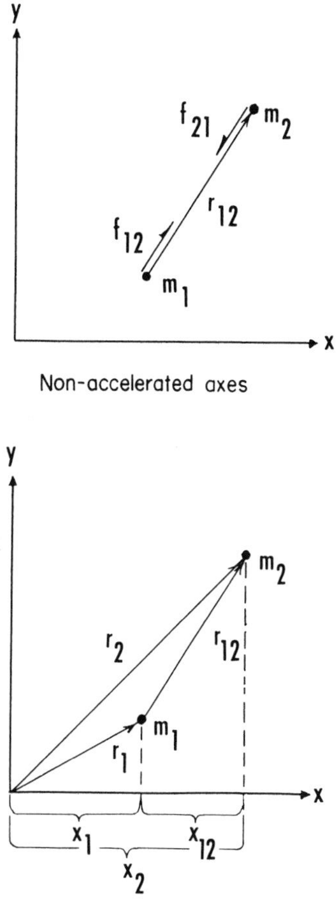

FIG. 8. Two-body problem.

Since astrodynamicists have been able to determine the product of Gm to a much higher precision than one can measure either G or m separately, the use of k^2 instead of G is always preferable and has been the accepted astronomical practice for hundreds of years.

A brief discussion of the length unit is also appropriate here. For heliocentric orbits the mean distance or semimajor axis of the Earth's orbit, termed the *astronomical unit* (a.u.), is the characteristic length unit while for geocentric orbits the equatorial radius of the Earth has been chosen as the characteristic length unit (see Herrick, *et al.*[37]). Hence r and a are measured in a.u. or equatorial radii depending upon the situation. Illustrative examples have been included at the end of Chapters 2 and 3 to show the utility of this system of characteristic units.

As a conclusion to our discussion of the equation of relative motion, let us briefly investigate an interesting disparity that seems to exist. This apparent disparity arises from the fact that

$$|\ddot{\mathbf{r}}| \neq \ddot{r}$$

that is, $\mathbf{r} \cdot \dot{\mathbf{r}} = r\dot{r}$ from Eq. (7) and, consequently

$$\dot{\overline{(\mathbf{r} \cdot \dot{\mathbf{r}})}} = \dot{\overline{(r \ \dot{r})}}$$

or

$$\mathbf{r} \cdot \ddot{\mathbf{r}} + \dot{\mathbf{r}} \cdot \dot{\mathbf{r}} = \dot{r}^2 + r\ddot{r};$$

but $\dot{\mathbf{r}} \cdot \dot{\mathbf{r}} = \dot{s}^2$ by Eq. (6) and

$$\mathbf{r} \cdot \ddot{\mathbf{r}} = \mathbf{r} \cdot \left(\frac{-\mu\mathbf{r}}{r^3}\right) = -\frac{\mu}{r}$$

by Eq. (11) so that

$$r\ddot{r} = (\dot{s}^2 - \dot{r}^2) - \frac{\mu}{r} = (r\dot{v})^2 - \frac{\mu}{r} \text{ or } \ddot{r} = r\dot{v}^2 - \frac{\mu}{r^2}.$$

On the other hand,

$$|\ddot{\mathbf{r}}| = \frac{-\mu|\mathbf{r}|}{r^3} = \frac{-\mu}{r^2}.$$

Where, then, does the mysterious $r\dot{v}^2$ come from? To answer this question in the most succinct manner we must carefully consider our "point of view." The quantity $\ddot{r}$ is simply the second time rate of change of r, where r is the magnitude of the distance from the focus to the object. Clearly, the vantage point from which we examine $\ddot{r}$ is at the focus and we measure or "sight" *along* the radius vector. In other words, we are in truth measuring r with respect to a *rotating* coordinate system as we follow it around and continuously reckon its derivative. The vector $\ddot{\mathbf{r}}$, on the contrary, is the acceleration vector as measured in inertial space *not* from the viewpoint of a rotating coordinate system. The difference between $|\ddot{\mathbf{r}}|$ and $\ddot{r}$ is, therefore, a fictitious radial acceleration whose value we have computed to be $r\dot{v}^2$.

1.7. Perturbations

Kepler's laws of motion and the preceding two-body formulas are valid only for the case of two bodies that are alone in the Universe, e.g., a single planet moving around the Sun. It is clear that a perfect description of the motion of an object can be obtained only if the forces acting on the object from all other centers are considered. Since this description is one of the central problems of astrodynamics, the following brief introductory discussion is included.

Non-two-body forces are often termed perturbative forces. In general, however, *perturbative forces* can be defined as forces acting on an object other than those forces that cause it to move on some *reference orbit.* In the case of planetary motions, astronomers adopted the two-body elliptical motion of an object as the reference motion. Hence, all non-two-body forces such as those arising from the other planets are characterized as perturbative forces. Of course, other than elliptical reference motions can be considered. Boris Garfinkel[7] and Sterne[8] have determined an analytical reference motion for an object moving around a spheroid, while Baker[9] has determined a closed analytical form for motion through an atmosphere without gravity. Other such reference motions are, of course, possible and it is only required that the solution be an analytical one (see Chapter 8).

As the term has been defined in the foregoing, perturbations need not necessarily be small. For example, Comet 1770 Lexell was so accelerated by a close approach to Jupiter in 1779 that it left the solar system on a hyperbolic orbit and has never been observed again. Comet Wolf, however, survived two encounters with Jupiter; the first, in 1875, wherein its perihelion distance was shortened from 2.5 to 1.5 a.u. and period of revolution adjusted accordingly, whereas the second conjunction restored the original conditions. The aphelion distance of 5.5 a.u. remained quite undisturbed during the entire procedure. In these cases, the perturbative forces were much larger than the force causing the heliocentric motion of the comet.

It is also important to recognize that perturbations are differential effects. This is a point that has often been overlooked. For example, the magnitude of the perturbative forces acting on the Moon due to the Sun are greater than the forces acting on the Moon due to the Earth. Nevertheless, the Moon definitely moves in a *geocentric* trajectory. The perturbations of an object such as the Moon caused by the Sun should be reckoned only as the differences between the attraction of the Sun acting on the center of the reference coordinate system at the Earth and the attraction of the

Sun acting on the Moon. From this point of view, it is clear that most of the perturbative effect of the Sun on the Earth and on the Moon causes them to move together in elliptical heliocentric orbits. Only the difference between the accelerations due to the Sun on the Earth and on the Moon can be counted as perturbative accelerations on the Moon (see Section 7.2).

Aside from the presence of other bodies, there are additional sources of perturbative forces. The Earth and many of the planets are not homogeneous in spherical concentric layers. For example, the equatorial bulge of the Earth exerts a perturbative force on nearby satellites that is greater in magnitude than the perturbative forces caused by the Sun or the Moon. Other perturbative forces of a nongravitational nature such as drag and light pressure will be taken up in Chapter 10.

Two-body orbits can be determined in closed analytical form; however, when perturbative forces are considered, recourse must be taken to more sophisticated methods of computation. These fall into two general categories. The first is termed *general perturbations* and involves the series expansion and analytical integration of an orbit by a Fourier or power series. The second is called *special perturbations* and involves a numerical integration. Three special perturbation methods will be considered in Chapter 8. They are Cowell's, Encke's, and variation-of-parameter methods. Other methods, for example, variation of elements and Hansen's are particularly important for the determination of lunar vehicle orbits, but will not be considered in detail here.

As will become apparent to the reader later, the motivation behind the astrodynamicist's use of certain of these apparently cumbersome perturbational procedures is that such methods allow for much faster and more accurate computations. For example, a number of analysts have found a tenfold decrease in computational time afforded by Encke's method in the computation of Earth to Moon orbits! Such economy cannot be overlooked even when high-speed electronic computers are available.

2 THE MINOR PLANETS

The remarkable story of the minor planets might almost be classed under the heading of "science fiction," with romantic overtones introduced by such characters as Eros, Amor, and Adonis; a martial element provided by Priam, Hector, Achilles, and other Greek and Trojan warriors; and a thrilling "surprise ending" undreamed of by 19th century astronomers in the successful flights of "man-made minor planets." This story forms an interesting backdrop and introduction to the principles and uses of astrodynamics.

It began in the mid-18th century with what we would now consider an irrational prediction by the German astronomer Bode. Those were the days when the new science of celestial mechanics, inaugurated by Newton's universal law of gravitation and implemented by the calculus of Newton and Leibnitz, was triumphantly solving the puzzles that had plagued astronomers ever since Hipparchus discovered precession of the equinoxes and the Moon's evection. Scientists and poets alike, optimistically concluded that all the laws of the universe would ultimately be found to be as simple and direct as the inverse square law of gravitation. In our own era Einstein's long search for a unified field formula may be a last remnant of that naive optimism.

2.1. Initial Discoveries

2.1.1. Bode's Prediction

In his translation of Bonnet's "Observations Concerning Nature" (1772), Professor Titius of Wittenberg appended an idea of his own, which has come down in history as "Bode's law," while the name of the author has been forgotten. Write down the names of the planets known in 1772 placing a question mark between Mars and Jupiter, and under each name write a 4; then place a 0 under Mercury, a 3 under Venus, a 6 under Earth and continue across the row doubling the number each time. Add the numbers under each planet and point off one decimal place from the right. You will then have before you a close approximation to the distances of the planets from the Sun, expressed in units of the Earth's mean distance, the astronomical unit (a.u.).

Mercury	Venus	Earth	Mars	(?)	Jupiter	Saturn	(Uranus 1781)
4	4	4	4	4	4	4	4
0	3	6	12	24	48	96	192
0.4	0.7	1.0	1.6	2.8	5.2	10.0	19.6 a.u.

or numerically $(4 + 3 \times 2^N)/10$ where $N = -\infty, 0, 1, 2, 3, \ldots$

The empty place between the terrestrial and major planets inspired Bode[11], Director of the Berlin Observatory, to declare eloquently: "Is it not highly probable that a planet actually revolves in the orbit which the finger of the Almighty has drawn for it? Can we believe the Creator of the world has left this space empty? Certainly not!" Herschel's discovery in 1781 of a trans-Saturnian planet at approximately the distance found by extrapolation from Bode's law, was hailed as a "happy verification" of the formula, and an association of European astronomers was formed to search the skies for the "missing link" between Mars and Jupiter.

2.1.2. Piazzi's Discovery

Piazzi, first Director of the observatory at Palermo, Sicily, was not a member of the European association. He was concerned only with adding more and more stars on every clear night to the great star catalog that he was compiling as his life-work. He was disturbed to find that a certain star that Wollaston had listed as "Mayer 87" was not to be found in Mayer's original catalog; but on searching the region of the sky where the star should have been he discovered, indeed, a starlike object of the eighth magnitude. When he found on the following night that the "star" had moved slightly, he naturally assumed that he had discovered a comet, although no coma or tail was discernible. He wrote to Bode on January 24, "On the first of January, [1801] I discovered a comet in Taurus. . . . On the 11th it changed its heretofore [westward] retrograde motion into [eastward] direct motion." On January 23 it was back in its original right ascension and declination, having passed the stationary point, and was diminishing in brightness as the distance between it and the Earth rapidly increased.

From such uncometary behavior, Bode was convinced that the eighth major planet whose existence he had proclaimed 30 years earlier had at last been located. After following the new member of the Sun's family for 41 nights, Piazzi's work was interrupted by illness, and when he looked for it again he could find no trace of it in the multitude of stars. Thus, by March 20, the date on which Bode received the letter of January 24, the new planet had disappeared from view. Piazzi named his discovery Ceres, in honor of the tutelary deity of Palermo, and the name of the goddess of harvests has proved most appropriate. The subsequent harvest has been an abundantly fruitful one for celestial mechanics and orbit theory and has led directly into the new field of astrodynamics.

At the time of the discovery of the first minor planet in 1801 there was every reason for believing that Ceres would be lost forever; for even if another accidental discovery should occur in the future there would be no possibility of identification since the elements of the orbit were not known. Up to 1801, orbits had been derived only for the major planets and an occasional comet. In regard to the former, the periods of revolution were precisely known from observations of the motion covering many centuries (except in the case of Uranus) and the mean motion, n, and semimajor axis, a, could be readily found from the period by Kepler's third law. In the case of Uranus, an approximation to the mean distance from an extrapolation of Bode's law was used in computing a preliminary circular orbit, which was then corrected to an ellipse as more observations became available. Like Ceres, Uranus was first thought to be a comet by its discoverer, William Herschel[12], on account of its disk and motion with respect to the stars. The fact that the eccentricity and inclination to the ecliptic of Uranus' orbit were small simplified the problem. Also it was found that Uranus had been observed and listed as a star 20 times during the century before Herschel's discovery! Moulton[13] discusses methods by Newton, Olbers, and others for obtaining the elements of a *parabolic* comet orbit; and here again the theory was made simpler by the fact that in a parabola the eccentricity is unity and the major axis infinite, leaving only the ω, i, Ω, and T_0 or M_0 to be determined. (See Section 6.5 for a discussion of Olbers' method.)

2.1.3. Gauss' Orbit

In September, 1801, the great German mathematician Gauss[5], then 24 years of age, began to think about the problem of determining the orbit of a heavenly body "without any hypothesis and from observations not covering a long interval and not allowing selection for special methods," but he put the thoughts aside to attend to more immediate problems. A few weeks later Piazzi's observations of Ceres from January 1 to February 11 of that year were published, and the discovery of the eighth planet became the "subject of universal conversation."

The case of Ceres was made particularly difficult by the fact that the small planet had already passed opposition at the time of discovery and was moving very slowly as it approached the stationary point. It began to retrace its path only 10 days after discovery and in the 41-day duration of Piazzi's observations, it had covered a geocentric arc of only 3°. This was equivalent to a heliocentric arc of 9°. Gauss' first orbit was necessarily hurried and crude, but it made possible the rediscovery of the small planet on December 31, 1801 and accordingly celestial mechanics made an important advance into the future. (See Section 6.4 for a discussion of Gauss' method.)

2.1.4. Discovery of Pallas, Juno, and Vesta (cf. Leuschner[14])

While searching for Ceres on March 28, 1802, Olbers at Bremen Observatory happened upon a second small planet that became known as Pallas. Juno and Vesta followed Pallas in 1804 and 1807 respectively. After Vesta there was a dearth of new discoveries for 38 years. The first four minor planets had been of magnitude 7.0 to 7.5 and had shown measurable disks that indicated diameters as follows:

Average Diameters of Minor Planets

Ceres	488 mi.
Pallas	304
Vesta	248
Juno	118

Astraea, discovered in 1845, was 2.5 to 3.0 magnitudes fainter, and consequently much more difficult to identify as a member of the solar system. In spite of the difficulty, the discovery of Astraea revived the waning interest in the search for new minor planets.

The visual observations of the 19th century were most laborious. The discovery of a new object was the result of the patient examination of fields of view, star by star, and a time-consuming careful comparison with inadequate star charts and catalogs in the search for an unidentified object. When a starlike body was found in a position for which no star had been charted, the next step was to make micrometric measurements of the differential right ascensions and declinations from comparison stars. If observations on the following night showed that the object was in motion with respect to the background of stars, it must then be observed over as long a period as possible so that a fairly accurate orbit could be determined before it disappeared in the Sun's rays. If cloudy weather intervened before the orbit could be secured, the new planet was lost.

2.1.5. First Photographic Discovery

In 1891, a new chapter in the story of the minor planets was begun when the first (numbered) discovery by photography was announced by Wolf at Heidelberg. Unfortunately (323) Brucia was observed only from December 22 to January 1, and the orbit derived from these data was not accurate enough for recovery of the planet at the next opposition. Brucia was rediscovered, however, in 1923 at the Naval Observatory in Washington and identified by the elements of the orbit.

The impetus which photography gave to minor planet observation is illustrated by the fact that the last nine years of the century produced 130 new and increasingly fainter objects as compared with 322 during the previous 90 years of visual observations.

2.2. Dynamical Effects

2.2.1. Kirkwood's Gaps

As early as 1857 Daniel Kirkwood[15] predicted that the orbits of minor planets would be found to be clustered in rings about the Sun, separated by empty spaces where their mean motions would have been commensurable with that of Jupiter. He called attention to the analogous distribution of the moonlets that form the rings of Saturn and which studiously avoid regions in which their motions would be in definite ratios with those of Saturn's satellites. In the case of the minor planets, he pointed out that the powerful attraction of Jupiter would have the effect of clearing the "regions of avoidance." When Kirkwood announced his theory, the orbits of only 46 minor planets were known. By 1866 the number had doubled and his theory was amply confirmed.

Kirkwood assumed that when the solar system took shape there was a broad belt of nebulous material between the orbits of Mars and Jupiter—a planet that could not coalesce out of the primary substance owing to the irresistible pull of the major planets, particularly Jupiter. He reasoned that at a distance, for example, of 3.27 a.u. from the Sun—which would place a body between the orbits of Bertha and Johanna—a mass would make precisely two revolutions to Jupiter's one. All its conjunctions with Jupiter for an indefinite time would occur in the same part of its orbit. Thus, the attraction of the great planet would act as if to give the small mass a push always in the same direction, and the orbit would accordingly become more and more eccentric or elongated, until it finally carried the body out of the danger zone and into a more populous region of the nebulous belt. There it would collide and coalesce with other masses moving at slightly different velocities and the result would be the formation of a small planet. The orbit would be very different from the original one according to Kirkwood and the space where the mean motion would have equaled exactly twice that of Jupiter would be left empty. On either side of these gaps planets are subject to strong perturbations when in conjunction with Jupiter.

2.2.2. Hirayama's Investigation

A Tokyo astronomer, Hirayama (cf. Brouwer[16]) began a detailed investigation of the distribution of minor planet orbits in 1917 when there were 790 numbered asteroids, and extended it from time to time as more objects were discovered until 1928 when the number had arrived at 1046. He found that the small planets were not distributed at random within a given ring, but that they fell into definite "families" when classified according to their fundamental orbital characteristics such as mean motions, eccentricities, inclinations to the ecliptic and nodes, after being freed from "induced oscillations" or secular variation in the elements produced by Jupiter, i.e., perturbations proportional to the time. Hirayama interpreted these statistics as indicating that the members of a certain "family" are the fragments of a larger body that broke up for some unknown reason millions of years ago. Whatever the cause of the breaking—whether an explosion, a collision with a smaller body, or instability due to too rapid rotation—each fragment received an impetus that added an increment to its original velocity, and caused the components to separate gradually yet retain certain recognizable characteristics from the original orbit while being acted upon by Jupiter and Saturn. As the result of secular perturbations, the fragments are eventually irregularly scattered and situated along the original path.

2.2.3. Recent Findings

In recent years Brouwer has made a detailed investigation of the secular variations of the orbits of minor planets by both Jupiter and Saturn[16], including perturbations of the second order arising from their mutual interaction, and applied them to 1537 of the 1563 objects for which orbits were published in *Kleine Planeten* for 1947. In general, Brouwer's study confirmed and amplified that of Hirayama. The original families were considerably enlarged due to additional material and some modification of boundaries and the deviations were due to the use of new values for the masses and of second-order perturbations by Saturn as well as Jupiter. He found 29 groups containing members ranging from 4 to 62 each.

Brouwer examined Kuiper's theory that at the origin of the solar system five to ten planets the size of the largest minor planets were formed at a distance of 2 to $3\frac{1}{2}$ a.u. from the Sun. These eventually broke up into fragments due to explosion, rapid rotational instability, tidal actions, or collisions. Although the probability of collision between two such bodies in 2×10^9 years is about 0.1, there is a point in favor of the collision theory in that the probability of later collisions is greatly augmented by the increase in the number of bodies resulting from one or two collisions.

Baade estimates from an examination of asteroid trails on plates taken with the 100-in. at Mount Wilson that there must be 44,000 minor planets of magnitude 19.0 or brighter. A vast number of these are undoubtedly very small, perhaps less than a mile in diameter.

E. W. Brown made the statement some years ago on the assumption that the asteroids were formed at the same time as the principal planets that "The origin of asteroids circulating between the orbits of Mars and Jupiter cannot be deduced by gravitational methods from their present orbits." But according to Brouwer, his objection loses force if the groups have originated much more recently. Thus a statistical study of the asteroids as a whole and in "families" may shed considerable light on the problem of origins in the solar system. In general, it is agreed that there should have been a planet between Mars and Jupiter but it could not coalesce from the primeval substance because of the disrupting force exerted by the great planet.

2.3. Theory of Orbits

2.3.1. General

The determination of the orbits of minor planets challenged the greatest minds of the 19th century and there was hardly a noted astronomer who did not have a hand in the development of the theory and application of orbit methods. A similar circumstance arises today as astrodynamicists are faced with new problems arising from the advent of space travel. The new members of the solar system presented not only an irresistible challenge for the advancement of celestial mechanics, but also an unlimited field for the testing of new ideas. Each planet was different from every other one. Very early in the minor planet era it was found that an orbit based on the observations of a single opposition was not sufficient for defining the motion at future oppositions, without taking into account perturbations by Jupiter, and sometimes other principal planets.

As the equations of motion of the three-body problem—e.g., Sun-planet-Jupiter—cannot be integrated analytically except in the particular cases of the Lagrangian straight line and equilateral triangle solutions, several new methods of dealing with perturbations were developed. The perturbations are either periodic or secular (see Chapter 7 for a discussion of the n-body problem).

To illustrate the unequaled importance of minor planets as experimental laboratories for trying out new astrodynamical theories and methods, we cite the following examples.

2.3.2. Ceres

In 1805, after computing several orbits for the first small planet, Gauss developed the perturbative function that was later adapted by Hansen in his method of general perturbations (see Chapter 9). Encke computed special perturbations by Jupiter using his own method of numerical integration, with ephemerides for 1837–1871 (see Chapter 8). Heiligenstein derived elements from seven oppositions 1818–27, including special Jupiter perturbations in the elements. Damoiseau computed a number of terms of the general perturbations. Schubert deduced elements from 250 positions in 14 oppositions 1832–54, applying perturbations from the tables of Encke and Wolfers with a correction for the secular variation of the obliquity of the ecliptic, which decreases at the rate of $0''.46$ a year due to planetary perturbations. Elements were derived by Godward from 15 oppositions

1857–76 by a differential correction of residuals from ephemerides in the British Nautical Almanac, and included perturbations by Venus, Earth, Mars, Jupiter, and Saturn.

G. W. Hill used Ceres to illustrate his modification of Hansen's method of general perturbations, deriving first-order terms due to Jupiter in order to determine an orbit from 10 normal places (see Section 6.6.1) between 1802 and 1890 and including secular perturbations by Mars, Jupiter, and Saturn using Gauss' method, as well as periodic perturbations by Mars and Saturn from Damoiseau's tables, which he found to require emendation.

On the basis of Hill's orbit, Merfield computed secular perturbations due to the eight principal planets by Gauss' method as developed by Hill. Wolf applied Gylden's theory of absolute or general perturbations to the changes in the radius vector. Vilyev derived general perturbations by Hansen's method, and Komendantov based an orbit on 12 normal places between 1913 and 1922, including Jupiter's action according to Numerov's method of special perturbations. He later extended the calculation to 1926, and added the effect of Saturn's attraction.

2.3.3. Pallas

This account of Ceres, with considerable variations, tells the story of Pallas, Juno, Vesta, and many others of the long line of small planets that followed them. Each presented a different problem, for no two were alike. Pallas, for example, differed from Ceres in having a large eccentric angle (14°, i.e., $\sin^{-1} e$) and inclination to the ecliptic (35°). Gauss exercised his new method of least squares by deriving an orbit from three sets of elements based on four oppositions each—1803–7, 1804–9, and 1805–9—and developed a method of numerically integrating the perturbations in the elements necessitated by the large e and i. In 1811, he derived mean elements using Laplace's elements of Jupiter's orbit and found a large libration in the mean motion due to the commensurability that 1894 revolutions of Pallas equal 737 of Jupiter. He obtained a value of 1:1047.86 for the mass of Jupiter, which is remarkably close to the value in current use, i.e., 1:1047.355.

Space permits only a superficial account of the tremendous advances in celestial mechanics following the discovery of the minor planets. Fortunately for the new science of astrodynamics and the investigation of the orbits of artificial satellites and interplanetary vehicles, these great developments came long enough ahead of the far-reaching discoveries in the field of astrophysics for a solid foundation to be laid in the theory of orbital motion under the action of disturbing forces. This chapter would not be complete, however, without some mention of specific problems to which the theory of planetary motion has been applied: (i) the correction of the astronomical unit and solar parallax (see Section 5.1); (ii) the determination of the masses of the principal planets (see Section 5.4); and (iii) the equilateral triangle solution of the three-body problem of Lagrange (see Section 7.1.2).

2.4. Future Investigations

Although the very existence of the small planets was first inferred from the presence of an apparently empty region between the orbits of Mars (1.5 a.u.) and Jupiter (5.2 a.u.) and for nearly a century they showed no tendency to stray across the orbits of the principal planets, there have been several notable exceptions, as will be seen in the case of the Trojans (see Section 7.1). A vast number of these small bodies may revolve, like Hidalgo, outside the orbit of Jupiter, and also outside the range of existing telescopes because of their small size, low reflecting power, and enormous distances.

One of the most remarkable of these exceptions was found by Baade in 1949, and its definitive orbit with perturbations by all the planets as far out as Neptune was derived by Herrick[17]. It was numbered 1566 and appropriately named Icarus, because it approaches closer to the Sun than any other known object, recalling to mind the reputed intramercurial planet Vulcan, observed during a total solar eclipse but never seen again. Icarus is closer to Mercury than Venus about one eighth of the time and will afford an excellent opportunity for a new determination of the mass of Mercury early in May 1968, when it should pass within 8,000,000 miles of that planet.

In June 1968, Icarus will approach within 4,000,000 miles of the Earth and will thus provide an unparalleled opportunity for a redetermination of the solar parallax and mass of the Earth–Moon system. On this literally "flying visit," Icarus will be brighter than the 15th magnitude for only 12 days, due to the rapid motion of 50′ per hour, and as its geocentric parallax will equal four times that of Eros in 1931, the perturbative effects of the Earth will be correspondingly 16 times as great. Moreover, due to the high eccentricity (0.826) and nearness to the Sun, the orbit of Icarus should illustrate the well-known relativity effect, i.e., a revolution of the line of apsides amounting to 10″ per century, as compared with Mercury's 43″ (see Section 10.5).

An extremely interesting and ingenious method for determining the mass of the Moon from observations of 619 Triberga has been suggested by

Brouwer and Ashbrook[18]. To date, the most exact value of this constant was based on observations of Eros, but it is unfortunately affected by systematic errors of the fundamental star system. Triberga is unique among minor planets in that its period of revolution is almost exactly four times that of the Earth, i.e., 4.0011 years, and three times its synodic period is 3.996 years. Still another remarkable fact is that 3.996 years is close to 49½ synodic months, which means that "the position of Triberga at an epoch of maximum easterly displacement by the lunar equation will nearly coincide with its position four years later at maximum westerly displacement."

From precise observations of Triberga, therefore, repeated over a number of oppositions and essentially independent of errors in the comparison star places (providing the same stars can be used at corresponding pairs of oppositions four years apart) it is expected that a more independent and exact value for the mass of the Moon than any found heretofore may be determined.

Another unique and challenging object is (1362) Griqua for which Rabe computed elements based on six oppositions from 1935 to 1956, applying perturbations to 1977. He found that the mean motion increases from 596″ in 1933 to 607″ in 1977, passing through the point of 2:1 commensurability with Jupiter in 1943. At the same time the eccentricity increased from 0.34 to 0.36. In the perihelion oppositions of 1959 September, 1965 October, and 1971 November, the predicted perturbations in longitude due to Jupiter are between 25° and 61°. The possibility of obtaining a more exact mass of Jupiter than any found thus far is pointed out by Rabe.

2.5. Simple Illustrative Examples

Minor planets offer a number of problems that are amenable to direct solution via the simple astrodynamical principles introduced in Sections 1.3 and 1.4. Consider first the speed required to place a payload on a circular heliocentric orbit in the minor planet belt between Mars and Jupiter. The semimajor axis of this "artificial minor planet" is, in terms of the characteristic heliocentric length unit, 3 a.u. Let us choose an elliptical transfer orbit to carry us from the Earth to the artificial planet orbit whose perihelion is at the Earth at time of launch and whose aphelion is at the point of final injection onto the artificial planet orbit. The rigorous solution of this "three-body problem" (i.e., Earth, vehicle, Sun) would require the application of perturbative techniques to be discussed in Chapters 7, 8, and 9. A simpler and very nearly correct solution utilized to show the feasibility of the mission can, however, be obtained on the basis of two-body analysis if the attraction of the Earth is neglected. Actually we need not introduce such a severe assumption but rather consider the vehicle after it has receded, say 1,000,000 miles from the Earth. From the Earth's standpoint this is an immense distance and the Earth now exerts a negligible influence on the space vehicle; but from the standpoint of the Sun the vehicle is still quite close to the Earth (only 1/100 a.u. away) and, consequently, can still be considered as being at the point of initial injection onto the transfer ellipse at perihelion. The velocity that the vehicle has relative to the Earth as it recedes far away from the Earth (i.e., it asymptotically approaches a final recessional speed—termed $\dot{s}_\infty$ in Section 12.1.2—that is usually much less than the initial booster burnout speed) must be added to the Earth's velocity around the Sun. The sum of these two velocities then will give the velocity of the vehicle relative to some nonaccelerated (i.e., inertial) solar-system coordinate system at the point of initial injection onto the elliptical heliocentric transfer orbit. See Fig. 9.

If the Earth is assumed to revolve on a circular orbit with a semimajor axis $a_\oplus = 1$ a.u., then the major axis of the transfer orbit, $2a_T$, will be $2a_T = 1 + 3$ or $a_T = 2$ a.u. Utilizing $\tau \triangleq k_s(t - t_0)$, the *vis-viva* Eq. (3) reduces to

$$\dot{s}^2 \triangleq \left(\frac{ds}{d\tau}\right)^2 = \left(\frac{ds}{k_s dt}\right)^2 = \mu\left(\frac{2}{r} - \frac{1}{a}\right), \tag{13}$$

where $\mu \triangleq m_1 + m_2$, m_1 is the mass of the Sun in characteristic units, i.e., solar masses, and m_2 is the mass of the vehicle in these same units. Clearly $m_1 \gg m_2$ and, consequently, $\mu = 1$.† The units of $\dot{s}$ can be ascertained by an examination of Eq. (13) for the special case of an assumed circular Earth orbit. In this case $r = a_\oplus$ and Eq. (13) reduces to $\dot{s} = 1/\sqrt{a_\oplus} = 1$ since $a_\oplus$ for the Earth equals unity in the characteristic unit of length—the a.u. Evidently the units of $\dot{s}$ are in terms of circular-satellite speed at unit distance (which is given the symbol V_{co}), i.e., in this case the units are in terms of the mean speed of the Earth (V_{co} = 29.766 km/sec, 18.495 mi/sec, or 97,656 ft/sec). Thus the speed relative to an inertial coordinate

† It is often useful not to set μ exactly equal to unity in order to partially take into account perturbative forces and still utilize two-body formulas. As an example, for minor planets between the orbits of Mars and Jupiter we can lump the masses of Mercury, Venus, Earth, and Mars with that of the Sun and thereby partially account for the perturbative influence of these bodies.

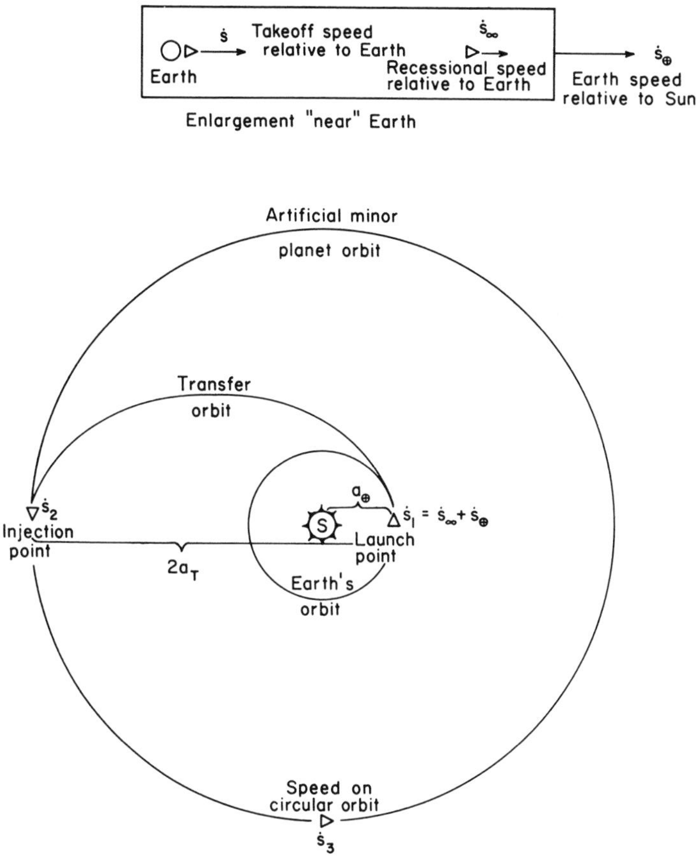

FIG. 9. Artificial minor planet.

system at initial injection onto the transfer orbit at $r_1 = 1$ (in terms of the characteristic speed unit) is

$$\dot{s}_1{}^2 = \frac{2}{1} - \frac{1}{a_T} = 2 - \frac{1}{2} = \frac{3}{2} \text{ or } \dot{s}_1 = \sqrt{\frac{3}{2}}.$$

At aphelion on the transfer ellipse (i.e., the point of injection of the payload onto the artificial minor planet orbit) $r_2 = 3$, so that

$$\dot{s}_2{}^2 = \frac{2}{3} - \frac{1}{2} = \frac{1}{6} \text{ or } \dot{s}_2 = \frac{1}{\sqrt{6}}.$$

The speed required to establish the payload on the circular 3 a.u. orbit is the difference between $\dot{s}_2$ and the circular orbit speed at 3 a.u., which is

$$\dot{s}_3^2 = \frac{1}{3} \text{ or } \dot{s}_3 = \frac{1}{\sqrt{3}}.$$

Thus the final injection speed to change from the transfer to the artificial minor-planet orbit is $\dot{s}_3 - \dot{s}_2 = 1/\sqrt{3} - 1/\sqrt{6} \simeq 0.169$ or in terms of km/sec = (0.169)(29.766) = 5.03 km/sec.

An almost identical analysis could be utilized to give the speed necessary to transfer a payload to a circular Earth satellite orbit. In this case the characteristic units are different, e.g., the length is measured in terms of Earth's equatorial radius (not astronomical units), the mass in terms of Earth masses (not solar masses), and the speed is in terms of circular-satellite speed at unit distance, which in this case amounts to the speed of a circular geocentric satellite grazing the Earth's surface around the equator (i.e., V_{co} = 7.905,258 km/sec, ≃4.912 mi/sec, or = 25,936 ft/sec). If the circular satellite orbit chosen were to be at an altitude of two Earth radii (or at distance from the geocenter of three Earth radii), then $\dot{s}_1$ at perigee of the transfer orbit (now truly reckoned at the Earth) would again be $\sqrt{3/2}$ but this time in terms of *geocentric* circular-satellite speed. In this regard it should be noted that the actual injection onto the transfer orbit will probably not occur at the Earth's surface ($r_1 = 1$) but rather at some booster burnout altitude, e.g., at an altitude of 0.05 Earth radii (or about 200 miles), in this case $r_1 = 1.05$ and

$$\dot{s}_1^2 = \frac{2}{1.05} - \frac{1}{2}.$$

The incremental speed necessary to change from the transfer orbit to the circular-satellite orbit is again $\dot{s}_3 - \dot{s}_2 = 0.169$, but because of the geocentric units it amounts to only (0.169)(7.905) = 1.33 km/sec.

The choice of the preceding perhaps unfamiliar set of units is not only convenient, due to the simplification of formulas, but also *mandatory* for reasons of accurate constants.

3 THE COMETS

Comets are the most mysterious and unpredictable members of the solar system, and consequently, also serve as historical introduction to astrodynamics. The word "planet" means "wanderer," but the "comets" or "hairy stars" are the actual wanderers of celestial spaces. Planets move in the same direction in orderly paths of low eccentricity and almost in the same plane, and their positions can be predicted far into the future. Comets, on the other hand, may flash into view from any direction and at any angle, and their orbital eccentricities may be anything from zero to more than one. In brightness they range from the faintest that can be photographed by the largest telescope to objects so brilliant that, in spite of their transparency and diffuseness, are perceptible to the unaided eye against a sunlit sky. Comets rapidly increase in luminosity as they near the Sun, for they shine only by virtue of sunlight, either as reflected from their solid meteoritic material (cosmic dust and rock fragments) or as the result of fluorescence of their gaseous elements caused by absorption of ultraviolet radiation and re-emission in the visible spectrum.

3.1. Characteristics of Comets

3.1.1. Structural Characteristics

The "ideal" comet consists of a *nucleus* or densest part, a *coma* or surrounding gaseous sheath, and the *tail* (or tails) that usually develop due to the expulsion of matter from the head as the comet approaches the Sun. The frequently observed explosions, attributed to the intense heating of frozen gases, cause dust and gases to be ejected in all directions, and the material is forced by solar radiation pressure and the pressure of a "solar wind" of protons and electrons to stream out in a direction exactly opposite to that of the Sun. Twelve or more comets, however, have developed temporary spike-like projections or "antitails" *toward* the Sun, apparently composed of ejected material not affected by radiation pressure. They are explained, perhaps, as the projection of normal tails on the sky. Thus cometary masses are continually decreasing while they are in the Sun's neighborhood, and at best, they cannot exceed 1/10,000 the mass of the Earth, according to all the evidence. For example, Comet 1889V Brooks spent two days within the satellite system of Jupiter describing an arc of 313° around the planet, without producing an observable effect on Jupiter's moons; but the comet's period of revolution was changed from 29 to seven years by the attraction of the great planet. In 1770, Lexell's Comet came so close to the Earth that some disturbance in the Earth's motion was anticipated, but no such effect was observed. As their volumes exceed those of the planets and sometimes even the Sun itself, the densities are inconceivably small.

One of the least understood, and possibly most significant features of comets is the continuous variation in volume, even when allowance is made for indistinctness of outline and the angle of projection on the sky. As a general rule, comets appear to contract as they approach within 2 a.u. of the Sun. Halley's Comet, for example, when first seen at a distance of 3 a.u. exhibited a coma 14,000 miles across; but it had increased to 220,000 miles by the time the comet was 2 a.u. from the Sun. During the short interval to perihelion passage, 0.5 a.u. from the Sun, the diameter had shrunk to 120,000 miles, then as the comet receded, it increased with great rapidity to 300,000 miles at 1 a.u. distance. A year later, at 4 a.u., the coma had again diminished to a diameter of 30,000 miles. Similarly, Encke's Comet has been observed to contract from a diameter of 300,000 miles at aphelion (4 a.u.) to 3000 miles at perihelion (0.34 a.u.).

3.1.2. Orbital Characteristics

Of the 100,000 comets which may, in the course of centuries, come close enough to be observed from the Earth, the orbits of only 1000 have been determined. All comets are believed to be periodic, and therefore, more or less permanent members of the solar system, and their average period is estimated to be 30,000 to 40,000 years. Obviously, the comets that have been observed to return to the Sun again and again are the exception rather than the rule. Of the 1000 comets for which orbits have been computed, fewer than 100 have periods of revolution less than 100 years; some 40 or 50 have periods of between 100 and 1000 years, and the periods of the remainder are very uncertain. Fewer than 30 comets are known to have been observed on two or more returns to the Sun. About 50 comets have periods less than 12 years and move in the same direction and approximately the same plane as Jupiter, indicating beyond question that sometime in the past they have approached close enough to have their motions brought under the control of the great planet.

It is difficult to pinpoint the position of a comet exactly enough for a precise orbit determination, due to the diffuseness of the image. The observed arc is often so short, compared with the greatly elongated ellipse, that one conic section will represent it about as well as another. Hence, it is usual to compute parabolas for newly discovered comets from which ephemerides may be derived for following the comet further. Strömgren traced 20 definitely hyperbolic orbits backward beyond Jupiter and Saturn, applying perturbations, and found that all were traveling in ellipses when they entered the populated region of the solar system. However the question of hyperbolic meteorite orbits still remains inconclusively answered. See Baker's discussion of this matter.[19]

Comet Encke has two unique and unexplained features: the period of 3.3 years is the shortest comet period known; and the orbit is gradually shrinking at a nonuniform rate, while the period diminishes correspondingly by 2.5 days per century. Two other members of Jupiter's captive family may also have accelerated motions. On the other hand, three short-period comets are suspected of being slightly retarded in their motion, i.e., their periods are growing longer. In both these effects, the causes of the phenomena are not explained. Bessel, however, suggested that the acceleration may be the result of ejection of a jet of material from the comet. Hence comets may be looked upon as the historical prototypes of modern thrust-propelled interplanetary vehicles.

3.2. Halley's Comet

3.2.1. History

Kepler was six years old when the great daylight comet of 1577 inspired Tycho Brahe to proclaim that comets were not the Aristotelian bursting into flames of vapors arising from the Earth's surface into a sublunar sphere of fire just outside the atmosphere. Tycho could find no diurnal parallax for the comet and concluded that it moved in a circular path outside the orbit of Venus. Kepler observed the motions of the great comets of 1607 and 1618 and saw that they passed between the Sun and the Earth. Newton tells us in the *Principia* that Kepler was the first to try to measure the distance of a comet by four observations, and that he believed they moved in straight lines.

Oddly enough, Kepler never thought of applying his remarkable laws of planetary motion to comets. It remained for Halley (1705)[20] to prove that one comet at least, and by inference most comets, moved in a highly eccentric ellipse and returned to the Sun at regular intervals. He calculated the parabolic orbits by Newton's graphical method for 24 historical comets for which sufficiently approximate observations were available, including the bright comet of 1682 that he himself had observed. On tabulating the orbital elements he discovered that there were several for which the longitudes of the node and perihelion and the inclination to the ecliptic were nearly identical, and when he saw also that the intervals between their apparitions were multiples of 75–77 years, he realized that a single comet, moving in an eccentric ellipse, had made repeated returns to perihelion. He correctly attributed the slight inequalities in the intervals to perturbations by the major planets and cited as corroboration the uncertainty in the orbit of Saturn due to the attraction of Jupiter. He traced the comet which bears his name back to 1305, and it was later identified with comets recorded in the Chinese annals back to 240 B.C. and probably 467 B.C.

3.2.2. The Computations of Clairaut and Others

Clairaut computed perturbations by Jupiter and Saturn and predicted that Comet Halley would next pass perihelion on 1759 April 13, pointing out, however, that the date might be changed a whole month due to the uncertainty in the masses of the great planets as well as the possibility of an encounter with unknown members of the solar system. Actually the comet passed the Sun on March 13, vindicating Clairaut's prediction and confounding the ridicule of scoffers who had looked for the return a year earlier, refusing to believe that the action of Jupiter could retard the motion by 518 and that of Saturn by 100 days.

In France, Damoiseau and de Pontecoulant calculated Jupiter and Saturn perturbations forward and predicted that Comet Halley would next return on 1835 November 4 and 12 respectively, but neither astronomer considered it necessary to include the action of the terrestrial planets.

In Germany, Rosenberger carried the calculation from the 1682 perihelion passage, including perturbations by Mars, Earth, and Venus in addition to those of the major planets, and arrived at two possible dates for the 1835 return: November 3 on the hypothesis that the comet traversed a path through a resisting medium, and November 11 without it. His compatriot, Lehmann, investigated the orbit from the 1607 apparition, observed by Kepler, and obtained November 26 as the date of perihelion passage. The actual date proved to be November 16, which was very close to the average value. In England, Cowell and Crommelin carried the investigation forward from 1835 to the 1910 return, and backward into ancient times to establish the identity with historic comets. When Comet Halley passed between the Sun and the Earth in May 1910 the tail extended for 150,000,000 miles, and was longer than the radius of the Earth's orbit! The Earth passed through it, but without noticeable effects.

3.3. Life and Origin of Comets

3.3.1. Biela's Comet

Several periodic comets for which ephemerides were available have vanished from view but none with such a sensational leave-taking as Biela's Comet. When this object was discovered by von Biela in 1826, it was then found to have been observed for a few weeks in 1772 and 1805, when it had a diameter of 30,000 miles as measured by Schröter. A member of Jupiter's family, Comet Biela first made news when Olbers predicted that it would cut across the Earth's orbit in 1832. As it happened, the Earth was 50,000,000 miles from the point where the comet crossed its path, and no damage was done. Then on its return in 1845 astronomers were astonished to see that Comet Biela was accompanied by a faint nebulous companion which rapidly increased in luminosity until for a time it was brighter than the principal component. Maury at the U. S. Naval Observatory followed the curious pair for several weeks, noting the fluctuations in brightness and color, the development of tails as they approached the Sun, and strangest of all the formation that he describes as follows:

"No. 2 appears to have thrown a light arch of cometary matter from its head over to that of the other; and their tails stretching off below the field, gives these two objects the singular and beautiful appearance of an arched way in the heavens through which the stars are sometimes seen to pass."

On the next return of Comet Biela in 1852, one component was about

$\frac{1}{2}°$ or 1,500,000 miles behind the other, but it was difficult to know which was the original and which the companion. Neither was observed again after the five weeks perihelion passage of 1852, although a search was made in 1859 and 1865.

3.3.2. Comets and Meteor Showers

In 1866, Schiaparelli demonstrated the connection between meteor showers and comets when he proved that the Perseid swarm moved in the same path as Tuttle's Comet. And in 1867 d'Arrest and Weiss showed that the meteor shower known from their radiant as Andromedes, pursued the same trajectory as the vanished Comet Biela.† On the night of November 27, 1872, just a century after the comet was originally discovered, a brilliant display of meteors fulfilled their prediction when four observers in Italy counted 33,000 "shooting stars" in $6\frac{1}{2}$ hr. Again on November 27, 1885 another spectacular shower was observed in Italy, when it was estimated that 75,000 meteors per hour entered the Earth's atmosphere. The numbers have greatly diminished in subsequent perihelion passages, and although the Earth still sweeps up some debris from Comet Biela it is obvious that either the swarm has been dispersed by Jupiter perturbations or diverted so that the Earth no longer passes through it. In this latter regard, Dubin has estimated from satellite data, and Van de Hulst from zodiacal light data, that between 5 and 10,000 tons of meteoritic material (primarily from mesometeoritic comet debris) enter the Earth's atmosphere per day!

It has recently been proposed that certain short-lived or ephemeral natural satellites of the Earth might be produced during such meteor

† There exist three different categories of meteorites, not all of which are associated with comets. In order to differentiate among these categories, it is essential to introduce and to define certain basic terms.

1. For those very small meteorites (having a characteristic dimension of a few microns) that are stopped by the atmosphere, without being consumed in flight or without producing luminous phenomena visible at the Earth's surface, the name "micrometeorite" has been proposed by Whipple. (The term "ultratelescopic meteorite" was first applied to tiny meteorites by Öpik.)

2. For those meteorites that are sufficiently massive to become fallen meteorites and whose origin appears to be related to that of the minor planets, the name "macrometeorite" is proposed.

3. For those intermediate meteorites (having a characteristic dimension of the order of a fraction of an inch) that are stopped by the atmosphere, consumed, and are seen as common "meteors," the name "mesometeorites" is proposed. The origin of these bodies appears to be related to the disintegration of comets.

showers (cf. Mebane[21], Baker[22], and O'Keefe[23]). Also the possibility that slowly moving and luminous "cometoids" pass through the atmosphere has been suggested by Robey[24,25].

Several comets have been known to subdivide, the earliest on record having been reported by Euphorus in 371 B.C. In 1916, Taylor's Comet 1915e broke into nearly equal parts. On their expected return in 1928, neither component was found, both had disappeared. Young observed that the nucleus of the Great Comet 1882 III became greatly elongated on approach to the Sun, extending to 50,000 miles. Then six starlike condensations appeared like a "string of pearls" along the comet-body. Passing perihelion, the great comet swung through an arc of 300° at a tremendous speed less than a solar radius from the Sun's surface, and then broke into four sizable comets that gradually drew apart. Due to the slight difference in the initial velocities with which they separated, the four comets were found to move in ellipses with periods of revolution of 670, 770, 880, and 960 years respectively. They will therefore return to the Sun at long intervals, recognizable only by a similarity in the orbital elements, (cf. Olivier[26]).

A month after its discovery, Comet Brooks 1889 V was seen by Barnard to eject four secondary nuclei which moved at first in approximately the same orbit while gradually separating. Two vanished within a few days. The other two miniature comets continued to follow their paths for a month, when one became too faint to observe. The fourth increased in luminosity until it was brighter than the principal comet; but when the latter returned to the Sun in 1896, it was alone.

3.3.3. Origin of Comets

The theory that several comets may have originated from the partition of a single great comet is supported by various lines of evidence. Hoek (1866) plotted on a projection of the celestial sphere the aphelia of the 190 periodic comets then known and found among them seven distinct "families" containing four to twelve members each. The persistent clustering in spite of the perturbations to which they must have been subjected over the centuries indicated a common origin for the components, presumably in some great generating comet. Hoek calculated the paths of 1860 III, 1863 I and 1863 VI to A.D. 757 and found that in that year each was exactly 600 a.u. from the Sun. The slight differences in their periods of revolution could be explained by a relative velocity amounting to only 2 ft/sec at the time of partition. Bredikhine (1888) also investigated "families" of comets moving in similar orbits that could not possibly be due to returns of a single comet because of the short and irregular intervals between them. From the similarity of the orbits of 1843 I, 1880 I, and 1882 III and their periods of 732, 769, and 772 years respectively, he deduced that the parent comet must have passed perihelion in the year 1110. Eddington (1913) diagrammed aphelia of 317 periodic comets and corroborated the tendency to cluster as well as the regions of avoidance which Hoek had noticed, where no aphelia were present (cf. Bredikhine[27]).

In considering the origin of great comets there are certain general points of agreement. For example, comets are evidently far more numerous than most of us would suspect from the evidence of our eyes. Obviously the ones we are able to observe must formerly have been much larger and brighter than they are now. The rapid disintegration in the Sun's neighborhood resulting from explosions and the ejection of material in the form of one or more "tails" that cannot return to the main body indicates that comets possess a finite life span a great deal shorter than those of the more durable planets. This leads to one of two conclusions:

(i) If comets were formed at the same time as the rest of the solar system, 5 to 10×10^9 years ago, they must be held in a reservoir in some region remote from the Sun and planets. Öpik and Oort have advanced the theory that a cometary "halo" surrounds the solar system at enormous distances from the comparatively small region occupied by the known planets. Occasionally one of these bodies is accelerated by the attraction of a passing star and leaves the comet sphere for an unknown destination. At other times, according to the theory, a comet may be retarded by stellar perturbations and begin to fall toward the Sun with increasing speed.

(ii) An alternative theory suggests that comets may have joined the Sun's family at a more recent date. Laplace (1796) explained comets as relatively small condensations of nebulous material (cosmic dust particles and gases) which wander through interstellar space until, chancing to come within the attraction of a star such as the Sun, they are drawn into hyperbolic orbits and begin to fall inward toward the center of attraction. He believed that the effect of passing through the "resisting ethereal medium" and the attraction of all the planets on both the inward and outward journey would retard the motion and change the initial hyperbolic trajectory into an ellipse.

Bredikhine pointed out that the Sun's path through the galaxy can be traced back to the vast nebulosity of the Orion region, where the Sun may have attracted to itself a great cloud of embryonic comets. Lyttleton[28] suggests that the solar system may have traversed several such cosmic gas and dust clouds in its circuits of the galaxy, each time attracting to itself, or rather to the center of mass of the solar system (which lies outside the Sun), an "accretion stream" of cometary condensations which fall inward on hyperbolic orbits until retarded by planetary perturbations.

3.4. Orbit Methods and Future Investigations

3.4.1. Orbit Methods

Newton characterized the derivation of a parabolic orbit from comet observations as *longe difficillimum* and confessed that he had tried many ways of solving the problem. He developed a graphical method requiring successive approximations that enabled Halley to establish the periodicity of comets. Several astronomers worked at the problem, but Olbers (1797) was the first to develop a simple analytical method that has stood the test of time (see Section 6.5).

Olbers argued that each observation gives a direction along which the comet must travel in a plane passing through the Sun. Only two points are required to fix a parabola when the focus is known. If three points in a plane are to fall on a parabola only one inclination to the ecliptic is possible; and a fourth position determines the line of nodes. Thus a parabolic orbit is completely specified by four observations without regard to the times or law of areas. When three observed directions are combined with Euler's equation relating the time intervals to the radii vectors and the chords, there are four equations for only three unknowns. In Olbers' method the unknowns are the "curtate distances," i.e., the projections of the geocentric distances on the plane of the Earth's orbit. Three points not in the same straight line fix the position of the plane; consequently two distances and the center of the Sun determine both the plane and the third distance. This relation gives Olbers' first equation. The requirement that the three positions of the comet must lie on a parabola with the Sun at the focus constitutes the second equation; and the relations between the two time intervals and the radii and chords provide the other two equations.

3.4.2. Future Investigations

From this brief discussion it may be observed that there are still a few unsolved problems in the theory of comets and their motions, the solutions of which might prove to be of interest to the student of astrodynamics. Planets travel in well-worn grooves, marked out for them by millions of years of mutual gravitational interaction. Their paths are prosaic and predictable. Comets, on the contrary, pursue experimental trajectories only partly predetermined by their initial impulse, somewhat like rockets soaring upward from a launching pad. We observe their behavior but must rely on known facts and conjecture to understand its causes. For example:

What causes the acceleration of Encke's Comet and the shortening of its major axis, all known perturbations having been accounted for? Is there a resisting medium along its path? Why do comets contract as they approach within 2 a.u. of the Sun, and expand again after leaving the Sun? Why do comets appear to avoid certain directions for the orientation of the lines of apsides? Why do some comets appear to have a retardation in longitude?

The answers to these and other questions, assuming that the observed effects are real, may be important to the interplanetary traveler.

3.5. Simple Illustrative Examples

As in the case of minor planet orbits it behooves us to take this opportunity to apply some of the simpler astrodynamic concepts presented in Chapter 1 to comets.

First let us determine the semimajor axis of Halley's Comet from the observed period of about 77 years. If P_0 is the Earth's period (characteristic heliocentric period) = 1 year and a_H is the semimajor axis of Halley's comet, then by Kepler's third law

$$\left(\frac{P}{P_0}\right)^2 = \left(\frac{77}{1}\right)^2 = \left(\frac{a_H}{a_\oplus}\right)^3 = \left(\frac{a_H}{1}\right)^3$$

or $a_H \cong 18$ a.u. The speed of Halley's comet relative to a heliocentric inertial coordinate system at $r = 1$ a.u. is obtained from the *vis-viva* equation (13)

$$\dot{s}^2 = \tfrac{2}{1} - \tfrac{1}{18}$$

or $\dot{s} \cong 1.39$. Assuming Halley's Comet intersected the Earth's orbit in a nearly perpendicular direction the *relative* speed between the Earth and Halley's Comet during the 1910 passage was

$$(\dot{s} \text{ relative})^2 = 1^2 + (1.39)^2 = 2.94$$

or $\dot{s}$ relative $= 1.71 = (1.71)(29.766) \cong 51$ km/sec.

Next let us suppose that you are to design a manned "artificial comet" to probe the solar system in the region between Mercury and Venus. Specifically that you wish to establish a circular orbit at $\frac{1}{2}$ a.u. from the Sun and then return to Earth again—all within a year. Let us see if such a plan is feasible.

In this case the heliocentric transfer orbit will have its aphelion at the Earth at time of launch and its perihelion at the point of final injection onto the $\frac{1}{2}$ a.u. circular orbit. The requisite speeds can be computed in a straightforward manner by using the *vis-viva* equation (13) exactly as was done in the last section i.e.,

$$\dot{s}_1^2 = \frac{2}{1} - \frac{1}{a_T}, \quad \dot{s}_2^2 = \frac{2}{\frac{1}{2}} - \frac{1}{a_T}, \text{ and } \dot{s}_3^2 = \frac{1}{\frac{1}{2}}.$$

In order to determine the transit times, however, recourse must again be made to Kepler's third law. The semimajor axis of this new transfer orbit is $a_T = (1 + \frac{1}{2})/2 = \frac{3}{4}$ a.u. Thus if P_0 is the Earth's period, then by Kepler's third law

$$\left(\frac{P}{P_0}\right)^2 = \left(\frac{a_T}{a_\oplus}\right)^3,$$

where $P_0 = 1$ year and $a_\oplus = 1$, so that $P = (\frac{3}{4})^{3/2} \cong 0.65$ years. Consequently, it takes about a third of a year outbound from the Earth to the circular orbit and about a third of a year inbound from the circular orbit on the transfer ellipse back to Earth. By a similar analysis the period of the circular orbit is $(\frac{1}{2})^{3/2} \cong 0.35$ years so that it would be possible to make one complete revolution around the Sun on the $\frac{1}{2}$ a.u. orbit and then return to the Earth's orbit via the transfer ellipse (from perihelion to aphelion) just in time to meet the Earth.

A somewhat analogous problem would be that of some Martians attempting to establish a 24 "Martian" hour equatorial satellite, i.e., to establish a satellite that would always remain over the same spot on the Martian equator as Mars rotated (the natural Martian satellite Deimos would almost fit the requirement by the way). The semimajor axis of this *areocentric* (Mars centered) satellite would then have to be obtained from its periodicity. The characteristic period, P_0, of an areocentric surface-circular satellite is about $1\frac{1}{2}$ Martian hours (by coincidence the surface circular-satellite or characteristic period, P_0, for a geocentric satellite is about $1\frac{1}{2}$ Earth hours). Hence

$$\left(\frac{P}{P_0}\right)^2 = \left(\frac{24}{1\frac{1}{2}}\right)^2 = \left(\frac{a}{1}\right)^3.$$

or $a = 6.35$ Martian equatorial radii or since one Martian equatorial radius is about 3413 km (see Table IX) the 24 "hour" satellite would be at an altitude of about 18,260 km above the Martian equator. The launch speed onto the transfer orbit from Mars' equator (neglecting Mars' rotation) would be

$$\dot{s}_1^2 = \frac{2}{1} - \frac{1}{a_T}$$

where $a_T = (1 + 6.35)/2$. While at apareon on the transfer orbit the vehicle speed would be

$$\dot{s}_2^2 = \frac{2}{6.35} - \frac{1}{a_T}.$$

The speed of the Martian 24-hour satellite is, similarly, $\dot{s}_3^2 = 1/6.35$. These speeds can be translated in terms of km/sec by noting that the Martian circular satellite or characteristic speed $V_{co} \cong 3.6$ km/sec (see Fig. 10).

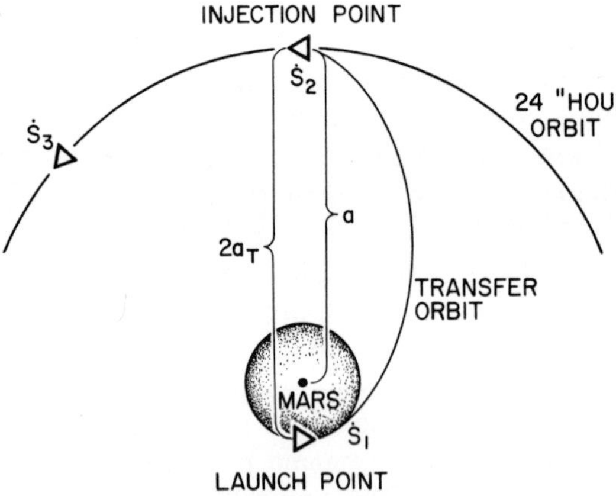

FIG. 10. 24 "Martian" hour satellite.

As a final example of the use of characteristic units consider the unit system that would probably be adopted by the very hypothetical "inhabitants" of a comet whose heliocentric orbit exhibits a semimajor axis of 4 a.u. Since the comet has negligible mass, and no easily definable equatorial radius, there would be no basis upon which to establish a "cometocentric" system of units. Nevertheless, the choice of the heliocentric units would be different from the choice made by Earthmen. The "inhabitants" of the comet would choose one complete revolution of their own body about the Sun as the basis for their own year. Since the period of the comet would be $4^{3/2} = 8$ Earth years, their year would be eight times our year. Furthermore, the characteristic heliocentric distance unit adopted by such beings, in terms of which they would measure the rest of the solar system, would be just four times our astronomical unit while the characteristic heliocentric speed would be $1/\sqrt{4} = \frac{1}{2}$ the Earth's mean orbital speed. The only common unit between us would be the solar mass.

With regard to the question of units it should be noted that the unit of τ can be derived from the unit of $\dot{s}$, i.e., $\dot{s} = 1 =$ (characteristic length)/(characteristic time) $=$ (radius)/τ so that τ is the time that is required for a circular satellite at unit distance to move one unit distance along its orbit. The actual size of this time unit in terms of other more conventional time units can be obtained from the basic definition that $\tau \triangleq k_e(t - t_0) =$ 13.447,052 min (or one "k_e^{-1} min") for geocentric orbits, $\tau = k_s(t - t_0) =$ 58.132,440,87 days for heliocentric orbits etc. (these are the times required, respectively, for a circular geocentric satellite at the unit distance of one Earth's radius to travel one Earth's radius and a circular heliocentric satellite at the unit distance of 1 a.u. (e.g., the Earth) to travel 1 a.u.).

A careful consideration of the foregoing examples and those presented in Chapter 2 will lead to a clearer understanding of the astronomical systems of units. The discussion of the actual numerical specification of these units will, however, be held in abeyance until Chapter 5. For additional numerical examples of the material contained in this volume, the reader is invited to refer to Herrick.[1]

4 GEOMETRY AND COORDINATE SYSTEMS

Before a study of astrodynamics can be undertaken it is necessary to acquire a clear understanding of the geometrical properties of two-body orbits and of various coordinate systems. Such an understanding must be based upon a command of the vocabulary of celestial mechanics. No attempt is made to justify the logic of this vocabulary: just as in the case of a foreign language it must be accepted by merit of its general usage and not revised to suit the taste of the individual. The majority of the nomenclature required will be introduced in the first three subsections.

The first two subsections deal with conic sections and their equations while the third discusses five principal coordinate systems, and the fourth section involves the actual determination of the coordinates of an observation station on the Earth's surface and of a vehicle in space. The fifth section includes a detailed presentation of the Moon-centered or selenographic coordinate system in order to indicate the complexity involved in a rigorous transformation to our nearest neighbor in space. The last subsection provides a key to the tables of planetary coordinates (which are indispensable for interplanetary coordinate transformations) and discusses the procedures used for their interpolation.

4.1. Conic Sections

4.1.1. General

According to Kepler's first law as extended by Newton, an object in a central force field (therefore exhibiting two-body motion) will trace out an orbit whose shape closely approximates a conic section with primary focus at the center of the principal attracting body.

Conic sections are, no doubt, well known to the reader. They may be considered as either ellipses or hyperbolas. The circle is a special case of the ellipse, whereas the parabola is the conic section that defines the boundary between the ellipse and the hyperbola. One of the most useful derivations of the equation of the conic results from the "directrix" definition, which describes a conic as the locus of points whose distances from the focus and the directrix remain in a constant ratio. This ratio is called the eccentricity, e (see Fig. 6). The x_ω-axis* is directed along the axis of symmetry of the conic from the focus to the directrix (therefore, directed to the point of closest approach or to the perigee, perihelion, or more generally, *perifocus*), the y_ω-axis is directed from the focus perpendicular to the x_ω-axis, r is the radial distance from the focus to a point on the conic, v is the angle between the x_ω-axis and r (termed the *true anomaly*), and p is the value of y_ω when $x_\omega = 0$ (i.e., the radius to the intersection of the conic with the y_ω-axis—termed the *parameter* or *semilatus rectum*). The equation of the conic can readily be found through consideration of Fig. 6:

$$p/e - r/e = r \cos v = x_\omega.$$

Therefore, the equation of the conic is

$$p = r(1 + e \cos v). \tag{14}$$

It can also be noted from Fig. 6 that if q be defined as the positive x_ω coordinate of the conic when $y_\omega = 0$ (radius to the intersection of the conic with the x_ω-axis), then letting $r = q$, we find that

$$p = q(1 + e).$$

The distance between the intersections (apsides) of the line of symmetry of the conic with the conic is termed the *transverse axis* or the *line of apsides*. In the case of an ellipse, one terms it the major axis. One-half of this length, the semimajor or semitransverse axis, is denoted by a. The distance between the center of the ellipse and either of the foci is termed c or ae. Consequently, it is clear that $q = a(1 - e)$ or $p = a(1 - e^2)$.

For nearly circular orbits it is often advisable to introduce the *argument of*

* The subscript ω indicates that the coordinate system is aligned with the perigee (-helion or -focus) direction.

latitude, $u \triangleq v + \omega$, where ω is defined in Chapter 1 as the argument of perigee (see Fig. 1).

4.1.2. Progression Through the Conic Sections

A simple demonstration of the change from one conic section to another can be carried out by the use of a flashlight. The flashlight beam approximates a cone and, by tilting it at different angles to the surface of a wall or blackboard, it is possible to observe the change from a circle (axis of flashlight perpendicular to the wall) to the ellipse, the parabola, and finally, when the angle of the axis is very oblique, to the hyperbola. Mathematically, it is possible to carry out a similar progression in a variety of ways. First of all, let us consider all those conics having a constant value for q (see Fig. 11). If the eccentricity e is 0, the ellipse degenerates into a circle. As e approaches unity, the ellipse becomes more and more elongated. This can be seen if one considers the distance from the focus to the far apsis, which is equal to $a(1 + e)$. When e reaches unity, the value of a necessary to keep q constant must necessarily go to infinity, since $q = a(1 - e)$. In this case the bounding conic is the parabola. If e becomes greater than unity, the parabola evolves into a hyperbola whose second branch appears to the right of the focus. If the focus-to-directrix distance is kept constant, the progression shown in Fig. 12 is obtained, and if the apsides are kept equidistant the progression shown in Fig. 13 is obtained. We can, therefore, outline the values for a and e associated with the conic sections by means of Table I.

Table I. Conic Sections

Conic	Eccentricity, e	Semitransverse axis, a
Circle	$e = 0$	$0 < a < \infty$
Ellipse	$0 \leq e \leq 1$	$0 < a < \infty$
Parabola	$e = 1$	$a = \infty$
Hyperbola	$1 \leq e < \infty$	$-\infty < a < 0$

As can be seen by inspection of Table I, the ellipse, parabola, and hyperbola all admit a value of e equal to unity. The rectilinear ellipse is simply a line segment connecting the two foci; the rectilinear parabola is a line from the focus along the transverse axis to plus infinity; and the rectilinear hyperbola is composed of two branches, one extending from one focus to

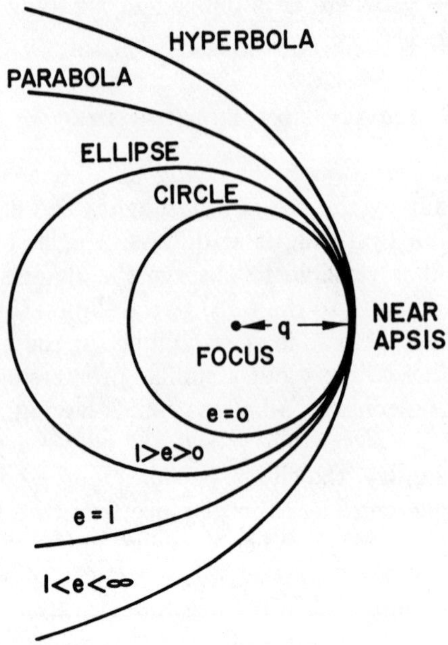

FIG. 11. Conic sections for constant q (after Herrick[1]).

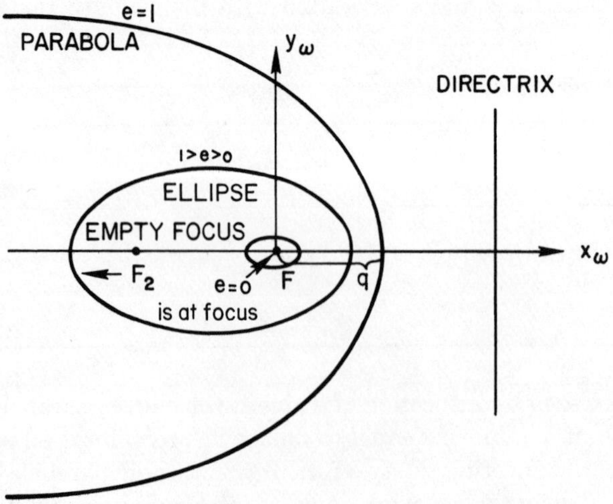

FIG. 12. Conic sections for constant focus to directrix distance.

plus infinity, the other extending from the second focus to minus infinity. It is sometimes difficult to conceive of such rectilinear orbits as having any physical significance with respect to actual two-body trajectories. The difficulty can often be overcome by considering the limiting case, as when an ellipse becomes more and more elongated and e approaches unity. This

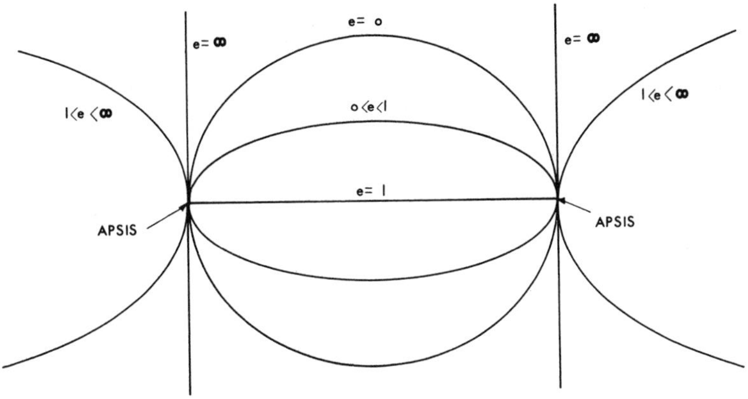

FIG. 13. Apsides fixed.

geometrical limit has also been demonstrated mathematically by Sundman[29] who analytically continued the orbits beyond the critical instant when it passed through the focus by expanding the equations of motion in ascending powers of $t^{1/3}$ and as a consequence obtaining a second-order branch point.

4.2. Equations for the Ellipse, Parabola, and Hyperbola

4.2.1. General

The polar coordinates r and v do not particularly lend themselves to the introduction of the relationships between time and position (e.g., Kepler's equation) that will be discussed in a later chapter. As will be seen, it proves to be more convenient to introduce certain auxiliary quantities, i.e., D, E, and F. The equations of the parabola, ellipse, and hyperbola will then be formulated in terms of these variables respectively.

4.2.2. The Ellipse

For elliptical orbits, the auxiliary quantity, E, called the *eccentric anomaly*, is defined as shown in Fig. 14. The equations of the coordinates referred to the orbit plane in terms of E are as follows:

$$\begin{aligned} x_\omega &= a(\cos E - e), \\ y_\omega &= a\sqrt{1 - e^2}\sin E, \\ r &= a(1 - e\cos E). \end{aligned} \tag{15}$$

We will present the derivation of these relationships because it will serve as a guide to the derivation of the following parabolic and hyperbolic formulas. From the geometry of Fig. 14 it is clear that

$$r\cos v = x_\omega = a\cos E - ae = a(\cos E - e).$$

Introducing this equation into the equation of a conic, we find that

$$r = p - ex_\omega = a(1 - e^2) - ae(\cos E - e) = a(1 - e\cos E).$$

Finally, y_ω can be most directly found from

$$y_\omega{}^2 = r^2 - x_\omega{}^2 = a^2(1 - e^2)\sin^2 E$$

so that

$$y_\omega = a\sqrt{(1 - e^2)}\sin E \qquad Q.E.D.$$

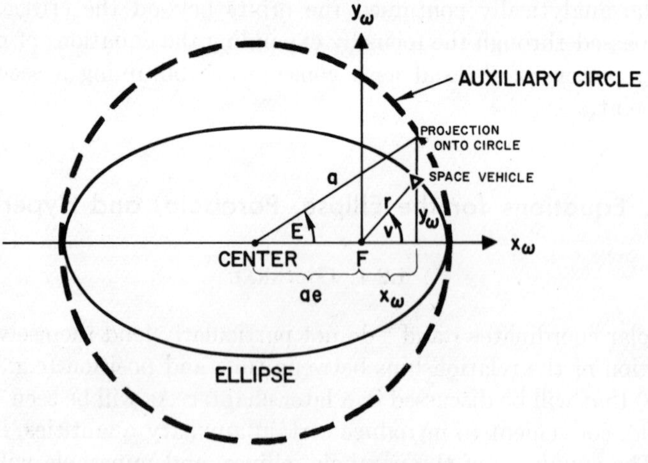

Fig. 14. Eccentric anomaly.

4.2.3. The Parabola

In the case of the parabola, an auxiliary quantity D is defined as $r\dot{r}/\sqrt{\mu}$. If it is recognized that $p = r^4\dot{v}^2/\mu$ (as will be shown in Chapter 6), and that in the case of a parabola $e = 1$ and $a =$ infinity, then $D = \sqrt{2q} \tan v/2$. Thus the equations for the parabola can be formulated as

$$x_\omega = q - D^2/2,$$
$$y_\omega = \sqrt{2q}\, D, \tag{16}$$

and

$$r = q + D^2/2.$$

As a sidelight to this discussion of parabolic orbits, it is appropriate to discuss briefly *Tisserand's criterion* as it is applied to nearly parabolic comet orbits. If a comet changes radically in size and brightness during a single apparition and if, at the same time, the orbital elements are altered by a chance encounter with an outer planet, how is the comet to be recognized with any certainty? If two comets, appearing several years apart, are suspected of being one and the same the identity may be proved or disproved by starting with the orbit of one and calculating perturbations across the gap. Then, if the final elements are the same as those of the suspect, the identity is considered established beyond reasonable doubt. But this is a laborious process; and Tisserand looked for a simple relation among the elements that remains unchanged by perturbations. The following equation, known as Tisserand's criterion, is useful for establishing the identity of two comets whose elements are a_1, e_1 and i_1; a_2, e_2 and i_2:

$$1/a_1 + 2\sqrt{a_1(1 - e_1^2)} \cos i_1 = 1/a_2 + 2\sqrt{a_2(1 - e_2^2)} \cos i_2. \tag{17}$$

The derivation of Eq. (17) can be found in reference 13, pp. 295 to 298, and will not be presented here.

4.2.4. The Hyperbola

In the case of the hyperbola, where a assumes a negative value, recourse must be taken to hyperbolic functions. The elliptical formulas may be transformed directly to the hyperbolic formulas by substituting for E the value iF and by observing the convention that $i = \sqrt{-1}$ and $\sqrt{1 - e^2} = +i\sqrt{e^2 - 1}$ (e is greater than unity for the hyperbola). A more descriptive definition of F can be obtained by consideration of a reference rectangular hyperbola (with $e = \sqrt{2}$). In this case, F can be associated with the reference hyperbola in a manner analogous to the definition of E by means of a reference circle. The equations for the hyperbola formulated in terms of F are as follows:

$$x_\omega = a(\cosh F - e),$$
$$y_\omega = -a\sqrt{e^2 - 1}\sinh F, \tag{18}$$

and

$$r = a(1 - e\cosh F).$$

All of the preceding equations are derived in more detail by Herrick.[1]

A more general universal variable, $\tilde{X}$, has also been developed by Herrick that is equally useful for the ellipse ($e \neq 0$), parabola, and hyperbola. In terms of $\tilde{X}$

$$x_\omega = q - \frac{\tilde{X}^2}{2!} + \frac{\tilde{X}^4}{a4!} - \frac{\tilde{X}^6}{a^2 6!} + \cdots,$$

$$y_\omega = \sqrt{p}\left[\tilde{X} - \frac{\tilde{X}^3}{a3!} + \frac{\tilde{X}^5}{a^2 5!} - \frac{\tilde{X}^7}{a^3 7!} + \cdots\right]$$

and

$$r = q + e\left[\frac{\tilde{X}^2}{2!} - \frac{\tilde{X}^4}{a4!} + \frac{\tilde{X}^6}{a^2 6!} - \cdots\right].$$

For the ellipse $\tilde{X} \triangleq \sqrt{a}\,E$, for the parabola $\tilde{X} \triangleq D$, and for the hyperbola $\tilde{X} \triangleq \sqrt{-a}\,F$.

4.3. Principal Coordinate Systems

4.3.1. Rectangular Coordinates

After centuries of experience, astronomers have found that the spherical polar coordinates, i, Ω, and ω, i.e., the orientation angles, are not well adapted to the analytical developments of orbit determination and recourse has been taken to rectangular coordinates. These Eulerian angles are, however, useful for descriptive purposes and are often determined as a by-product at the end of a computation.

In order to introduce the more commonly employed orientation vectors (those used in the rectangular coordinate development), it is necessary that five principal coordinate systems be defined. Each of these coordinate systems will be specified according to its usual origin, fundamental plane, and principal direction. Note that certain systems are clearly not inertial, some are quasi-inertial, and others completely inertial (ordinarily, dependent on the exact specification of the principal direction).

4.3.2. Geographic System

The first system is the common *geographic* system. The origin is the Earth's center (geocentric). The fundamental plane is the equatorial plane, on which directions are measured east or west from the intersection of this plane and the Greenwich meridian (i.e., a semicircle stretching from the North to the South Pole and passing through the Greenwich Observatory, England). The longitude is measured either East (λ_E) or West (λ_W)

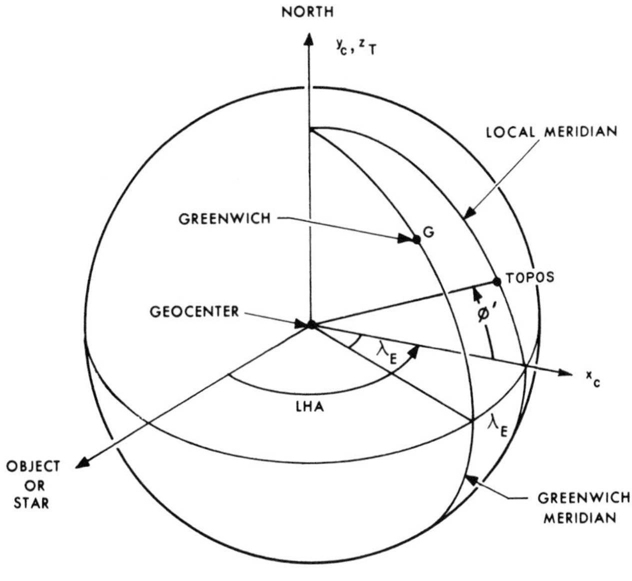

Fig. 15. Geographic coordinates.

from the Greenwich (also called *prime*) meridian. Geocentric latitude, ϕ', is measured along a meridian or by the angle at the center between the radius and the equatorial plane: positive if north and negative if south of the equatorial plane (see Fig. 15). The geographic system is obviously not an inertial one as it rotates with the Earth through 360° with respect to the Sun in $24^h 3^m 56\overset{s}{.}6$ sidereal time, or 24 mean solar hours.*

* The superscript h refers to hours, m to minutes, and s to seconds, while the superscripts d and y refer to days and years, respectively.

It may be worthwhile to digress briefly on the subject of latitude. There are three latitudes commonly employed in astronomical parlance: (i) geocentric, (ii) geodetic, and (iii) astronomical. *Geocentric latitude*, ϕ', is defined above as the angle measured at the Earth's center between the equatorial plane and a radius to the station; *geodetic latitude*, ϕ, is the angle between the equatorial plane and a normal to a *reference spheroidal surface*, Z_g, as shown in Fig. 16. The reference spheroid is an oblate ellipsoid whose surface most nearly approximates the mean sea-level surface of the Earth (geoid). Such a spheroid is characterized by a "flattening," "ellipticity," or "oblateness," f, where

$$f = (a - b)/a \tag{19}$$

and a is the semimajor and b the semiminor axis of the ellipse of revolution forming the spheroid. *Astronomical latitude*, ϕ_a, is defined as the angle between the local *astronomical zenith*, Z_a, or vertical (as determined by a plumb-bob or, more basically, by the direction of the local gravitational

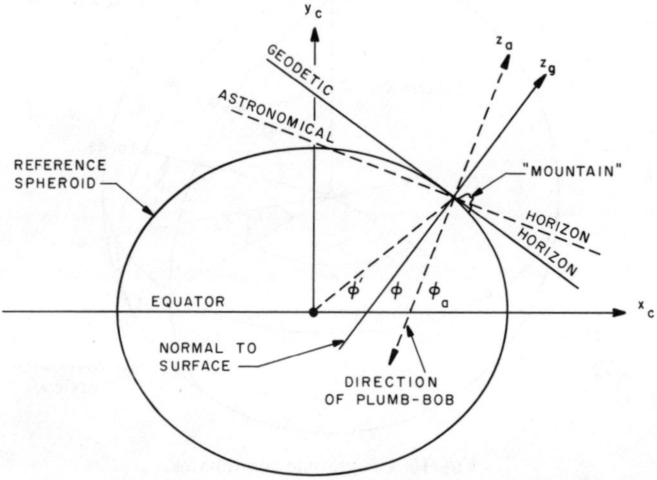

FIG. 16. Geocentric, geodetic, and astronomical latitude (after Herrick[1]).

field) and the equatorial plane. Since astronomical latitude is based upon the local gravitational field, resulting from the mean sea-level geoid and certain anomalies (such as the "mountain" shown in Fig. 16), it differs from the geodetic latitude by a small quantity, which is usually negligible. This difference is termed "station error." The *astronomical horizon* is simply a horizon plane perpendicular to Z_a. (Z_a is also centrifugal-force affected.)

There exist a variety of such reference spheroids each representing an approximation to the geoid and characterized by a flattening, f, and equatorial radius a_e. See Table II.

TABLE II. REFERENCE SPHEROIDS

Name	$a_e(m)$	$1/f$
Airy	6,376,542.000	299.300
Army Map Service (Hough)	6,378,270.000	297.000
Bessel	6,377,397.155	299.153
Clark 1866	6,378,206.400	294.979
Clark 1880	6,378,249.145	293.465
International	6,378,388.000	297.000
Krassovsky	6,378,245.000	298.300

It should be noted in passing that the angle between the observer's astronomical meridian and some star (or other distant object) is termed the *local hour angle* (LHA) and, as discussed in Chapter 11, is employed in the definition of time. See Fig. 15.

4.3.3. TOPOCENTRIC OR HORIZON SYSTEM

The second of these is the *topocentric* (from the Greek *topos*, a place) or horizon system, the origin of which is taken at the observer. In this system

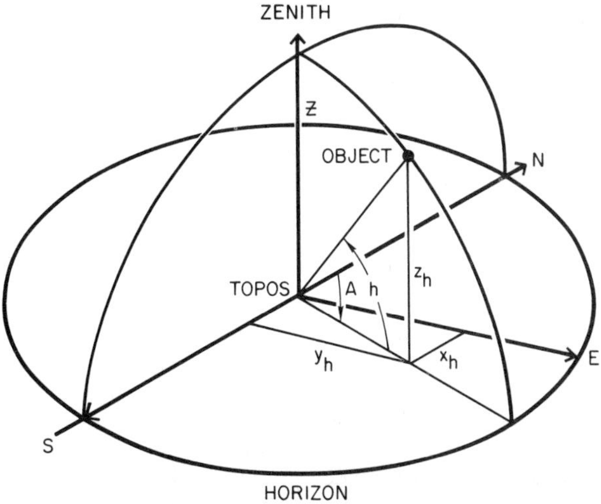

FIG. 17. Horizon or altazimuth system (after Herrick[1]).

(shown in Fig. 17), the x_h-axis is directed toward the south point, the y_h-axis toward the east and the z_h-axis is directed to the astronomical zenith. Such a coordinate system is being carried around by the Earth's rotation and is, therefore, not inertial. The angle from the north direction measured east in the x_h, y_h plane (horizon plane) is defined as azimuth, A, and the angle measured from this plane toward the zenith is defined as the altitude, h. (An alternate definition of azimuth, which is often employed by astronomers, specifies that it is measured west of the south direction.)

4.3.4. Equatorial System

The third system, often employed in geocentric orbit computations, is called the *equatorial* coordinate system. Its center is usually, but not exclusively, taken at the Earth's center (e.g., it is often taken at the topos). As was noted in the introduction, the x-axis of this system is directed towards the vernal equinox. The z-axis is directed parallel to the Earth's polar axis towards the North celestial pole and the y-axis is directed so as to form a right-handed coordinate system. As we have said before, the direction to the vernal equinox is not constant as the result of both the precession and nutation of the Earth's axis, the latter being caused primarily by the influence of the Moon. Hence, in specifying the equatorial coordinates of an object, it is also necessary to state what vernal equinox is referred to as principal direction. For example, star catalogs may be referred to the equinox of 1900, 1965, etc.* The rates of change of the right ascension, α, and declination, δ, due to precession are given by

$$\frac{d\alpha}{dt} = m + n \sin \alpha \tan \delta, \qquad \frac{d\delta}{dt} = n \cos \alpha, \tag{20}$$

where

$$m = +3^{\mathrm{s}}.073{,}27 + 0^{\mathrm{s}}.000{,}018{,}6(t - 1950),$$

$$n = +20''.042{,}6 - 0''.000{,}085(t - 1950),$$

or

$$= +1^{\mathrm{s}}.336{,}17 - 0^{\mathrm{s}}.000{,}005{,}7(t - 1950),$$

where α is counted in hours, minutes, and seconds, i.e., 24^h is equivalent

* Actually, one specifies an "equator and equinox" of a certain date, since the direction in which α is measured also depends upon the time-varying orientation of the equator. It is likewise necessary to specify whether the equator is a *mean* or a *true* one (see Chapter 10 of Herrick[1]). The *mean* equinox and equator of a date is their position *without* the effect of periodic nutation (18.6 year period) included, i.e., considering only the slow steady shift of precession (26,000 year period). The *true* or *apparent* is their actual position with nutation added. See pp. 237 and 238 for the *mean* and *apparent* sidereal times, which are measured relative to the mean and the apparent vernal equinox.

to 360°. The definition of the angles α (right ascension) and δ (declination) can be gleaned from inspection of Fig. 18 [rates given by (20) are per year].

It should be emphasized that this equatorial coordinate system is defined by *directions* from a particular origin and not by the equatorial plane itself. In other words, the center of the equatorial coordinate system may be at the geocenter, topocenter, heliocenter, selenocenter, etc. The celestial equator, however, is the same in every case, since although these centers are relatively far apart, to all intents and purposes they are all at the center

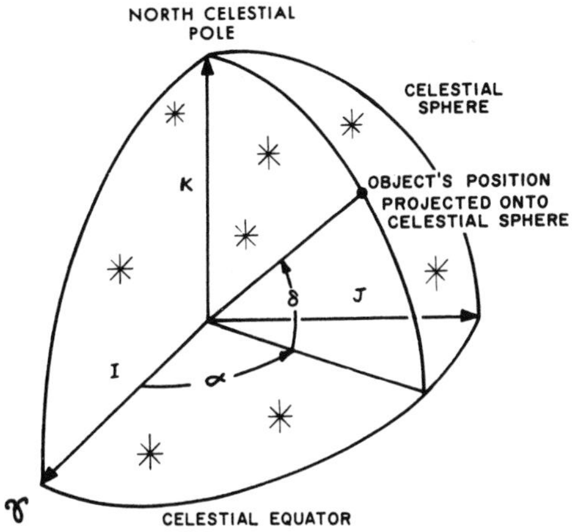

FIG. 18. Definition of α and δ.

of the infinite celestial sphere. For the same reason, the right ascensions and declinations of *stars* remain essentially the same irrespective of the equatorial coordinate center. Because stars are at such enormous distances little parallax or star-image displacement occurs in, for example, the translation of the center of coordinates from the Earth to Venus. For closer objects such as interplanetary space vehicles, on the other hand, the coordinates would depend to a very great extent on the choice of the center.

4.3.5. Ecliptic System

The fourth system, often employed in the case of heliocentric orbit computation, is referred to the *ecliptic* as fundamental plane. The x-axis is directed to the vernal equinox as in the equator system, whereas the z-axis

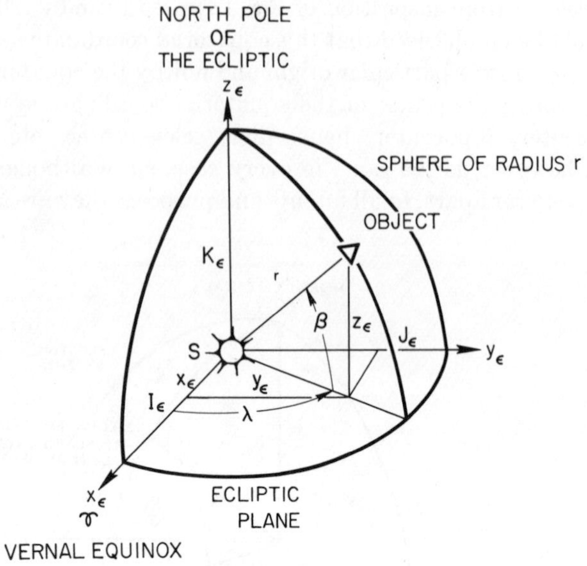

FIG. 19. Ecliptic system.

is directed along the normal to the ecliptic plane. Fig. 19 indicates the definition of celestial longitude, λ, and celestial latitude, β.

4.3.6. Orbit Plane Systems

The fifth coordinate system is referred to axes in and perpendicular to the orbit plane and may be separated into four subsystems. The origin, in every case, is at the central attracting body and the z-axis is normal to the orbit plane. The x-axis may be directed to perifocus (denoted by x_ω); or along the line of nodes (denoted by x_Ω); or to an inertial direction in the orbit plane Υ' ($x_{\Upsilon'}$); or, in fact, to the object itself forming a rotating system. The y-axis in each case is at right angles to the x-axis in the orbit plane in a direction such that x, y, and z form a right-handed coordinate system. The angle b is measured normally to the orbit plane and is utilized only in the analysis of perturbative forces that act at right angles to the plane i.e., for an object on a two-body orbit $b = 0$ in the absence of perturbative forces. The angle u $(=\omega + v)$ is called the *argument of latitude* and the angle l $(=\Omega + \omega + v)$ is called the *true longitude*.

For geocentric orbits, the *line of nodes* is defined as the line of intersection

TABLE III. SELECTED NOMENCLATURE FOR THE REFERENCE COORDINATE SYSTEMS

Coordinate System	Origin	Fundamental Plane	Principal Direction	Spherical Coord.	Rectangular Coordinates	Unit Vectors
Geographic	Geocenter	Equator	Greenwich Meridian	λ, ϕ'	x_c, y_c, x_T, y_T, z_T[a]	$\mathbf{I}_c, \mathbf{J}_c, \mathbf{K}$
Horizon	Topos	Horizon	North	A, h	x_h, y_h, z_h	$\mathbf{S}, \mathbf{E}, \mathbf{Z}$
Equatorial	Geocenter Topocenter Heliocenter etc.	Equatorial	Vernal Equinox	α, δ	x, y, z	$\mathbf{I}, \mathbf{J}, \mathbf{K}$
Ecliptic	Geocenter Heliocenter	Ecliptic	Vernal Equinox	λ, β	$x_\epsilon, y_\epsilon, z_\epsilon$	$\mathbf{I}_\epsilon, \mathbf{J}_\epsilon, \mathbf{K}_\epsilon$
Orbit	Focus	Orbit	Perifocus	v, b[b]	x_ω, y_ω	$\mathbf{P}, \mathbf{Q}, \mathbf{W}$
			Lines of Nodes	$u\ (= \omega + v), b$[b]	x_Ω, y_Ω	$\mathbf{N}, \mathbf{M}, \mathbf{W}$
			Υ'	$l\ (= \Omega + \omega + v), b$[b]	$x_{\Upsilon'}, y_{\Upsilon'}$	$\mathbf{F}, \mathbf{G}, \mathbf{W}$
			$\mathbf{r}$	—	—	$\mathbf{U}, \mathbf{V}, \mathbf{W}$

[a] See Eqs. (24) and (111).

[b] $b = 0$ for unperturbed two-body motion.

of the equatorial and orbit planes. In general, it is the intersection line of any reference plane with an orbit plane, e.g., the ecliptic and the orbit plane of Mars. It is often useful to define the antinodes as the intersection points (with the orbit) of a line (in the orbit plane) perpendicular to the line of nodes.

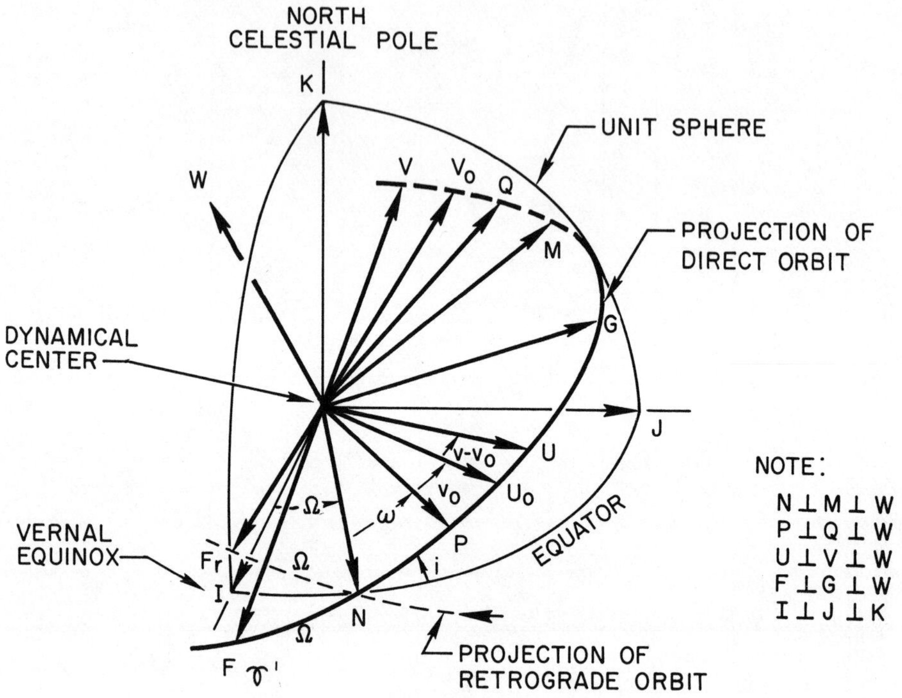

FIG. 20. Unit vectors.

In the foregoing systems and subsystems certain unit vectors are employed to define the different directions. Table III and Fig. 20 will demonstrate these unit vectors and also summarize the foregoing remarks: other unit vectors are discussed by Herrick.[1] Figure 21 gives a schematic illustration of the relation between the Earth, unit sphere (i.e., the sphere that defines unit vectors), and the celestial sphere. Since the celestial sphere is hypothesized to be at infinity, its center can be thought of as coinciding with the origin of any of the systems.

After centuries of experience, celestial mechanics has found the use of these unit vectors to be far more convenient than the orientation angles i, Ω, and ω for the definition of the orbit plane's orientation, i.e., for a transformation from the equatorial (or other) system into the orbit plane sys-

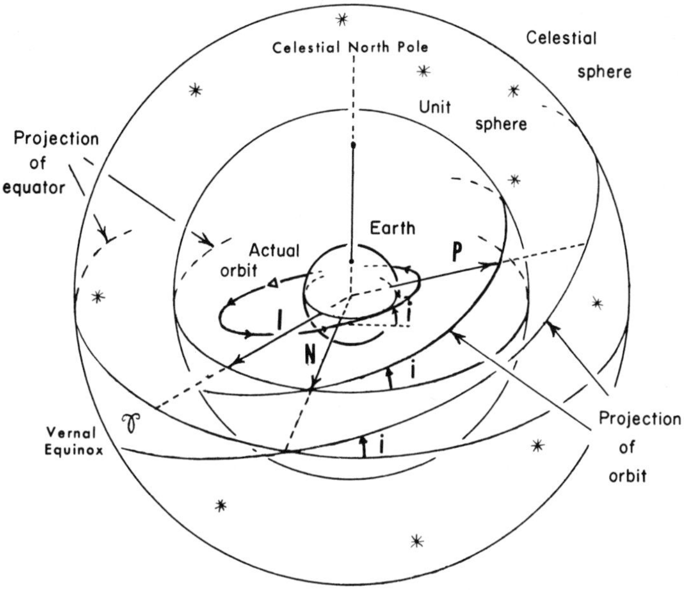

FIG. 21. Earth, unit, and celestial spheres.

tem. For example, the transformation of the coordinates of a space vehicle in the equatorial system (x, y, z) into the orbit plane (**P**, **Q**, **W**) system (x_ω, y_ω) in terms of unit vectors is simply

$$x_\omega = \mathbf{r} \cdot \mathbf{P} = xP_x + yP_y + zP_z$$

and

$$y_\omega = \mathbf{r} \cdot \mathbf{Q} = xQ_x + yQ_y + zQ_z \tag{21}$$

and vice-versa

$$\mathbf{r} = x_\omega \mathbf{P} + y_\omega \mathbf{Q}$$

$$x = x_\omega P_x + y_\omega Q_x \qquad x \to y,\, z. \tag{22}$$

If i, Ω, and ω were employed instead, then it would be necessary to form

$$x_\omega = x(\cos\omega\cos\Omega - \sin\omega\sin\Omega\cos i) + y(\cos\omega\sin\Omega + \sin\omega\cos\Omega\cos i) + z(\sin\omega\sin i), \text{ etc.} \tag{23}$$

See Chapter 5 in Herrick[1] and Eqs. (32) and (33) of this volume where the P's and Q's must be formed for the Moon's orbit.

The use of unit vectors not only leads to a concise method for specifying directions and executing coordinate rotations, but is also computationally more efficient since it circumvents the generation of or interpolation from tables of trigonometric functions—a very time-consuming process even for electronic computers. As is demonstrated in Chapter 6, the entire orbit determination, computation, and prediction can be accomplished *without* the use of trigonometry functions (except for a very limited number in Kepler's equation) if the unit vectors **P**, **Q**, and **W** are utilized instead of i, ω, and Ω. Furthermore, very useful checks are provided by the use of these vectors e.g., $\mathbf{P} \cdot \mathbf{P} = 1$, $\mathbf{P} \cdot \mathbf{Q} = 0$, $\mathbf{W} = \mathbf{P} \times \mathbf{Q}$ etc.

As an example of the utilization of these systems it is noted that for low eccentricity orbits, the **N**, **M**, and **W** reference system is preferable to one identified with perigee (**P**, **Q**, **W**) since this latter system is poorly defined and, in fact, the perigee, **P**, is completely undefined for $e = 0$. For equatorial orbits on the other hand, **N** is undefined and the **F**, **G**, **W** system is to be preferred.

It is left as an exercise for the reader to derive the inverse relationships, i.e., to express the descriptive i, Ω, ω in terms of the orbit plane unit vectors listed in Table III.

4.4. Coordinates of a Station and a Space Vehicle

The determination of the coordinates of an observation station, or rather the coordinates of the geocenter referred to a station, **R**, offers an illustrative example of the application of coordinate systems to the practical problem of observation. The components of the station vector referred, for instance, to the true equator and equinox of date in the equatorial geocentric system are

$$\mathbf{R}\begin{cases} X = -r_c \cos\phi' \cos\theta = -(C+H)\cos\phi\cos\theta = -x_c\cos\theta = -x_T, \\ Y = -r_c \cos\phi' \sin\theta = -(C+H)\cos\phi\sin\theta = -x_c\sin\theta = -y_T, \\ Z = -r_c \sin\phi' \qquad\quad = -(S+H)\sin\phi = -y_c = -z_T, \end{cases} \tag{24}$$

where r_c is the geocentric distance of the station, ϕ' is the geocentric latitude, H is the height above a reference spheroid expressed in Earth equatorial radii, ϕ is the geodetic latitude of the station, and θ is the angle between the station and the vernal equinox measured at the geocenter (i.e., the local hour angle of the equinox or sidereal time. See Section 11.1 for the procedure to be followed in order to determine this time, θ.) The values of C and S are

$$C \triangleq 1/\sqrt{1-(2f-f^2)\sin^2\phi} \qquad \text{and} \qquad S \triangleq C(1-f)^2,$$

where f is the flattening of the reference spheroidal form of the Earth. It is preferable to specify the station coordinates in terms of S, C, H, and ϕ rather than in terms of r_c and ϕ' since the geodetic latitudes and heights above sea level are usually tabulated while the geocentric latitudes and distances are not. (Cf. *American Ephemeris and Nautical Almanac 1963*, Table VII *S and C*, and pp. 484–485.) In Eq. (24) x_c and y_c are the time-constant coordinates of a station in the rotating meridional plane of the station while x_T, y_T, and z_T are the time-varying coordinates of a station referred to the geocenter.

The rates of change of the components of the station vector are

$$\dot{\mathbf{R}} \begin{cases} \dot{X} = \omega(C+H)\cos\phi\sin\theta, \\ \dot{Y} = -\omega(C+H)\cos\phi\cos\theta, \\ \dot{Z} = 0, \end{cases} \tag{25}$$

where ω is the Earth's angular rotational velocity (strictly referred to a fixed equinox) in radians per k_e^{-1} min, $\omega = 0.058{,}834{,}478{,}0$.

For any time, t, the value of θ in radians is given by

$$\theta = \theta_{g0} + 0.004{,}375{,}269{,}50(t - t_0) + \lambda_E, \tag{26}$$

where θ_{g0} is the Greenwich sidereal time in radians at some epoch, t_0, (e.g., time of injection onto orbit), $t - t_0$ is the solar time in minutes since the epoch, and λ_E is the east longitude of the station in radians.

If the geocentric coordinates of the space vehicle are given by x, y, z; the topocentric equatorial by ξ, η, ζ, (i.e., the components of $\boldsymbol{\varrho}$); and the coordinates of the geocenter relative *to* the station by X, Y, Z, then

$$\boldsymbol{\varrho} \begin{cases} \xi = x + X, \\ \eta = y + Y, \\ \zeta = z + Z, \end{cases} \qquad \dot{\boldsymbol{\varrho}} \begin{cases} \dot{\xi} = \dot{x} + \dot{X}, \\ \dot{\eta} = \dot{y} + \dot{Y}, \\ \dot{\zeta} = \dot{z} + \dot{Z}. \end{cases} \tag{27}$$

Or in terms of the unit vector $\mathbf{L}$ directed from the observer to the space vehicle

$$\boldsymbol{\varrho} = \rho\mathbf{L} = \mathbf{r} + \mathbf{R} \qquad \dot{\boldsymbol{\varrho}} = \dot{\rho}\mathbf{L} = \dot{\mathbf{r}} + \dot{\mathbf{R}}$$

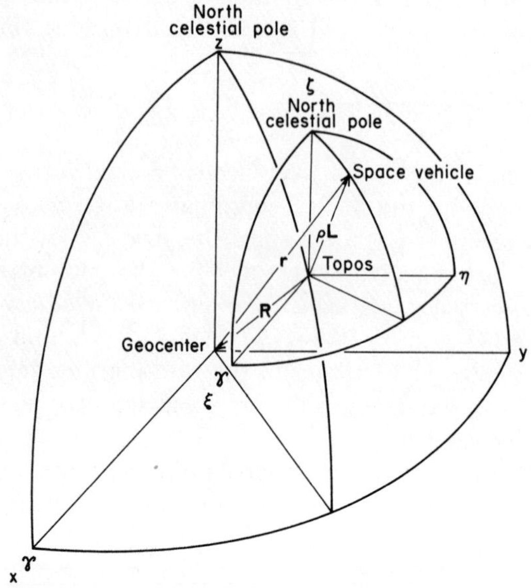

FIG. 22. The vector **L** in topocentric equatorial coordinates.

as shown in Fig. 22. The range from the observing station to the object (e.g., space vehicle), ρ, is given by

$$\rho = +\sqrt{\xi^2 + \eta^2 + \zeta^2},$$

the range-rate is given by

$$\dot{\rho} = (\xi\dot{\xi} + \eta\dot{\eta} + \zeta\dot{\zeta})/\rho,$$

the x, y, z components of a unit vector from the station to the object are given by

$$L_x = \xi/\rho, \qquad L_y = \eta/\rho, \qquad L_z = \zeta/\rho,$$

and the topocentric declination, δ, of the object viewed from the station is, therefore,

$$\delta = \tan^{-1}[L_z/+\sqrt{L_x^2 + L_y^2}] \text{ or } \delta = \sin^{-1} L_z \tag{28}$$

while the topocentric right ascension is

$$\alpha = \tan^{-1}[L_y/L_x] \tag{29}$$

with the quadrant determined by inspection of the signs of both numerator and denominator.

The x_h, y_h, z_h components of this same topocentric unit vector are

$$L_{x_h} = \xi_h/\rho;\ L_{y_h} = \eta_h/\rho,\ L_{z_h} = \zeta_h/\rho,$$

where

$$\xi_h = \xi \cos\theta \sin\phi + \eta \sin\phi \sin\theta - \zeta \cos\phi,$$

$$\eta_h = \eta \cos\theta - \xi \sin\theta,$$

and

$$\zeta_h = \xi \cos\theta \cos\phi + \eta \cos\phi \sin\theta + \zeta \sin\phi.$$

The altitude, h, of the object viewed from the station is, therefore,

$$h = \tan^{-1} [L_{z_h}/+\sqrt{L_{x_h}{}^2 + L_{y_h}{}^2}] \text{ or } h = \sin^{-1} [L_{z_h}]$$

while the azimuth is

$$A = \tan^{-1} [-L_{y_h}/L_{x_h}].$$

If the x, y, z geocentric coordinates of a space vehicle are computed from some orbit determination scheme (see Chapter 6), then the observations of this vehicle from a given station at time, t, can be *represented* by the foregoing formulas. This specification of the topocentric coordinates of an object for the purpose of observation is ordinarily published in tabular form and is called a local *ephemeris*.

For more general utilization an ephemeris should be useful for more than one observatory, thus the "impersonal" *geocentric* α and δ or x, y, z are tabulated. Transformation to topocentric α and δ or L_x, L_y, L_z is then carried out, by the preceding formulas, locally at the observatory.

The inverse operation, i.e., to determine the x, y, z coordinates of a space vehicle from an observed set of data such as ρ, h, A, can be carried out in a similar fashion. In this case the unit vector **L** is obtained from

$$L_x = -\cos\theta \sin\phi \cos h \cos A + \cos\theta \cos\phi \sin h - \sin\theta \cos h \sin A,$$

$$L_y = -\sin\theta \sin\phi \cos h \cos A + \sin\theta \cos\phi \sin h + \cos\theta \cos h \sin A,$$

$$L_z = \cos\phi \cos h \cos A + \sin\phi \sin h, \tag{30}$$

while $\xi = \rho L_x$, $\eta = \rho L_y$, and $\zeta = \rho L_z$ and X, Y, and Z are determined exactly as before. Finally,

$$x = \xi - X, \quad y = \eta - Y, \quad \text{and} \quad z = \zeta - Z. \tag{31}$$

4.5. Selenographic Coordinate System

4.5.1. General

A specific example of a less common coordinate system is the lunar or selenographic system. The following transformation to this system has been devised by Koskela[30] and has found extensive application to lunar-trajectory analysis.

The selenographic coordinate system takes into account the geometrical and physical librations in lunar longitude and latitude. The *geometrical libration* in latitude is the result of the inclination of about 6°.5 between the lunar equator and the lunar orbit plane. The Moon's north pole is tipped 6°.5 toward the Earth at one time during the month, and half a month later the south pole is so presented. The geometrical libration in longitude is due to the eccentricity of the Moon's orbit. The rotation of the Moon on its axis is practically uniform, but since the orbit is elliptical, the angular velocity around the Earth is not constant, and therefore, we can see alternately around the eastern and western limbs. This libration in longitude amounts to about 7°.75 to both the east and west.

The *physical librations* are the result of the Moon being a triaxial ellipsoid and not a sphere. The longest diameter is directed toward the Earth and the shortest along the axis of rotation (see Section 5.3). Because of the geometrical librations, the longest diameter does not always point directly toward the Earth, and therefore the attraction of the Earth on this bulge will cause the Moon to oscillate or librate slightly about its equilibrium position (cf. Klemperer and Baker).[31,32,33]

4.5.2. Definition of Terms

Selenographic latitude is measured from the lunar equator, positive to the north; i.e., in the hemisphere containing *Mare Serenitatis*. Selenographic longitude is measured along the lunar equator. The lunar prime meridian is defined as being the one that passes through the mean center of the Moon, where the mean center is taken to be the point on the lunar surface intersected by the lunar radius that is directed towards the Earth's center when the Moon is at the mean ascending node and when the node coincides with the mean perigee or mean apogee. The longitude is measured positive toward the west; i.e., toward *Mare Crisium*. (See *Mean center* in glossary.)

The sums of the geometrical and physical librations in longitude and latitude are tabulated for every day of the year in the *American Ephemeris and Nautical Almanac* as the Earth's selenographic longitude and latitude, i.e., the selenographic latitude and longitude of the point on the Moon's surface where the line of centers between the Earth and the Moon intersects this surface. When the libration in latitude, i.e., the Earth's selenographic latitude, is positive, the mean center of the Moon's disk is displaced to the south leaving a region of the north limb exposed to view. These librations are tabulated to the nearest 0°.01, which represents 0.16 nautical miles on the Moon's surface (similarly for longitude libration).

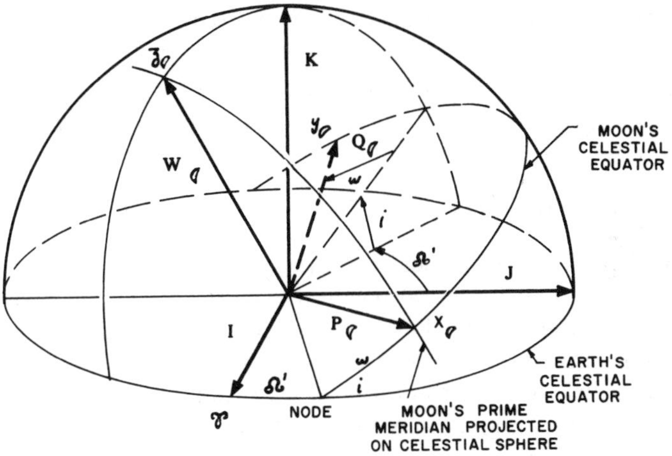

FIG. 23. Celestial sphere centered at Moon.

The orientation relationship between the geocentric equatorial coordinate system and the selenographic coordinate system is shown in Fig. 23 as they are both projected onto the celestial sphere. The $z_☾$-axis points to the pole of the Moon's equatorial plane. The $x_☾$ and $y_☾$ axes lie in the Moon's equator plane, the $x_☾$ axis being directed to the lunar prime meridian and $y_☾$ completing the right-handed set of coordinates. $\mathbf{P}_☾$, $\mathbf{Q}_☾$, $\mathbf{W}_☾$ are unit vectors along the $x_☾$, $y_☾$, $z_☾$ axes; Ω' is the distance measured along the celestial equator from the vernal equinox, ♈, to the node of the Moon's celestial equator (i.e., the line of intersection between the Earth's celestial equator and the Moon's celestial equator); i is the inclination of the Moon's mean equator to the Earth's true equator; and ω is the distance measured on the *Moon's* equator from its node to the lunar prime meridian. The Moon's equator is, of course, defined as being perpendicular to the axis of the Moon's monthly rotation in inertial space. (See the *American Ephemeris and Nautical Almanac* 1960, p. 501.)

4.5.3. Transformation

4.5.3.1. Rotation

The rotation from selenocentric equatorial coordinate axes to selenographic coordinate axes is given by the standard equations for the orientation vectors in terms of the Moon's orientation angles i, Ω', and ω (see Eq. (23)):

$$\mathbf{P}_{☾} = \mathbf{I}(\cos\omega\cos\Omega' - \sin\omega\sin\Omega'\cos i) + \mathbf{J}(\cos\omega\sin\Omega' + \sin\omega\cos\Omega'\cos i) + \mathbf{K}(\sin\omega\sin i),$$

$$\mathbf{Q}_{☾} = \mathbf{I}(-\sin\omega\cos\Omega' - \cos\omega\sin\Omega'\cos i) + \mathbf{J}(-\sin\omega\sin\Omega' + \cos\omega\cos\Omega'\cos i) + \mathbf{K}(\cos\omega\sin i),$$

and

$$\mathbf{W}_{☾} = \mathbf{I}(\sin\Omega'\sin i) + \mathbf{J}(-\cos\Omega'\sin i) + \mathbf{K}(\cos i). \tag{32}$$

where **I**, **J**, **K** have their usual definition as unit vectors directed to the vernal equinox, north celestial pole of the Earth etc. (but not necessarily with origin at the Earth). For example, if x', y', z' are the *selenocentric* equatorial coordinates of an object (i.e., measured from the lunicenter but directed parallel to the axes of a geocentric equatorial system) and if $x_{☾}$, $y_{☾}$, $z_{☾}$ are the *seleno*-graphic coordinates of this same object, then

$$x_{☾} = \mathbf{r}'\cdot\mathbf{P}_{☾} = x'(\cos\omega\cos\Omega' - \sin\omega\sin\Omega'\cos i) + y'(-\sin\omega\cos\Omega' - \cos\omega\sin\Omega'\cos i) + z'(\sin\Omega'\sin i)\ \text{etc.,} \tag{33}$$

cf. Eqs. (23) and (45).

The values for i and Ω' are tabulated to the nearest 0°001 in the *American Ephemeris and Nautical Almanac* for intervals of 10 days. Values for $\sin\omega$ and $\cos\omega$ must be found before the rotation indicated by Eqs. (32) and (33) can be carried out.

In Fig. 24 $\mathbf{L}_{☾}$ is a unit vector along OE, the radius of the Moon that is directed toward the center of the Earth. The librations in longitude and latitude are l and b, respectively. They are available from the *American Ephemeris and Nautical Almanac*. The components of $\mathbf{L}_{☾}$ are

$$L_{x_{☾}} = -\cos\delta\cos\alpha,$$

$$L_{y_{☾}} = -\cos\delta\sin\alpha,$$

and

$$L_{z_{☾}} = -\sin\delta, \tag{34}$$

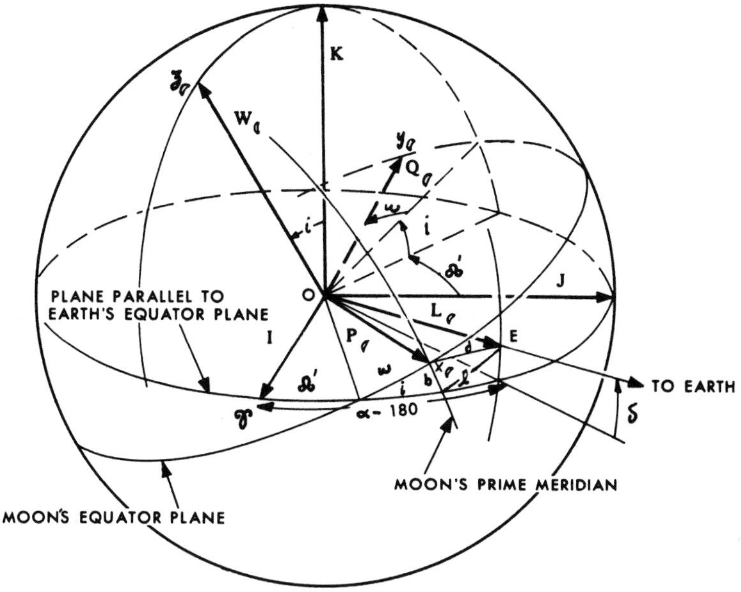

FIG. 24. Coordinate system relationships for the Moon.

where α is the right ascension of the Moon and δ the declination. Applying the law of cosines to the triangle with sides b, l, d (the angle d is defined in Fig. 24),

$$\cos d = \cos b \cos l$$

so that

$$\mathbf{P}_☾ \cdot \mathbf{L}_☾ = \cos d = \cos b \cos l.$$

Similarly

$$\mathbf{Q}_☾ \cdot \mathbf{L}_☾ = \cos b \sin l. \tag{35}$$

From Eqs. (32), (33), and (34)

$$\begin{aligned}\mathbf{P}_☾ \cdot \mathbf{L}_☾ = &-(\cos\omega\cos\Omega')(\cos\delta\cos\alpha) + (\sin\omega\sin\Omega'\cos i)(\cos\delta\cos\alpha)\\ &-(\cos\omega\sin\Omega')(\cos\delta\sin\alpha) - (\sin\omega\cos\Omega'\cos i)(\cos\delta\sin\alpha)\\ &-\sin\omega\sin i\sin\delta.\end{aligned} \tag{36}$$

Simplifying Eq. (36) and using Eq. (35), one finds that

$$\begin{aligned}\cos b\cos l = &-\cos\omega\cos\delta\cos(\Omega'-\alpha)\\ &+\sin\omega[\cos i\cos\delta\sin(\Omega'-\alpha) - \sin i\sin\delta].\end{aligned} \tag{37}$$

Likewise, using Eqs. (32), (33), and (34) we find that

$$\cos b \sin l = \mathbf{Q}_{☾} \cdot \mathbf{L}_{☾} = \sin \omega \cos \delta \cos (\Omega' - \alpha) + \cos \omega(\cos i \cos \delta \sin (\Omega' - \alpha) - \sin i \sin \delta]. \quad (38)$$

Dividing Eq. (37) by sin ω, Eq. (38) by cos ω, and subtracting, it is found that

$$\frac{\sin l \sin \omega}{\cos l} - \cos \omega = \frac{\cos \delta \cos (\Omega' - \alpha)}{\cos b \cos l}. \quad (39)$$

Dividing Eq. (37) by cos ω, Eq. (38) by sin ω, and adding, one obtains

$$\frac{\cos l \sin \omega}{\sin l} + \cos \omega = \frac{\cos i \cos \delta \sin (\Omega' - \omega) - \sin i \sin \delta}{\cos b \sin l}. \quad (40)$$

Addition of Eq. (39) and Eq. (40) yields

$$\sin \omega = \frac{\cos l}{\cos b} [\cos i \cos \delta \sin (\Omega' - \alpha) - \sin i \sin \delta] + \frac{\sin l}{\cos b} [\cos \delta \cos (\Omega' - \alpha)]. \quad (41)$$

Also

$$\cos \omega = \frac{\sin l}{\cos b} [\cos i \cos \delta \sin (\Omega' - \alpha) - \sin i \sin \delta] - \frac{\cos l}{\cos b} [\cos \delta \cos (\Omega' - \alpha)]. \quad (42)$$

With sin ω and cos ω known, the rotation indicated by Eqs. (32) and (33) can now be carried out.

The right ascension, declination, and horizontal parallax, $\pi_{☾}$, of the Moon are obtained from the *American Ephemeris and Nautical Almanac.* These quantities can be used to find the rectangular geocentric equatorial coordinates of the Moon. Let the magnitude of the geocentric radius vector to the Moon be $r_{\oplus☾}$, then

$$x_{\oplus☾} = r_{\oplus☾} \cos \delta \cos \alpha,$$

$$y_{\oplus☾} = r_{\oplus☾} \cos \delta \sin \alpha,$$

and

$$z_{\oplus☾} = r_{\oplus☾} \sin \delta. \quad (43)$$

$r_{\oplus\text{☾}}$ is found from the Moon's *horizontal parallax* by

$$r_{\oplus\text{☾}} = \frac{a_e}{\sin \pi_{\text{☾}}} \tag{44}$$

where a_e is the Earth's equatorial radius. Reference is made to the *Lunar Ephemeris* and Baker[2] for the details of obtaining $x_{\oplus\text{☾}}$, $y_{\oplus\text{☾}}$, and $z_{\oplus\text{☾}}$.

4.5.3.2. *Translation*

Let

$$x'_{\text{☾}\Delta} \triangleq x_{\oplus\Delta} - x_{\oplus\text{☾}}, \ (x \to y, z)$$

be the coordinates of the vehicle (Δ) with respect to the Moon in coordinates translated to the center of the Moon, i.e., selenocentric equatorial coordinates, and by using Eq. (32) to rotate into selenographic coordinates there results

$$\begin{aligned} x_{\text{☾}\Delta} = \mathbf{r}'_{\text{☾}\Delta} \cdot \mathbf{P}_{\text{☾}} = x'_{\text{☾}\Delta}(\cos \omega \cos \Omega' - \sin \omega \sin \Omega' \cos i) + y'_{\text{☾}\Delta}(\cos \omega \sin \Omega' \\ + \sin \omega \cos \Omega' \cos i) + z'_{\text{☾}\Delta}(\sin \omega \sin i), \end{aligned}$$

where $\mathbf{r}'_{\text{☾}\Delta}$ is a radius vector from the center of the Moon to the vehicle, with components given in terms of the selenocentric equatorial coordinates. Similarly $y_{\text{☾}\Delta}$ and $z_{\text{☾}\Delta}$ can be found to be

$$\begin{aligned} y_{\text{☾}\Delta} = \mathbf{r}'_{\text{☾}\Delta} \cdot \mathbf{Q}_{\text{☾}} = x'_{\text{☾}\Delta}(- \sin \omega \cos \Omega' - \cos \omega \sin \Omega' \cos i) \\ + y'_{\text{☾}\Delta}(- \sin \omega \sin \Omega' + \cos \omega \cos \Omega' \cos i) + z'_{\text{☾}\Delta}(\cos \omega \sin i), \end{aligned}$$

and

$$z_{\text{☾}\Delta} = \mathbf{r}'_{\text{☾}\Delta} \cdot \mathbf{W}_{\text{☾}} = x'_{\text{☾}\Delta}(\sin \Omega' \sin i) + y'_{\text{☾}\Delta}(- \cos \Omega' \sin i) + z'_{\text{☾}\Delta}(\cos i). \tag{45}$$

These last three equations give the position of the vehicle in selenographic coordinates when the positions of the vehicle and Moon in geocentric coordinates and the three rotation angles are known.

4.5.4. Latitude, Longitude, Altitude, and Velocity

The selenographic longitude and latitude of the vehicle can be calculated from the selenographic coordinates given by Eqs. (45).

Latitude is obtained from

$$\phi_{☾} = \sin^{-1} [z_{☾\Delta}/r_{☾\Delta}] \tag{46}$$

where

$$r_{☾\Delta} = +\sqrt{x_{☾\Delta}^2 + y_{☾\Delta}^2 + z_{☾\Delta}^2},$$

while selenographic longitude is obtained from

$$\lambda_{☾} = \tan^{-1} [y_{☾\Delta}/x_{☾\Delta}]. \tag{47}$$

The sign of $x_{☾\Delta}$ and $y_{☾\Delta}$ must be noted in order to obtain the correct quadrant for $\lambda_{☾}$.

The height of the vehicle above the surface given by the mean radius of the Moon, $r_{☾}$, is, clearly,

$$H_{☾\Delta} = r_{☾\Delta} - r_{☾}.$$

The selenographic components of relative velocity are

$$\dot{x}_{☾\Delta} = \dot{\mathbf{r}}'_{☾\Delta} \cdot \mathbf{P}_{☾} = \dot{x}'_{☾\Delta} (\cos \omega \cos \Omega' - \sin \omega \sin \Omega' \cos i) + \dot{y}'_{☾\Delta} (\cos \omega \sin \Omega' + \sin \omega \cos \Omega' \cos i) + \dot{z}'_{☾\Delta} (\sin \omega \sin i) + \omega_{☾} y_{☾\Delta},$$

$$\dot{y}_{☾\Delta} = \dot{\mathbf{r}}'_{☾\Delta} \cdot \mathbf{Q}_{☾} = \dot{x}'_{☾\Delta} (- \sin \omega \cos \Omega' - \cos \omega \sin \Omega' \cos i) + \dot{y}'_{☾\Delta} (- \sin \omega \sin \Omega' + \cos \omega \cos \Omega' \cos i) + \dot{z}'_{☾\Delta} (\cos \omega \sin i) - \omega_{☾} x_{☾\Delta},$$

and

$$\dot{z}_{☾\Delta} = \dot{\mathbf{r}}'_{☾\Delta} \cdot \mathbf{W}_{☾} = \dot{x}'_{☾\Delta} (\sin \Omega' \sin i) + \dot{y}'_{☾\Delta} (- \cos \Omega' \sin i) + \dot{z}'_{☾\Delta} (\cos i), \tag{48}$$

where $\dot{\mathbf{r}}'_{☾\Delta}$ is a velocity relative to the rotating selenographic system with components given in selenocentric equatorial coordinates, i.e.,

$$\dot{x}'_{☾\Delta} = \dot{x}_{\oplus\Delta} - \dot{x}_{\oplus☾} \qquad x \rightarrow y, z$$

and $\omega_{☾}$ is the angular rate of rotation of the Moon in radians per "k_e min."

4.6. Coordinates of the Planets

In order to indicate the tables that are presently available from which one can obtain the coordinates of the planets in the equatorial and ecliptic coordinate systems, the following listing, prepared by Hilton[34] is presented. The list indicates the sources of data as well as; (i) type of coordinates, (ii) reference system, (iii) format, (iv) accuracy and consistency, (v) interval of tabulation, and (vi) availability of differences.

The reader should note that most of the tables listed give coordinates relative to an *equatorial coordinate system*. Even when both the ecliptic and equatorial coordinates are given the interval is much smaller for the equatorial system (thereby allowing for a more accurate interpolation). It is also called to the reader's attention that the more recent planetary coordinates listed in the *American Ephemeris and Nautical Almanac* are listed in terms of *Ephemeris Time* (see Section 11.1 for the procedure to be followed in order to obtain Ephemeris Time).

4.7. List of Ephemerides

Planetary Coordinates for the Years 1800–1940, 1940–1960, 1960–1980, H. M. Stationery Office, (3 Vols.). These are intended for the calculations of perturbations on objects that do not approach the planet closely.

I. Venus, Earth-Moon barycenter, Mars, Jupiter, and Saturn: (i) Cartesian, latitude and longitude, radius; (ii) mean equator and equinox of 1950.0; (iii) available on decimal cards; (iv) the Cartesian coordinates are tabulated to five decimals of an astronomical unit but the last place is in doubt. Latitude and longitude are to thousandths of a degree for Earth, Venus, and Mars, and to one more figure for Jupiter and Saturn; (v) the interval is 10 days from 1920 to 1980 for all except Saturn, which is tabulated at 20-day intervals from 1920 to 1940. Before 1920 only Jupiter and Saturn are tabulated to day intervals; (vi) no differences are given.

II. Uranus and Neptune: (i) Cartesian, latitude and longitude, radius vector; (ii) Mean equator and equinox of 1950.0; (iii) available on decimal cards; (iv) the Cartesian coordinates are listed to four decimals of an astronomical unit, angles to thousandth of a degree; (v) the interval is 40 days from 1920 to 1980, 120 days before 1920; (vi) no differences are given.

III. The 1960–1980 volume also lists the coordinates of the barycenter of the Sun and the four inner planets to four decimal places of an astronomical unit at 10-day intervals.

IV. Mercury: (i) Cartesian only; (ii) mean equator and equinox of date; (iii) cards; (iv) three decimals; (v) 10 days from 1960 to 1980, only; (vi) no differences.

V. Pluto (taken from reference: *Coordinates of the Five Outer Planets*, 1653–2060 Volume XII): (i) Cartesian only; (ii) mean equator and equinox of 1950.0; (iii) cards; (iv) four decimals of an astronomical unit; (v) 40 days from 1920 to 1980; (vi) no differences.

Astronomical Papers prepared for the use of the *American Ephemeris and Nautical Almanac*, U. S. Government Printing Office.

I. Coordinates of Venus—Volume XV, Part III: (i) Cartesian, longitude, and latitude; (ii) mean equator and equinox of 1950.0; (iii) decimal cards available from U. S. Naval Observatory and 704 tapes available from Eglin Field; (iv) requires study; (v) 4-day interval from 1800 to 2000; (vi) the tapes have been supplied with differences.

II. Solar coordinates or the coordinates of the Sun with respect to the center of the Earth—Volume XIV: (i) Cartesian; (ii) mean equator and equinox of 1950.0. (In the yearly *American Ephemeris and Nautical Almanac,* the coordinates are also given referred to the mean equator and equinox of the beginning of the appropriate year); (iii) decimal cards from the U. S. Naval Observatory were reduced to 704 tapes by University of California Radiation Laboratory and are available from Eglin Field; (iv) seven decimals of an astronomical unit; (v) 4-day intervals from 1800 to 2000 in the Astronomical Papers; (1-day interval for the current year in the Almanac); (vi) second difference modified to take account of the fourth difference are supplied at the 4-day interval. (The Almanac lists first and second differences.)

III. Earth-Moon Barycenter Coordinates are also given in Volume XIV: (i) Cartesian; (ii) mean equator and equinox of 1950.0; (iii) cards and tapes; (iv) seven decimals of an astronomical unit; (v) 4-day interval between 1800 and 2000 plus the 10-day dates not divisible by four; (vi) only the tapes include differences.

IV. *Coordinates of the Five Outer Planets,* 1653–2060 Volume XII:(i) Cartesian; (ii) mean equator and equinox of 1950.0; (iii) cards and tapes; (iv) nine decimals of an astronomical unit; (v) 40-day interval; (vi) second and fourth differences.

V. *Improved Lunar Ephemeris 1952 to 1959* and *American Ephemeris and Nautical Almanac* from 1960 on: (i) ecliptic and equatorial angular coordinates, parallax; (ii) true equator and equinox of date; (iii) cards; (iv) milliseconds of time; (v) 12 hours for ecliptic coordinates and parallax; hourly for equatorial coordinates; (vi) no differences on cards.

If coordinates are tabulated at a constant interval, w, intermediate values can be interpolated using Lagrangian coefficients.[35] For high-order formulas this can mean considerable shifting of data inside the computer memory as the problem proceeds from one interval to the next. Therefore, it may become preferable to carry some differences and to use other interpolation formulas (e.g., Everett's). The coefficients of the difference are polynomials in

$$s = \frac{t_i - t_0}{w},$$

where t_0 is the start of the interval, w is the time interval between entries in the table (assumed equal thruout), and t_i is the intermediate time.* When there are many such t_i in one interval, it may save computing time to re-form the interpolation formula into a power series in s. The coefficients of the powers of s are the derivatives expressed as functions of the differences. Thus the determination (interpolation) of some tabulated quantity X at the time t_i follows from†

$$X(t_i) = (1 - s)X(t_0) + E''_0\delta^2X(t_0) + sX(t_1) + E''_1\delta^2X(t_1), \qquad (49)$$

where E''_0 and E''_1 are the so-called *Everett's coefficients:*

$$E_0'' \triangleq \frac{s(s-1)}{3!}(2 - s) \text{ and } E''_1 \triangleq \frac{s(s-1)}{3!}(s + 1).$$

Such interpolation is capable of producing the full accuracy of the table. Other interpolation and extrapolation formulas are discussed in the following paragraphs.

The planetary coordinates are nearly periodic functions. A complete harmonic analysis to the accuracy required by astronomical observations corresponds to the "theories" upon which the national almanacs are based (i.e., general perturbations—see Chapter 9). These involve very many terms, but a limited part of a planet's orbit could be represented to satisfactory accuracy by a few sine and cosine terms.

By means of the two-body expression for acceleration, i.e.,

$$\ddot{\mathbf{r}} = -\mu\mathbf{r}/r^3,$$

the higher derivatives may be expressed in terms of position and velocity. This reduces the extrapolation formulas to the so-called f and g series, (cf. pages 227–229 in Moulton).[13]

$$\mathbf{r}_i = f_i\mathbf{r}_0 + g_i\dot{\mathbf{r}}_0, \qquad (50)$$

where f_i and g_i are functions of t_i, i.e.,

$$f_i = 1 + \tau_i^2\bar{f}_2 + \tau_i^3\bar{f}_3 + \cdots$$

and

$$g_i = \tau_i + \tau_i^3\bar{g}_3 + \cdots$$

* Often one employs h instead of w, where $h \triangleq wk$. In this case h is the time interval expressed in characteristic units.

† The δ signify central differences as defined in, e.g., reference 35 and in the list of definitions under *numerical differentiation.*

where

$$\bar{f}_2 = -\tfrac{1}{2}r_0{}^3,\ \bar{f}_3 = \dot{r}_0/2r_0{}^4 \cdots$$

and

$$\bar{\bar{g}}_3 = -\tfrac{1}{6}r_0{}^3,\ \cdots$$

with

$$\tau_i = k(t_i - t_0).$$

This development is based upon series expressions and on the equations of motion (see Chapter 11 in Herrick[1]) and neglects the perturbations on the planet by other planets.

If we neglect also the fourth and higher differences, we arrive at Wood's method for obtaining approximate positions by quadrature of the second difference equation:

$$\delta^2\mathbf{r} = h^2\ddot{\mathbf{r}} = -\mu h^2\mathbf{r}/r^3 \tag{51}$$

where $h \triangleq wk_s$ (and k_s is the Gaussian gravitational constant). It may be desirable to include in the numerical integration the higher difference

$$\delta^2\mathbf{r} = h^2\{\ddot{\mathbf{r}} + \tfrac{1}{12}\delta^2\ddot{\mathbf{r}} - \tfrac{1}{240}\delta^4\ddot{\mathbf{r}} + \cdots\}$$

or better

$$\mathbf{r}_i = h^2\{\delta^{-2}\ddot{\mathbf{r}} + \tfrac{1}{12}\ddot{\mathbf{r}} - \tfrac{1}{240}\delta^2\ddot{\mathbf{r}} + \cdots\}. \tag{52}$$

Inclusion of perturbations leads to Cowell's method and to a large-scale integration such as that which produced the "Coordinates of the Five Outer Planets." (See Chapter 8.)

Here it is noted that there are quantities that change more slowly than the coordinates, namely the elements and related parameters of the planetary orbit. These elements or parameters may likewise be tabulated and interpolated, expressed in power or harmonic series, or integrated (e.g., by variation-of-parameters formulas, see Chapter 8). The interval of tabulation or integration can be much larger than for the coordinates. The drawback is in the additional formulation needed to obtain coordinates from the elements. The major difficulty in this respect, the solution of Kepler's equation, may be circumvented by its expansion in series.

The independent variable of the tabulations listed in the foregoing is considered to be a uniform time. This description fits neither the mean solar time by which clocks are set nor the sidereal time that furnished the observational basis. They depart from uniformity because of the periodic, secular, and irregular variations in the rotation of the Earth. The mean solar time determined by the rotation of the Earth is styled Universal Time (UT). Consequently, a new standard, the tropical year 1900.0, has been adopted. The "ephemeris mean day" is obtained from this by dividing by 365.242,198,79. Ephemeris Time (ET) measured in this unit differs from UT by an amount which is determined by a comparison of observed and calculated positions of the Moon. Since this determination cannot be made instantaneously, an approximation to ET is now made by use of atomic clocks. See Section 11.1 for a more complete discussion of time.

5 ASTRODYNAMIC CONSTANTS

Improved astrodynamic constants are required to predict orbits of space vehicles with high precision. A distinction may be drawn, however, between feasibility or preliminary orbits, which need not be particularly accurate and are useful for rough prediction (e.g., see the simple illustrative examples of Chapters 2 and 3); and definitive orbits, which must be more accurate if they are to be employed in any realistic computation. For example, the landing error on the Moon resulting from uncertainties in the current values of the geocentric constants amounts to between 50 and 100 miles, while the error at a Martian intercept due to uncertainties in the heliocentric constants at this time amounts to between 5,200 and 52,000 miles. Such errors are greater than can be tolerated in the observational data, and consequently considerable effort is now being devoted to the reduction of these uncertainties.[36]

Gravitational constants fall into four categories: *geocentric, selenocentric* (or Moon-centered), *heliocentric,* and *planetocentric* (planet-centered). There are also important constants in the areas of atmospheric and vehicle properties, such as the atmospheric density and its variation, and the drag encountered in the transitional region between the free-molecule flow and slip-flow regimes. These latter drag forces will be discussed in Chapter 10 which deals with nongravitational forces. A more complete development of the subject of gravitational astronomical constants has been carried out by Herrick *et al.,*[37] and by Wolaver.[38]

5.1. Heliocentric Constants

5.1.1. General

The basic constant of gravitation to be determined in the case of heliocentric orbits is k_s.* Theoretically, three equations could be employed for its determination. The first equation is simply a statement of the acceleration due to gravity at a given distance from the Sun, $g_s(r)$:

$$g_s = k_s^2\mu/r^2, \tag{53}$$

where in this case μ is the Sun's mass. Unfortunately, it is impossible to set up gravity-measuring stations on the solar surface and the determination of g_s must be abandoned.

The second equation that can be employed to determine k_s is a statement of Kepler's third law, (cf. Eq. (2))

$$k_s^2\mu P_\oplus{}^2 = (2\pi)^2 a_\oplus{}^3;$$

where $P_\oplus$ is the period of revolution and $a_\oplus$ is the semimajor axis of the Earth–Moon heliocentric orbit and μ is the sum of the Earth, Sun, and Moon masses; or

$$k_s = \frac{2\pi a_\oplus{}^{3/2}}{P_\oplus \sqrt{\mu}}. \tag{54}$$

It is apparent that if one defines the semimajor axis $a_\oplus$ of the Earth–Moon center-of-mass orbit to be exactly 1 a.u. then, given precise information on the sum of the masses of the Earth, Sun, and Moon (in solar-mass units) and the sidereal period of the Earth (orbital period of the Earth reckoned with respect to an inertial system), k_s can be found very accurately. This is the method Gauss employed in 1809. Unfortunately, Gauss apparently did not recognize that it is the Earth–Moon center of mass whose motion most closely approximates a heliocentric ellipse, or he considered the lunar mass to be negligible in view of the inexactness of the other quantities. Thus he omitted the mass of the Moon from μ. An error in the value for P, as it happened, very nearly canceled the other inaccuracies.

* According to Dirac's cosmological theory, there might be a slow time variation of k_s, but so small as not to affect our computations.

A third equation that might be utilized is the *vis-viva* or energy integral,

$$\left(\frac{ds}{dt}\right)^2 = k_s^2\mu(2/r - 1/a_\oplus). \tag{55}$$

If the masses of the Sun, Earth, and Moon are well determined; if $a_\oplus = 1$ a.u.; if r, the Earth's distance from the Sun is known in astronomical units; and if the speed ds/dt of the Earth can be measured; then, in principle a determination of k_s is possible. ds/dt can be obtained for example from the relative line-of-sight (radial) velocities of stars found by measures of the Doppler shift in high dispersion spectra.[39] As yet, however, this third method is subject to systematic errors and hence less exact than the second method; and only when very precise measures of the Doppler shift in the 21-cm interstellar line of neutral hydrogen become available, will this velocity method be found to yield an accurate estimate of k_s in laboratory units[40,41].

The original evaluation in 1809 of the Gaussian constant of gravitation k_s was not sufficiently accurate for modern needs, owing to lack of precise knowledge of the astronomical constants, which include the mass of the Earth–Moon system, the period of the Earth's revolution about the Sun, and its mean distance from the Sun. If astronomers held strictly to the definition of these constants, they would have to recompute k_s every time new information became available. Following the logic of Newcomb, it was finally decided to bring order out of chaos by retaining Gauss' original value of k_s and treating the Earth like any other planet by allowing its semimajor axis to depart from a value of exactly unity (e.g., at present $a_\oplus = 1.000,000,230$ a.u.). Thus, as new information on μ and P became available it was not necessary to discard all previously computed planetary orbits, but rather only to scale them slightly. As will be shown, this same logic can be applied to geocentric orbits. Note that the accuracy to which k_s^2 can be determined as the product of the values of G and $m_\odot$ where G is the cgs gravitational constant and $m_\odot$ the mass of the Sun as determined in the laboratory, is completely inadequate compared to the astronomically determined value $k_s = 0.017,202,098,950$.

5.1.2. Solar Parallax

Because of the unavoidable choice of the astronomical unit as unit of planetary distance and the necessary employment of laboratory (e.g., mks) units for initial specifications of interplanetary trajectories, an exact value of the astronomical unit in laboratory units is essential. Unfortunately, it is difficult to determine this value since, until the invention of radar, no highly accurate astronomical measurements in laboratory units were possible. Essentially, the question is one of determining the *solar parallax*, $\pi_\odot$, which is related to the mean distance by the equation:

$$\pi_\odot \triangleq a_e/\text{a.u.}, \tag{56}$$

i.e., the reciprocal of the Earth's mean distance from the Sun expressed in units of the Earth's equatorial radius or the angle at the Sun subtended by the Earth's equatorial radius.†

The solar parallax is too small (8″.8) to measure directly. The relative scale of the solar system in astronomical units is known with sufficient accuracy for most purposes, the uncertainty amounting to 10,000 miles per a.u. (1 a.u. $\cong$ 93,000,000 miles), but the more exacting requirements of interplanetary navigation demand that the distances of the planets be known with greater accuracy in the same terrestrial units in which vehicular velocities are given.

In the past decade or two, new values for the solar parallax have been derived by several independent methods. Two of these depend upon the close approach of a minor planet to the Earth; a third is determined from radial velocities of stars; and the most recent method involves the reflection of radar beams from the planet Venus. The lack of exact agreement among these improved values indicates the presence of systematic errors, which will eventually, no doubt, be removed.

(i) When a minor planet with a well-determined orbit comes so close to the Earth that its distance in terrestrial units can be found by triangulation, the value of the astronomical unit can then be derived by equating the observed distance to the equivalent length in astronomical units given by the orbit calculation. Successful applications of the geometrical method were carried out at Cambridge and Greenwich Observatories using observations of 433 Eros, which approaches at perihelion oppositions to within 14,000,000 miles of the Earth.[42]

(ii) An even more effective use can be made of the motions of a minor planet during a close approach to the Earth from the dynamics of the orbit. The dynamical method consists in observing the departure of the actual motion from the calculated heliocentric orbit, in which the significant perturbations by all the planets have been taken into account, and deducing

† More rigorously $\sin \pi_\odot = a_e/\text{a.u.}$ but because the angle $\pi_\odot$ is so small, $\sin \pi_\odot$ can very accurately be approximated by $\pi_\odot$ expressed in radians.

the mass of the Earth–Moon system from the deviations. In a monumental work on the motions of 433 Eros, Rabe based a least squares solution on residuals from observations made between 1926 and 1945, including a close approach to the Earth in 1930–31.[43] He derived corrections to 17 adopted constants: the six elements of the orbit of Eros; the obliquity of the ecliptic and the positions of the equator and equinox; the mean longitude, eccentricity, and perihelion of the Earth's orbit; the constant of precession; and finally, the masses of the four inner planets. Since the astronomical unit is connected with the Earth–Moon mass by Kepler's harmonic law, the solar parallax can be determined.

Specifically, Kepler's third law is combined with the formula relating the acceleration of gravity at the Earth's equator, g_e, i.e.,

$$k_s^2 \mu P_\oplus^{\,2} = (2\pi)^2 a_\oplus^{\,3},$$

$$g_e = \frac{k_s^2 m_\oplus (1)}{a_e^2}$$

($k_e^2 = m_\oplus k_s^2$, $m_\oplus$ in solar masses, cf. p. 16) so that

$$\frac{m_\oplus}{\mu} = \frac{g_e a_e^2 P_\oplus^{\,2}}{(2\pi)^2 a_\oplus^{\,3}}. \qquad (57)$$

Since $\mu = m_\odot + m_\oplus + m_☾$ is determined from Rabe's reduction of 433 Eros data and the other constants are well known, it is then possible to solve for $a_\oplus$ (already given in terms of astronomical units) in terms of a_e and apply Eq. (56) to obtain the solar parallax. (Actually, g_e is measured on a rotating Earth so that a correction for rotation must be applied to the second of Eqs. (57) by modifying (1) cf. Eq. (60) where $(1) \rightarrow \mu$.)

(iii) Fundamentally, the spectroscopic method of determining the solar parallax involves measuring the line-of-sight (radial) velocity by the Doppler shift of its spectral lines six months or so apart, when the star's longitude differs from that of the Sun by 90° and the star is on the meridian (to avoid introducing a component of velocity due to the Earth's rotation). One half the difference of the two radial velocities will give the Earth's average speed in its orbit. On the assumption that the orbit is a circle, its dimensions are readily found. Without such an assumption an evaluation using the *vis-viva* integral can be employed as was noted earlier.

(iv) In February, 1958, Price *et al.*[44] of the Lincoln Laboratories of M.I.T. sent radar beams at 440 mc of about 400 miles pulse width (2 msec) to Venus and received the echo. If the distance traversed by the beam can be accurately determined from the observed travel time and the known velocity of light, the value of the astronomical unit is readily found. This is essentially the method, in reverse, which Michelson used to determine the speed of light by observing the time it required to traverse a known distance and be reflected back to the source.

The astronomical distance of Venus, i.e., from the center of the Earth to the center of Venus, is known with considerable accuracy in astronomical units. But the radar beam traveled from a station on the Earth's surface to a point at some unknown depth below the unseen surface of Venus; and its velocity was affected by the ions in the Earth's atmosphere and possibly in the impenetrable (to visible light) atmosphere of Venus, as well as by free electrons in the intervening space. Care must be exercised, therefore, in the employment of the radar method. Specifically, the following points must be considered. First, an up-to-date value for the speed of light, c, should be utilized. The work of Plyler who employed molecular spectra gave rise to $c = 299{,}792 \pm 6$ km/sec; that of Mulligan and McDonald gave $c = 299{,}792.8$; and the recent work of Froome who employed a microwave interferometer gave $c = 299{,}792.5 \pm 0.1$ km/sec (cf. reference 45). (The out-dated speed of light quoted in the *American Ephemeris* has no relevancy whatsoever in the determination of planetary position data and, for this reason, should not be employed.) Secondly, as pointed out by G. Westrom, the center-to-center Earth–Planet distance should be computed by considering the legs of the triangle with the vertices being the location of the Earth when the signal was transmitted, the location of the planet at reflection, and the location of Earth at reception. Such Earth and planet positions are obtained by accurate interpolation of the tables listed in Section 4.7. Third, a correction must be included for the surface-to-surface distances. The correction at Earth is simple, but at Venus (and other planets) the planetary radius to the reflecting level is more uncertain. Fourth, the decrease in speed and consequent curvature of the radar beam in interplanetary space due to refraction must be accounted for. If one assumes 10^3 electrons/cm^3, then 440 mc radiation will move at a speed of 299,792.4 km/sec (if we adopt $c = 299{,}792.5$ km/sec). Fifth, for the most exact determinations of solar parallax, optical observations of the target planet should be made simultaneously with the radar observations in order to improve the planetary position data listed in the ephemerides (which may be in error as much as $1''$).

In spite of the uncertainties introduced by these considerations, the radar-echo method may eventually yield a more exact value of the solar parallax than the geometrical, gravitational, or spectroscopic methods, although all these have made significant contributions[46] as will be seen from the comparison given in Table IV.

TABLE IV. VALUES OF THE SOLAR PARALLAX

Solar parallax	Author	Date	Method
8″.7966 ± 0″.047	Hinks	1901	Geometrical (Eros)
8.790 ± 0.001	Spencer Jones	1931	Geometrical (Eros)
8.799 ± 0.001	Witt and Noteboom (independently)	1893–1931	Geometrical (Eros)
8.7984 ± 0.0004	Rabe	1926–1945	Dynamical (Eros)
8.803 ± 0.004	Spencer Jones	1928	Spectroscopic
8.805 ± 0.007	W. S. Adams	1941	Spectroscopic
8.801,87[a] ± 0.000,05	Price *et al.*	Feb. 10, 1958	Radar echoes from Venus
8.801,80[a] ± 0.000,05	Price *et al.*	Feb. 10, 1958	Radar echoes from Venus

[a] Computed by George Westrom.

5.2. Geocentric Constants

5.2.1. POTENTIAL FUNCTION

In discussing geocentric gravitational constants, it is convenient to introduce the potential function, Φ, as defined by

$$\frac{\partial \Phi}{\partial x} \triangleq \frac{d^2x}{dt^2} \qquad x \to y,\, z.$$

This definition is somewhat older than potential theory and astronomers employed it initially without recognizing the true nature of potential energy. Consequently Φ is found to be proportional to the negative of the potential energy per unit mass.

For a purely central field (yielding two-body motion)

$$\Phi = k^2(m_1 + m_2)/r \tag{58}$$

so that

$$\frac{d^2x}{dt^2} = \frac{\partial \Phi}{\partial x} = -k^2(m_1 + m_2)x/r^3 \qquad x \to y,\, z.$$

Because of its asphericity the Earth does not produce a purely central-force potential and, if $m_2 \ll m_1$ (which is certainly the case for all Earth satellites of mass m_2 except the Moon), the Earth's field can be represented by

$$\Phi = \frac{k_e^2 m_1}{r}\left[1 + \frac{J}{3}\frac{1}{r^2}(1 - 3\sin^2\delta) + \frac{H}{5}\frac{1}{r^3}(3 - 5\sin^2\delta)\sin\delta + \frac{K}{30}\frac{1}{r^4}(3 - 30\sin^2\delta + 35\sin^4\delta) + \cdots\right], \tag{59}$$

where J, H, and K are the coefficients of the so-called second, third, and fourth harmonics of the Earth's gravitational potential, $m_1 = m_\oplus$ = the mass of the Earth in terms of Earth mass = 1, r is the radial distance from the dynamical center expressed in units of equatorial radii, and δ is the geocentric declination or the geocentric latitude of the sub-satellite point, i.e., $\sin\delta = U_z$. It should be noted that an axially-symmetric Earth is assumed (since there is no longitude dependence in Φ) and that a lack of symmetry in the northern and southern hemispheres is included in the third harmonic or H term. The first harmonic ($1/r$ term) is missing because of the choice of an equatorial coordinate system in which δ is measured relative to the center of the Earth. As of this writing, the best values for the foregoing coefficients, as determined from the orbit of $1958\beta_2$,[47] are:

$$J = (1623.41 \pm 4) \times 10^{-6},$$
$$H = (6.04 \pm 0.73) \times 10^{-6},$$

and

$$K = (6.37 \pm 0.23) \times 10^{-6}.$$

By means of satellite observations such constants can be determined as will be discussed in Chapter 9. The fifth harmonic is not sufficiently well known to justify its inclusion in the list.

5.2.2. Gravitational Constant

As in the case of k_s, one could determine k_e by any one of the three Eqs. (53), (54), or (55). Until the launching of the first artificial Earth satellite the best method was by use of

$$g_e = k_e^2\mu/a_e^2, \tag{60}$$

where g_e is the equatorial value of the acceleration of gravity and

$$\mu = 1 - A - \tilde{\omega} + J + \tfrac{1}{2}K + \cdots.$$

In this formulation A is the mass of an ellipsoidal shell of atmosphere in Earth masses and, as it does not contribute to the force at the Earth's surface, it must be subtracted; the constant $\tilde{\omega} \triangleq (a_e^3\omega^2/k_e^2)$ where ω = the angular rotation rate of the Earth, accounts for the component of the acceleration of gravity resulting from centrifugal force. The evaluation of μ, therefore, is really of an "effective" mass; a_e, on the other hand, must be determined by geodetic surveys of arcs on the Earth's surface involving corrections for the irregularities of the Earth's figure. Recent surveys have been made for improving the values of a_e and the flattening of the Earth f. In particular, the Army Map Service has measured arcs along meridians in both hemispheres from Alaska to Chile and a connection across the Mediterranean from Europe to Lake Tanganyika has also been established. These surveys give a value of a_e amounting to 6,378,270 $\pm$ 100 m, which has been revised in the light of recent satellite surveys to 6,378,145 $\pm$ 100 m. (At this writing the most up-to-date value for the flattening is $f = 1/(298.3 \pm 0.1)$.)

The acceleration due to gravity at the Earth's equator, g_e, is obtained from the general gravity formula:

$$g(\phi) = g_e(1 + \beta \sin^2 \phi + \gamma \sin^2 2\phi), \tag{61}$$

where g is the acceleration of gravity at any geodetic latitude ϕ. It is clear that β is related to the rotation of the Earth, while γ is nearly equal to K of Eq. (59). In fact, it can be shown[37] that f, J, β, and $\tilde{\omega}$ are interrelated by

$$\beta = f + \tfrac{3}{2}\tilde{\omega} + \cdots$$

and

$$J = f - \tfrac{1}{2}\tilde{\omega} + \cdots.$$

Thus, satellite observations that give rise to improved values of f and J also have an effect on g_e.

Given many observations of g throughout the world (at various ϕ's) Eq. (61) can be solved by least squares for β and γ as well as g_e. A value of g_e consistent with recent satellite observations is g_e = 9.780,320 $(1 + 3 \times 10^{-6})$m/sec^2.

Equation (54)—Kepler's third law—could be employed with accurate measurements of the Moon, i.e.,

$$k_e^2\mu_{\oplus☾}P_☾^2 = (2\pi)^2 a_☾^3.$$

In this case lack of exact knowledge of $\mu_{\oplus☾} = m_\oplus + m_☾$ and (until recent radar determinations by Yaplee, *et al.*[48]) of $a_☾$ make this method less accurate than the aforementioned method. From these recent lunar radar observations, for example, one obtains $a_e = 6{,}378{,}175$ m.

As was pointed out in the case of heliocentric constants, it is advisable to adopt a value for k_s and let the mean distance of the Earth's orbit vary as new data are found. We designate a g-radius analogous to the astronomical unit that originally was exactly equal to the Earth's equatorial radius and adopt[37]

$$k_e = 0.074{,}365{,}74.$$

Hence, as new geocentric gravitational data are obtained, only the *scale* of the orbits already determined need be changed. Such a procedure has the obvious advantage of not requiring a complete recomputation of older geocentric orbits as new information on our gravitational field becomes available. In keeping with such a procedure, the equatorial radius of the Earth, expressed in g-radii, is, at this date, $a_e = 0.999{,}990{,}22$ g-radii.

5.3. Selenocentric Constants

5.3.1. Lunar Distance or Parallax

Lunar or selenocentric gravitational constants include the semimajor axis, $a_☾$, of the Moon's orbit, the Moon's mass, and the coefficients describing the Moon's triaxial figure.

The *lunar parallax* or ratio of the Earth's equatorial radius, a_e, to the semimajor axis of the Moon's orbit, $a_☾$, was first determined by triangulation from the Cape and Greenwich Observatories; later from the dynamical considerations of the lunar orbital motion.† In 1952, O'Keefe and Anderson[49] derived a new value from photoelectrically recorded observations of star occultations, by reversing the usual process of reducing occultation observations in which the Moon's distance enters as one of the known quantities.

In 1956, Yaplee and associates at the Naval Research Laboratory began an experimental investigation of the method of radar echoes as a means of

† The Moon's *horizontal parallax*, tabulated in the *American Ephemeris* at intervals of 12 hours, is defined as the angle at the Moon subtended by the Earth's radius through a point T on the surface, when the angle at T is a right angle, i.e., when the Moon is 90° from the zenith of T. The true parallax at any other zenith distance z is found by multiplying the horizontal parallax by sin z. The mean equatorial parallax is the *mean* angle at the Moon's center subtended by the Earth's equatorial radius, when the angle at T (now situated on the equator) is 90°. In other words, $\sin \bar{\pi}_☾ \cong \bar{\pi}_☾$ (in radians) $= a_e/a$.

determining more exact values for the distances of astronomical objects than those given by the older methods. Using a wavelength of 10 cm (frequency 2860 mc), they found that the Moon was a very good reflector, with a smoother surface than had been anticipated, and that sweeps made over a six-hour period showed a consistency within half a mile in the results.[48] For each pulse transmitted, the return signal record showed four or five "spikes" or maxima, indicating multiple interference between several strong scattering areas. Some uncertainty may enter if N (the number of in-flight pulses that left the transmitter after the pulse whose echo is to be measured) is not known. In the case of the Moon, the ambiguity could amount to 400 mi. N can be found, however, since it equals the number of sweeps between the last transmitter pulse and the last received echo, unless the ion density in space is large enough to change the velocity of propagation. They found that the observed and calculated values of N agreed. By-products of the experiment will include the Earth's diameter; the ion density within a sphere of radius 250,000 miles surrounding the Earth; and the character of the Moon's surface obtained from the fine structure of the returned signals. A comparison of the values for the Moon's mean distance or semimajor axis is found in Table V.

TABLE V. MEAN DISTANCE OF MOON

Distance in km	Source
384,407.6 ± 4.7	O'Keefe and Anderson 1952
384,403 ± 1	Yaplee, Burton, Craig, and Roman 1957
384,400	*American Ephemeris 1960*

5.3.2. MASSES OF THE EARTH AND MOON

Although the *American Ephemeris and Nautical Almanac* for 1960 still carries Newcomb's values for the masses of the planets and Moon, several new determinations have been made in recent years based on more accurate observational data. The masses of the Earth–Moon system, for example, were independently calculated by Noteboom, Witt, and Rabe as by-products of the differential improvements of the orbit of 433 Eros, including exact perturbations by all the planets and covering a large number of oppositions and two close approaches to the Earth in 1901 and 1931 respectively. Rabe also derived corrections to the adopted masses of Mercury, Venus, and Mars as well as the current values of 7 astronomical constants, in the most recent of the least squares solutions for improving the elements of Eros (see Section 5.4).

Three new determinations of the Moon's mass have also emerged from the Eros calculations through corrections to the constant of the "Lunar Equation." As the result of solar perturbations, the Moon's orbit is lengthened in a direction at right angles to the instantaneous line joining the Earth and the Sun. The average figure thus produced is called the "variational orbit." (See Chapter 9). Due to the ellipticity of the Earth's orbit, however, the solar perturbative force continually fluctuates, as it is proportional to the reciprocal of the cube of the distance of the Sun. The consequent distortion of the variational orbit, called the "parallactic inequality" may amount to 127″ at maximum, or about 14.5 times the solar parallax.

If P is the parallactic inequality, $\mu_☾$ the mass of the Moon relative to the Earth, and $\pi_\odot$ the solar parallax, the following relationship holds[46]:

$$P = 14.5662 \frac{1 - \mu_☾}{1 + \mu_☾} \pi_\odot . \tag{62}$$

If any two unknowns can be found from observations, the third follows immediately. Rabe determined $\mu_☾$ from an improved value of P and of the solar parallax. Delano[50] based a differential correction (see Section 6.6.2) of the elements of Eros on the orbital data tabulated by Spencer Jones in order to reduce the residuals to the same order of magnitude as the accidental (or random) errors of the comparison star places and the observations. With improved elements of Eros and a correction to the Earth's mean longitude thus obtained, he again represented the observations and found that the residuals were as small as could be expected on the dates for which the parallactic inequality vanished. On the intermediate dates, however, the residuals showed a periodicity that identified them with the systematic errors in the constant of the lunar equation. He then made a final least squares solution for a correction to this constant, and derived two possible values. These, when combined with Spencer Jones' value of the solar parallax (8″.790), gave the mass of the Moon.

TABLE VI.

$m_{\oplus+☾}^{-1}$	Author	$m_☾^{-1}$	Author
329,390	Newcomb	81.45	Newcomb
328,370	Noteboom (1921)	81.375 ± 0.026	Rabe (1949)
328,390 ± 103	Witt (1933)	81.222 ± 0.027	Delano (1950)
328,466 ± 43	Rabe (1949)	81.219 ± 0.030	Delano (1950)

Table VI gives the new values of $m_{\oplus+☾}^{-1}$, the reciprocal of the mass of the Earth–Moon system, in units of the Sun's mass; and the reciprocal of the Moon's mass $m_☾^{-1}$ in units of the Earth's mass. Newcomb's values are given for comparison.

5.3.3. Lunar Potential

As we found in the case of the Earth, it is useful to introduce the concept of gravitational potential in order to define the gravitational field of an aspherical body. In keeping with the definition of Φ given in Eq. (58), the general value of Φ for the Moon, which is composed of a continuum of incremental masses dm, is

$$\Phi = k_m{}^2 \int \frac{dm}{s},$$

where s is the distance from dm to the point at which the potential is reckoned. The expansion of $1/s$ in terms of the zonal harmonics of Legendre functions is given by:

$$\Phi = \Phi_0 + \Phi_1 + \Phi_2 + \cdots,$$

where

$$\Phi_0 = \frac{k_m{}^2}{r} \int P_0(c)\, dm,$$

$$\Phi_1 = \frac{k_m{}^2}{r^2} \int \rho P_1(c)\, dm,$$

and

$$\Phi_2 = \frac{k_m{}^2}{r^3} \int \rho^2 P_2(c)\, dm, \quad \ldots; \tag{63}$$

and where r is the radial distance from the lunicenter to where Φ is reckoned, ρ is the distance from the lunicenter to dm, c is the cosine of the angle between $\mathbf{r}$ and $\boldsymbol{\rho}$, and $P_i(c)$ are the Legendre polynomials:†

$$P_0(c) = 1,$$
$$P_1(c) = c,$$
$$P_2(c) = \tfrac{1}{2}(3c^2 - 1), \quad \ldots.$$

† $P_i(c)$ is meant to symbolize the fact that P_i is a function of c; e.g., $P_2(c) = \frac{1}{2}(3c^2 - 1)$. Such a meaning for symbols enclosed in a parenthesis or bracket will be utilized throughout the text and should not be confused with a simple product.

It is clear that $\Phi_1 = 0$ by symmetry, Φ_0 is the potential of a point mass, and Φ_2 is a second harmonic or dipole term. Note that such a development in the case of the Earth gave rise to the J, H, and K coefficients. In the case of the Moon one cannot assume axial symmetry since the Moon's figure can be best approximated by that of a triaxial ellipsoid with semi-major axes a, b, and c. One then defines the moments of inertia about those axes by A, B, and C respectively. The c-axis of this triaxial ellipsoid is taken as coincident with the rotational or polar axis of the Moon, the a-axis points toward the Earth (apart from small librations), and b is perpendicular to a and c.

The best data, to date, on A, B, and C is given by Jeffreys:

$$\frac{C - A}{C} = 0.000{,}626{,}9 \pm 0.000{,}002{,}7.$$

In his paper Jeffreys[52] suggested that $(B - A)/C$ might have the very uncertain value of $0.000{,}118 \pm 0.000{,}051$. A better value, however, was given by Jeffreys in 1957 based on the observational data of Yakovkin[53] and cluster around

$$(B - A)/C = 0.000{,}209 \pm 0.000{,}001.$$

A, B, and C are related to a, b, and c by

$$\frac{B - A}{C} = \frac{a^2 - b^2}{a^2 + b^2} \text{ and } \frac{C - A}{C} = \frac{a^2 - c^2}{a^2 + b^2}. \tag{64}$$

An additional relationship must, therefore, be obtained before values for a, b, and c can be determined. One relatively simple way to resolve this problem is to make direct observations of the lunar radius. Irregularities occasioned by the presence of mountains and craters make this a difficult task. If, e.g., the mean meridional radius of the Moon's visible disk, $r_☾$, is given by

$$r_☾ = \frac{b + c}{2} = 1737.85 \pm 0.07 \text{ km},$$

as measured by triangulation, then (cf. page 10 in Alexandrov[51])

$$a = 1738.57 \pm 0.07 \text{ km} = 1.000{,}000 \text{ long lunar equatorial radius}$$
$$b = 1738.21 \pm 0.07 \text{ km} = 0.999{,}793 \text{ long lunar equatorial radius}$$

and

$$c = 1737.49 \pm 0.07 \text{ km} = 0.997{,}653 \text{ long lunar equatorial radius.}$$

In order to determine the gravitational potential of the Moon, one requires in addition to the specification of a, b, and c, a determination of the density distribution (see the work of Urey, *et al.*[54]) i.e.,

$$\Phi_0 = k_m^2 m_☾/r,$$
$$\Phi_1 = 0,$$
$$\Phi_2 = \frac{1}{2}\frac{k_m^2}{r^3}\left(\frac{4}{3}\pi abc\right)\Omega\lambda_1, \; . \; . \; . \; ,$$

where $k_m = 0.057{,}929$, and $m_☾ = 1$, and

$$\Omega \triangleq [a^2(3U_x^2 - 1) + b^2(3U_y^2 - 1) + c^2(3U_z^2 - 1)],$$

or through application of Eqs. (64) (or directly by MacCullagh's theorem[55])

$$\Phi_2 = \frac{k_m^2}{2r^3}[A + B + C - 3(AU_x^2 + BU_y^2 + CU_z^2)]$$
$$\equiv \frac{k_m^2 C}{2r^3}\left[\frac{(B - A)}{C}(1 - 3U_y^2) + \frac{(C - A)}{C}(1 - 3U_z^2)\right]$$

where $C = m_☾ a^2 = 0.334 \pm 0.002$ Moon masses (Moon radii)^2 as found by Jeffreys [52] (on the other hand for the constant density model $C = 0.399{,}9$ and for the compressional model $C = 0.397{,}9$), with z directed to the Moon's north pole, x perpendicular to it and directed to a meridian passing through the mean center of the Moon, and y directed so as to form a right-handed coordinate system—such a system is identical to the $x_☾$, $y_☾$, $z_☾$ selenographic system defined in Section 4.5.2 (U_x, U_y, and U_z being the components of a selenographic $\mathbf{U} = \mathbf{r}/r$ unit vector) and λ' is a function of the lunar density variation. In the case of constant density, $\lambda' = \rho_{AV}/5$. In case of Jeffreys' compressional model with constant bulk modulus $\lambda' = \rho_{AV}$ (0.199). Different values of λ' can be obtained for other assumptions.

5.4. Planetocentric Constants

5.4.1. Masses

The following section discusses and summarizes the values for planetocentric constants—particularly planetary masses and dimensions. We are indebted to George B. Westrom whose assistance was valuable in the preparation of this section.[56] The three methods generally available for the determination of the mass of a planet are: (i) perturbing action on minor planets; (ii) action on its own satellites; and (iii) perturbing action on other major planets. The relative uncertainties in the methods depend on a number of factors: the mass and nearness of approach of the satellite or body perturbed, the mass of the planet itself, etc.

5.4.1.1. Masses from Minor Planets

Early in the 19th century astronomers recognized the urgent need for more precise values of the masses of the principal planets and, conversely, they realized the exceptional opportunities for obtaining them afforded by minor planets with eccentric orbits. The strong disturbance in the motion of a minor planet that ventures too close to Jupiter, for example, produces significant residual differences between theory and observation, if the adopted mass of the planet is inexact or higher order terms are neglected. A correction to the mass can be derived from the differential improvement of the orbit. The perturbations are cumulative when there is a near commensurability between the mean motions of the minor planets and Jupiter. Thus, in the case of these highly perturbed orbits, the mass of Jupiter could be corrected along with the minor planet's orbital elements (see Chapter 6) to yield an improved planetary mass.

Obviously, such a small quantity as a correction to a major planet's mass could not be deduced from a differential correction of the orbital elements of an asteroid† until the most accurate orbit had been calculated from the available data and effective perturbations by other planets applied as well. As an example of the immense amount of patience and labor involved in such an undertaking, we cite the work of Leveau[57] on the orbit of 4 Vesta. On the basis of Farley's elements of Vesta derived from 12 normal places between 1840 and 1855, Leveau computed first-order perturbations due to Venus, Earth, Mars, Jupiter, Saturn, Uranus, and Neptune by Hansen's method; he computed second-order perturbations depending on the square of Jupiter's mass and on the product of the masses of Jupiter and Saturn. He then represented 215 normal places formed from 5,000 observations 1807–89 and deduced mean elements, using Newcomb's Tables of the Sun, and taking corrections to the masses of Mars and Jupiter into the solution. One large term had a period of 3000 years; a commensurability of 3:10 in the periods of Jupiter and Vesta produced a term with a period of 36 years. Leveau extended the computation later to

† *Asteroid* is synonymous with *minor planet*, but the latter term is to be preferred.

include observations to 1904 and made a new determination of the masses. His values, and comparable results obtained by other astronomers, are given in Table VII.

TABLE VII. MASSES OF MARS AND JUPITER FROM MINOR PLANETS

Minor planet	Author	Mass of Jupiter[a]	Mass of Mars[a]	Date
4 Vesta	Encke	1050.36		1825
4 Vesta	Leveau I	1045.63	3648,000	1890
4 Vesta	Leveau II	1046	3601,280	1904
13 Egeria	Hansen	1051.42		1865
24 Themis	Krüger	1047.538		1865
33 Polyhymnia	Newcomb	1047.34		1893

[a] Units are reciprocals of the solar mass taken as unity.

5.4.1.2. Masses from Satellites

In determining the mass of a planet from its satellites, one needs only to measure the distance from the satellite to the planet's center and the period of the satellite. Substitution into Kepler's third law gives the mass as a fraction of the solar mass. Since periods can be measured to great accuracy the major source of error is in the distance from the satellite to the planet. The error in the mass thus enters percentage-wise as the cube of the distance error; hence, the error is larger for the larger planets.

Mars has two satellites, Phobos and Deimos, whose periods are $27553^{s}.85$ and $109{,}074^{s}.9$ respectively. The semimajor axes are $12''.895 \pm ''.019$ and $32''.389 \pm ''.018$.[58] Since the error in the distance is much greater than in the periods we need consider only the error in the distance. Since the distance enters as the cube, the error in Deimos is only 0.4 that of Phobos.

Substitution of the above values into Kepler's third law gives the mass as a fraction of the solar mass. Since the mass of Deimos is negligible as compared to Mars, and the mass of Mars is negligible as compared to the Sun, one can write:

$$m_{♂} = \left(\frac{P_{♂}}{P_{D}}\right)^2 \left(\frac{a_{D}}{a_{♂}}\right)^3 m_{\odot},$$

where

$m_{♂}$ = the Martian mass, $P_{♂}$ = the period of Mars,
$m_{\odot}$ = the Solar mass, a_{D} = the semimajor axis of Deimos' orbit, and
P_{D} = the period of Deimos, $a_{♂}$ = the semimajor axis of Mars' orbit.

Table VIII shows considerable variation in the mass as determined from the two methods.

TABLE VIII. PLANETARY MASS

	Mars mass[a]	
3,079,000 ± 5702	Urey[b]	1952
3,110,000 ± 7700	Rabe[c]	1950
	Venus mass[a]	
406,358 ± 723	Fotheringham[d]	1926
403,490 ± 2400	Ross[e]	1928
411,300	Spencer Jones	1940
408,000	Clemence and Scott	1940
408,645 ± 208	E. Rabe[c]	1949
	Jupiter mass[a]	
1047.40 0.3	DeSitter	1908
	Saturn mass[a]	
3497.64 0.27	Hertz	1953

[a] Units are reciprocals of the solar mass taken as unity.
[b] From the orbit of Deimos.
[c] From perturbations on Eros.
[d] From perturbations of Mars, Earth, and Mercury.
[e] From perturbations of Mars and Earth.

5.4.1.3. Mass from Perturbations on Other Planets

In the case of Venus, no moons are present and recourse must be taken to estimates based upon the Venusian perturbation of Earth, Mercury, and minor planets. Values for the reciprocal of Venus' mass also may be found in Table VIII.

It should again be noted that the constants given in the *American Ephemeris and Nautical Almanac* are *not* up to date—in fact they are of 1901 "vintage." As has been pointed out by Clemence of the U. S. Naval Observatory, these old constants have been retained without revision for the sake of consistency between the old and new editions of the *Ephemeris*. The latest improved constants should nevertheless be utilized in all definitive interplanetary orbit computations; otherwise, as demonstrated in reference 36, there would result a significant increase in the corrective fuel required.

5.4.2. Diameters and Flattening

Accurate determination of the diameter of the solid surface of a planet having an atmosphere is exceedingly difficult. To determine the diameter one uses either some type of micrometer attached to a telescope or measurements of photographs. The principal uncertainties, discussed in some detail by Campbell[59] are aberration, irradiation, focus, and the atmosphere of the planet. He points out that practically all the errors give a diameter that is too large.

Table IX gives several of the older and some more recent determinations of the diameters of Mars and Venus. Most of the values are intended to display the size of the disk, which depends upon the thickness of the atmosphere.

Table IX. Planetary Diameters

	Mars diameter	
Equatorial diameter (km)		
6743 ± 22	See[a]	1901
6652 ± 11	Trumpler[b]	1927
6679 ± 42.3	Van de Kamp	1928
6860 ± 21.7	Rabe[c]	1929
6834 ± 50.2	Reuyl	1941
6826	Müller	1948
	Venus diameter	
Equatorial diameter (km)		
12,620	Rabe	1928
12,313 (solid planet)	Ross	1928
12,246	Kuiper	1949

[a] Average of determinations from 1651 to 1901.
[b] Determination of solid surface from motion of surface features.
[c] Reviewed previous determinations.

The flattening of a planet is defined as the ratio of the difference between the equatorial and polar diameters to the equatorial diameter. The flattening can be calculated from dynamical formulas by assuming hydrostatic equilibrium and a particular density distribution or it may be measured on photographs. Table X gives figures for the flattening of Mars.

TABLE X. MARS FLATTENING

$\frac{1^{a}}{192}$	Struve	1895
$\frac{1^{a}}{191.8}$	Woolard	1944
$\frac{1^{b}}{76.9}$	G. de Vaucouleurs	

[a] Dynamical from motion of satellites.
[b] Average of several optical determinations over more than 100 years.

5.5. Atmospheric Constants

5.5.1. General

For low-altitude satellites and space vehicles the "constants" associated with the atmosphere of the Earth are often vastly more important than those associated with the Earth's gravitational field. In the case of these atmospheric constants the problem is aggravated by their systematic annual, diurnal, and latitudinal variations and their random variation due to solar influences. Of the many constants involved in specifying an atmosphere (e.g., wind, temperature, molecular composition, etc.) we have singled out the model density profile for detailed discussion.

It must be emphasized at the outset that all model atmospheric density profiles are to some extent speculative. No model can accurately describe the entire atmosphere at any given time. The basic properties of any atmospheric model, i.e., pressure, density, and the ratio of temperature to the molecular weight of air, are related by the equation of hydrostatic equilibrium:

$$-dP = \rho g \, dH \tag{65}$$

and the equation of state:

$$\rho = \frac{Pm}{R^*T}. \tag{66}$$

In these equations, $-dP$ is the decrease in pressure due to an increase dH in altitude, ρ is the density and g the acceleration of gravity at altitude H,

m is the true molecular weight of the air, T is the true temperature, and R^* is the universal gas constant.

When the altitude function is known for any one of the basic properties, the altitude functions of the other properties are easily established. The temperature function is generally chosen as the defining property, although some model atmospheres have been derived without making any assumptions regarding the temperature distribution.[60,61]

All models of the atmosphere are based upon *Toussaint's temperature function* (1919), or minor variations thereof, for the 0–20 km region. Toussaint's temperature function is defined by 15°C at sea level, a constant gradient of -0.0065°C/m from sea level to 11,000 m (giving a temperature of -56.5°C for 11,000 m), and then a constant -56.5°C from 11,000 m to 20,000 m.

In 1952 the International Civil Aviation Organization (ICAO) adopted a standard atmosphere extending to 20,000 m. This model used Toussaint's temperature function, giving a tropopause altitude and temperature of 11,000 m and -56.5°C. The value of the acceleration of gravity at sea level, g_0, was taken to be 9.80665 m/sec^2. The ICAO atmosphere was accepted as the United States Standard Atmosphere on November 20, 1952.

The ICAO was not concerned with high altitudes. Various extrapolated models, such as those of Warfield, Grimminger, and the Rocket Panel, temporarily fulfilled the increasing requirements for atmospheric tables at higher altitudes.

5.5.2. ARDC Model Atmosphere 1956

The Air Research and Development Command (ARDC) Model Atmosphere[62] 1956 extends to 500,000 m*. (Where m* denotes geopotential meters; see Eq. (69)). It is consistent with the ICAO Standard Atmosphere and also with the Extension of the United States Standard Atmosphere 1956 which extended to 300,000 m*. The upper portion of the ARDC Model 1956 was determined from theoretical considerations before satellite inferred density data were available, and when the only published rocket density data above 100 km consisted of 10 scattered density points. Thus only general trends can be inferred at these high altitudes, and the atmospheric properties become more and more speculative with increasing height. This 1956 model has been widely accepted as being the best available representation of the atmosphere prior to satellite inferred density data. It was intended that the ARDC Model 1956 be modified whenever more reliable atmospheric data became available, and at the time of this writing it is to be replaced by the ARDC Model 1959 atmosphere.

It will be worthwhile to discuss the ARDC Model 1956 in some detail, because such a discussion will provide an understanding of the principles upon which model atmospheres are based, and also because the majority of models making use of satellite-inferred densities are simply modifications of the ARDC Model 1956 at high altitudes.

Since the acceleration due to gravity varies with altitude, it is convenient to use "geopotential altitude," H^*, defined by

$$g_0^* \, dH^* \triangleq g \, dH, \tag{67}$$

where g is the acceleration due to gravity in m/sec² at geometric altitude H (in meters), and if H^* is in geopotential meters (m*), then g_0^* is equal to 9.80665 m²/sec² m*. The integration of the equation of hydrostatic equilibrium and the resulting algebraic expressions are simplified by concealing the variable gravity in the geopotential altitude. By using

$$g = g_0 \left(\frac{R'}{R' + H} \right)^2 \tag{68}$$

as the relation for the variation of gravity in Eq. (67), and integrating, a nearly correct relationship between geopotential and geometric altitude is found as

$$H^* = \frac{H g_0}{g_0^*} \left(1 + \frac{H}{R'} \right)^{-1}, \tag{69}$$

where $R' = 6{,}356{,}766$ m (this is the effective Earth's radius at latitude 45° 32′ 40″ and is not to be confused with our revised value for the equatorial radius—see Minzner and Ripley[62] for a detailed discussion of this point). The ratio g_0/g_0^* has the dimension m^*/m but is numerically unity (i.e., at sea level $m = m^*$). The ordinary (geometric) meter should, of course, still be employed for the purpose of orbit determination, e.g., for entry into atmospheric density tables. See p. 167 for the determination of H.

To simplify the integration and computational equations involved in deriving an atmospheric model, Minzner has defined a *molecular-scale temperature*, T_m. Upon specifying the functional relationship of T_m with altitude, T_m may be taken as the defining property of the ARDC Model Atmosphere 1956. The molecular-scale temperature combines the two variables T and m by

$$T_m \triangleq \frac{T}{m} m_0 \tag{70}$$

where m_0 is a reference molecular weight, conveniently taken as the molecular weight of air at sea level. Thus, variations in molecular weight are taken into account without requiring their functional form.

The variation of the temperature parameter, T_m, with geopotential altitude, H^*, is arbitrarily taken to be piecewise continuous. This segmented function is selected so as to be consistent with the observed data. The slopes of these segments have constant derivatives (or gradients), L_m. Throughout any straight portion of the function then,

$$T_m = (T_m)_b + L_m(H^* - H_b^*). \tag{71}$$

where $(T_m)_b$ is the value of T_m at the base altitude, H_b^*, of any straight segment and also equal to the value of T_m at the top of the preceding segment, and L_m is the derivative of T_m with respect to H^* between the discontinuities. There is no justification for assuming this piecewise continuous function for the $T_m(H^*)$ relation other than that it is a convenient approximation and it follows tradition. The values of L_m and the associated values of H_b^* are selected so as to provide agreement with observed temperatures up to the highest altitudes for which reliable temperature measurements are available. The densities and pressures calculated with this temperature function agree with the observed values. At higher altitudes the temperature function is selected such that the densities derived by using it will agree with the observed values.

The derivation of the expressions for pressure and density at a given geopotential height, H^*, will be briefly outlined. The pressure relationship is obtained first, and the result is used in deriving the density function.

The equation of state, (66), is substituted into the equation of hydrostatic equilibrium, (65), giving

$$dP = -\frac{Pm}{R^*T} g\, dH. \tag{72}$$

The expression for molecular-scale temperature, (Eq. (70)), and the definition of geopotential (Eq. (67)) are substituted into Eq. (72), giving

$$\int_{P_b}^{P} \frac{dP}{P} = -\frac{m_0 g_0^*}{R^*} \int_{H_b^*}^{H^*} \frac{dH^*}{T_m}. \tag{73}$$

Making use of the assumed $T_m(H^*)$ relationship, (Eq. (71)), and performing the integration, there results for any straight portion of the curve,

$$\ln \frac{P}{P_b} = -\frac{m_0 g_0^*}{R^* L_m} \left\{ \ln \left[1 + \frac{L_m}{(T_m)_b} (H^* - H_b^*) \right] \right\}, \tag{74}$$

where P_b is the pressure at the base of any straight segment. The density at this point is by Eqs. (66) and (70)

$$\rho_b = \frac{P_b m_0}{(T_m)_b R^*},$$

and therefore

$$\frac{\rho}{\rho_b} = \frac{P}{P_b} \frac{(T_m)_b}{T_m}.$$

Taking the logarithm of this equation, we find that

$$\ln \frac{\rho}{\rho_b} = \ln \frac{P}{P_b} - \ln \frac{T_m}{(T_m)_b},$$

whereupon substitution of Eq. (71) and Eq. (74) gives the expression for the density at any point along a straight portion of the curve

$$\ln \rho = \ln \rho_b - \left(1 + \frac{m_0 g_0^*}{R^* L_m}\right) \left\{ \ln \left[1 + \frac{L_m}{(T_m)_b} (H^* - H_b^*) \right] \right\} \tag{75}$$

In the isothermal regions, where $L_m = 0$,

$$\ln \rho = \ln \rho_b - \frac{m_0 g_0^*}{R^*} \left\{ \frac{(H^* - H_b^*)}{(T_m)_b} \right\} \tag{76}$$

where $(T_m)_b R^*/m_0 g_0^*$ is called the "scale height."

The value of density at the base of any segment is the same as the density at the top of the preceding segment. Thus, ρ_b depends directly upon the sea level value of density, ρ_0, which is

$$\rho_0 = \frac{P_0 m_0}{(T_m)_0} R^*.$$

Adopting $P_0 = 101{,}325.0$ newtons/m^2, $m_0 = 28.966$, $(T_m)_0 = 288.16$°K, and $R^* = 8.31439 \times 10^3$ joules/°K kg, ρ_0 becomes $\rho_0 = 1.225\,013\,998$ kg/m^3. Values of ρ_b can now be determined for each successive layer by use of Eqs. (75) or (76).

Interim model atmospheres were devised by Schilling, Sterne, Folkart, Harris, and Jastrow when it was found that the ARDC Model 1956 did not fit the first reliable satellite-inferred density. The first of these very tentative models was based upon the ARDC Model 1956 and a density of 4.5×10^{-10} kg/m^3 at 220 km. This density point was inferred from observations of satellite 1957 α_2, and was about 8.7 times the density predicted by the ARDC Model 1956 at this altitude. Whitney made further extensions and the 1956 Model has now been superseded by the 1959 Model. The estimated divergence of this 1959 ARDC *Model* atmosphere from the actual atmosphere is estimated to be about $\pm 6\%$ at sea level and exponentially increases to about $\pm 60\%$ at 50 km.

5.5.3. Variations

Seasonal, diurnal, and latitudinal variations of atmospheric density are very poorly determined at this time. Pond feels that there is not yet sufficient data available to give a valid estimate of these variations. Champion is of the same opinion, although he considers the seasonal and diurnal density variations to be quite small. Whitney states that there appears to be a general increase of variability with altitude.

Champion and Minzner[63] investigated possible seasonal variations in density by plotting satellite perigee latitudes as a function of the time and then comparing the density points. As a very tentative conclusion, they suggest that the satellite inferred densities may be lower in the summer than in the winter. Later data may not confirm this.

One might expect somewhat higher temperatures in the high atmosphere during the daylight hours than at night. Until recently there has been no clear-cut evidence to support this expectation of systematic diurnal variations in atmospheric temperature and consequently in density. Jacchia, however, has announced the presence of a definite diurnal effect in the orbit acceleration of 1957 β 1. The observed semi-amplitude of this diurnal effect is roughly 10% of the acceleration (cf. Jacchia).[64]

As the result of the Earth's oblateness, a satellite at a fixed geocentric distance is much nearer the surface of the Earth at the equator than at the poles, and is therefore in a region of higher density. The latitudinal variations between the densities obtained from a number of rocket flights give conflicting conclusions. Whitney[65] has pointed out that recent satellite data give a good indication of latitudinal variations in density that are compatible with the well-known flattening of the geoid. This amounts to about 15% at 200 km. Other special-purpose balloon satellites will surely resolve this problem.

A correlation between density variation and solar phenomena has recently been inferred from satellite observations. The satellite accelerations show variations with mean periods of about 27–30 days. This period coincides with the rotational period of the Sun, suggesting a correlation with solar activity. All the satellites show approximately synchronous maxima and minima of accelerations, which implies worldwide variations of density. Jacchia[66] finds three types of fluctuations: (i) those that follow the rhythm of the solar flux—probably caused by solar ultraviolet; (ii) those that are connected with the position of perigee relative to the subsolar point (termed diurnal)—also due ultimately to solar ultraviolet; and (iii) those transients accompanying magnetic storms—caused by atmospheric heating resulting from solar corpuscular radiation. (Dessler has suggested that the hydromagnetic waves generated by enhanced solar wind may significantly heat the ionosphere, thereby causing an upward expansion and accounting for the 30 to 50% increase in satellite drag at 200 km.) At present, all these fluctuations (amounting to a maximum increase in density of 20–70%) are averaged out by deriving densities from mean accelerations averaged over several months.

It is an exceedingly difficult task to disentangle from one another the variations of density with altitude, latitude, and time, and with possible astrophysical variables. Some of these difficulties may be overcome with the use of additional satellites. For example, latitudinal and seasonal changes would be eliminated in the density data obtained from a satellite in an equatorial orbit. In a polar orbit there is no advance of the line of apsides, so seasonal changes in density could be studied to the best advantage.

In view of the fact that the density variations in the atmosphere are not yet clearly understood, it is dangerous to combine densities obtained from different satellites at random times. Therefore, at this time it seems best to proceed with a model based upon satellite accelerations that are averaged over long periods of time. An approach adopted by Whitney attempted to average out the latitudinal, diurnal, and seasonal variations. He thus processed all the observed points of each individual satellite to obtain one point per satellite, and employed these points in deriving his atmospheric models. On the other hand, Kallmann employed all the satellite-inferred density points of several satellites in deriving her models. Much more data are necessary before models can be derived that will actually account for all the observed variations of the atmosphere.

We are indebted to Paul Koskela who aided us extensively in the preparation of the foregoing section (cf. Baker *et al.*).[67]

MORE DETAILED ANALYSES

6 ORBIT DETERMINATION AND IMPROVEMENT

Orbit determination methods are applied to two different practical problems of astrodynamics:

(i) the *post computation* or prediction of the future position of a space vehicle based upon observational data; and

(ii) the *precomputation* of nominal or variant orbits prior to a launch in order to determine the orbital characteristics in advance.

The former problem, (i), must be faced by all range systems and is discussed in Section 11.2. The latter problem of precomputation, (ii), is of more direct concern to the designers of space probe orbits and is discussed in Chapter 12 and in Baker.[2]

In general, the determination of the orbit of a space vehicle, comet, or planet may follow one of three different procedures. One method, which is associated with the name of Willard Gibbs, makes use of three position vectors, $\mathbf{r}_1$, $\mathbf{r}_2$, $\mathbf{r}_3$, to define the conic section, without recourse to the dynamical equations. A second procedure, associated with the names Laplace and Lagrange, determines the orbit from $\mathbf{r}$, $\dot{\mathbf{r}}$, $\ddot{\mathbf{r}}$, i.e., the vectors of position, velocity, and acceleration at a certain date or time (usually termed the "middle date t_2" because numerical differentiation from observational data before and after this date are used to construct the derivatives). If, as is more usual, the acceleration is derived from the equations of motion (which arise from Newton's second law of motion and his universal law of gravitation), the orbit is determined from the position and velocity at the middle date. A third method, due to Gauss, combines two positions and the time interval between them with Kepler's law of constant areal velocity to define the orbit. These three orbit methods refer only to undisturbed or two-body motion, as, for example, that of a single planet around the Sun, or a satellite around a spherical Earth (all pairs of objects assumed to be alone in the Universe); but they can be extended by perturbation techniques, which will be described later, to include the effects of any number of bodies external to the two-body system.

6.1. Orbit from Position and Velocity

Although technically associated with the Laplacian and Lagrangian methods, the determination of orbital elements from the rectangular equatorial coordinates and their time-derivatives, x, y, z, $\dot{x}$, $\dot{y}$, $\dot{z}$, has a general application and is found in most methods. Consequently we shall preface the development of the various orbit determination procedures by assuming that the coordinates and their velocities are known and deriving expressions for the orbital elements from them. The first step will be to define the basic vectorial parameters **a**, **b**, and **h**, which arise from the integration of the equations of motion and the derivation of Kepler's first and second laws (cf. Chapter 8 in Herrick[1]). No attempt is made to derive these relationships in the most sophisticated manner—in fact, an *ad hoc* approach is taken to expedite the proof. The interested reader is directed to Herrick[1] for a more motivated approach.

6.1.1. Derivations

We will start with the geometrical relationship $r^2 = x^2 + y^2 + z^2$, and take successive derivatives with respect to the time:

$$r\dot{r} = x\dot{x} + y\dot{y} + z\dot{z} \triangleq \sqrt{\mu}D,$$

$$\dot{r}^2 + r\ddot{r} = \dot{x}^2 + \dot{y}^2 + \dot{z}^2 + x\ddot{x} + y\ddot{y} + z\ddot{z} \quad (\text{with } \dot{s}^2 = \dot{x}^2 + \dot{y}^2 + \dot{z}^2)$$

$$= \dot{s}^2 - \left(\frac{x^2\mu}{r^3} + \frac{y^2\mu}{r^3} + \frac{z^2\mu}{r^3}\right) = \dot{s}^2 - \frac{\mu}{r} \quad (\text{i.e., } \ddot{x} = -\mu x/r^3,\ x \to y,\ z)$$

$$= \sqrt{\mu}\dot{D}, \tag{77}$$

and finally

$$3\dot{r}\ddot{r} + r\dddot{r} = 2(\dot{x}\ddot{x} + \dot{y}\ddot{y} + \dot{z}\ddot{z}) + \frac{\mu\dot{r}}{r^2} = \sqrt{\mu}\ddot{D}$$

$$(\text{with } \ddot{x} = -\mu x/r^3,\ x \to y,\ z \text{ and } r\dot{r} = x\dot{x} + y\dot{y} + z\dot{z})$$

$$= -2\mu\frac{r\dot{r}}{r^3} + \mu\frac{r\dot{r}}{r^3} = -\mu\frac{r\dot{r}}{r^3} = -\mu^{3/2}D/r^3.$$

Consequently, one obtains the interesting relationship

$$\ddot{D} = -\mu D/r^3, \tag{78}$$

and since from the equations of motion, $\ddot{x} = -\mu x/r^3$, $x \to y, z$, the following three differential equations can be formed:

$$\ddot{D}x - D\ddot{x} \equiv 0 \qquad x \to y, z.$$

Their integral is obtained by parts and if we define $a_x \sqrt{\mu}$ to be the constant of integration, then,

$$\dot{D}x - D\dot{x} = a_x \sqrt{\mu} \qquad x \to y, z$$

or in vectorial form

$$\dot{D}\mathbf{r} - D\dot{\mathbf{r}} = \mathbf{a}\sqrt{\mu}. \tag{79}$$

The ambiguity in notation, i.e., that $|\mathbf{a}| \neq a$ the semimajor axis, should be noted at this point.

In order to understand the significance of $\mathbf{a}$, consider the scalar dot product $\mathbf{r} \cdot \mathbf{a}$,

$$\mathbf{r} \cdot \mathbf{a} = xa_x + ya_y + za_z = \frac{1}{\sqrt{\mu}}(\dot{D}r^2 - Dr\dot{r})$$

$$= \frac{r^2}{\mu}(\dot{s}^2 - \dot{r}^2) - r = \frac{r^2}{\mu}(r\dot{v})^2 - r,$$

where $r\dot{v}$ is the transverse component of velocity and $\dot{s}^2 = \dot{r}^2 + (r\dot{v})^2$. Since $\mathbf{r} \cdot \mathbf{a} = |\mathbf{r}|\,|\mathbf{a}| \cos(\angle \mathbf{a}, \mathbf{r})$, where $\angle \mathbf{a}, \mathbf{r}$ signifies the angle between $\mathbf{a}$ and $\mathbf{r}$,

$$\frac{r^4\dot{v}^2}{\mu} = r[1 + |\mathbf{a}| \cos(\angle \mathbf{a}, \mathbf{r})]$$

which is the equation of a conic; thus Kepler's first law has been derived. Comparison of this form with the previously derived equation of a conic

$$p = r[1 + e \cos v]$$

allows for the following interpretations:

$$p = a(1 - e^2) = \frac{r^4\dot{v}^2}{\mu}$$

$$|\mathbf{a}| = e,$$

and

$$\angle \mathbf{a}, \mathbf{r} = v;$$

consequently, **a** is a vector with magnitude e and directed towards perifocus along the semimajor axis:

$$\mathbf{a} = e\mathbf{P}. \tag{80}$$

The derivation of expressions involving **b** proceeds in a similar *ad hoc* fashion. Let us define

$$H \triangleq r - p$$

and determine from the equation of a conic that

$$H = r - p = -re \cos v;$$

therefore,

$$\dot{H} = \dot{r} = \sqrt{\frac{\mu}{p}}\, e \sin v.$$

$$\text{(i.e., } \dot{r} = pe \sin v\dot{v}/(1 + e \cos v)^2$$

$$= \frac{r^2\dot{v}}{p}\, e \sin v = \sqrt{\frac{\mu}{p}}\, e \sin v.)$$

Differentiating again, we find that

$$\ddot{H} = \sqrt{\frac{\mu}{p}}\, e \cos v\dot{v},$$

but

$$\dot{v} = \frac{\sqrt{\mu p}}{r^2} \qquad \text{and} \qquad e \cos v = \frac{(p - r)}{r}$$

so that

$$\ddot{H} = \frac{\mu(p - r)}{r^3} \qquad \text{or} \qquad \ddot{H} = \frac{-\mu H}{r^3}. \tag{81}$$

Consequently, multiplying by $\ddot{x} = -\mu x/r^3$, $x \to y, z$, we obtain the following three differential equations:

$$\ddot{H}x - H\ddot{x} \equiv 0 \qquad x \to y, z.$$

Their integrals are obtained by inspection, and if one defines $b_x \sqrt{\mu}$ to be the constant of integration of the first equation, then

$$\dot{H}x - H\dot{x} = b_x \sqrt{\mu} \qquad x \to y, z$$

or in vectorial form

$$\dot{H}\mathbf{r} - H\dot{\mathbf{r}} = \mathbf{b}\sqrt{\mu}. \tag{82}$$

Again, the ambiguity in notation, i.e., that $|\mathbf{b}| \neq b$ the semiminor axis, should be noted. In order to understand the significance of $\mathbf{b}$, consider the scalar dot product $\mathbf{r} \cdot \mathbf{b}$.

$$\mathbf{r} \cdot \mathbf{b}\sqrt{\mu} = \dot{H}r^2 - Hr\dot{r} = \dot{r}r^2 - (r - p)r\dot{r} = pr\dot{r}$$

and also

$$= \sqrt{\mu}\,|\mathbf{r}|\,|\mathbf{b}|\cos(\angle\mathbf{r}, \mathbf{b}).$$

But

$$\dot{r} = \sqrt{\mu/p}\; e \sin v$$

so that

$$e\sqrt{p}\sin v = |\mathbf{b}|\cos(\angle\mathbf{r}, \mathbf{b})$$

and one can therefore associate the angle $\angle\mathbf{r}, \mathbf{b}$ with $90°\text{-}v$ and $|\mathbf{b}|$ with $e\sqrt{p}$. Hence, $\mathbf{b}$ is a vector emanating from the focus and directed parallel to the semiminor axis, i.e.,

$$\mathbf{b} = e\sqrt{p}\,\mathbf{Q}. \tag{83}$$

The vector $\mathbf{h}$ is related to the angular momentum (per unit mass) and, hence, is determined by the following development of the two-body equations of motion (i.e., multiply by the right column and add)

$\ddot{x} = -\mu x/r^3$		$+z$	$-y$
$\ddot{y} = -\mu y/r^3$	$-z$		$+x$
$\ddot{z} = -\mu z/r^3$	$+y$	$-x$	

$$y\ddot{z} - z\ddot{y} = 0$$

$$z\ddot{x} - x\ddot{z} = 0$$

$$x\ddot{y} - y\ddot{x} = 0$$

The integral of this set of differential equations can again be found by inspection and, if we define $h_x\sqrt{\mu}$ as the constant of integration then the solutions are

$$y\dot{z} - z\dot{y} = h_x\sqrt{\mu} \qquad \begin{matrix} x \rightarrow y \\ \nwarrow z \swarrow \end{matrix} \tag{84}$$

(i.e., cyclical rotation of x, y, and z yields the other two equations). These three equations can be recognized as the three components of angular momentum or $\mathbf{r} \times \dot{\mathbf{r}}$, which is in turn simply equal to $r^2\dot{v} = \sqrt{\mu p}$. This, therefore, is the derivation of Kepler's second law of constant areal velocity or, equivalently, of angular momentum. Hence,

$$\mathbf{h} = \sqrt{p}\mathbf{W}. \tag{85}$$

6.1.2. Evaluation of Orbital Elements

It is clear, therefore, that given $\mathbf{a}$, $\mathbf{b}$, and $\mathbf{h}$ (actually any two of the three vectors would be sufficient), then the transverse axis, eccentricity, and orientation elements, i.e., the components of $\mathbf{P}$, $\mathbf{Q}$, and $\mathbf{W}$ along the equatorial coordinate axes may be obtained. The orbit determination evolves in a straightforward manner as follows:

The semimajor axis, a, is found from the *vis-viva* integral Eq. (13), given

$$\dot{s}^2 = \dot{x}^2 + \dot{y}^2 + \dot{z}^2, \text{ i.e.}$$

$$\frac{1}{a} = \frac{2}{r} - \frac{\dot{s}^2}{\mu}. \tag{86}$$

At this point in the calculation a decision can be made as to whether the orbit is an ellipse ($0 < a < \infty$), a parabola ($a = \infty$), or a hyperbola ($-\infty < a < 0$). Assuming that $0 < a < \infty$, one can then obtain $\dot{D}$ from Eq. (77), i.e.,

$$\frac{\dot{D}}{\sqrt{\mu}} = \frac{\dot{s}^2}{\mu} - \frac{1}{r} = \frac{1}{r} - \frac{1}{a} \tag{87}$$

while e and E are obtained from Eq. (15), i.e.,

$$e \cos E = 1 - \frac{r}{a} = \frac{r\dot{D}}{\sqrt{\mu}}$$

and also from

$$e \sin E = \frac{r\dot{r}}{\sqrt{\mu a}} = \frac{D}{\sqrt{a}}. \tag{88}$$

(Note that $\dot{r} = p^2 e \sin v\dot{v}/\{(1 + e \cos v)^2 p\} = r^2\dot{v}e \sin v/p$, therefore, $\sin v = \dot{r}\sqrt{p/\mu}/e$. But $y_\omega = r \sin v = r\dot{r}\sqrt{p/\mu}/e$, and $y_\omega = a\sqrt{1 - e^2}$ $\sin E$ also. Thus,

$$a\sqrt{1 - e^2} \sin E = \frac{r\dot{r}}{e}\sqrt{p/\mu} \quad \text{or} \quad e \sin E = r\dot{r}/\sqrt{\mu a}.)$$

Alternate formulas for low-eccentricity orbits may be found summarized in Chapter 8.

Given the eccentric anomaly, E, it is now possible to relate position to time by Kepler's equation:

$$E - e \sin E = M \triangleq n(t - T), \tag{89}$$

where M is called the *mean anomaly*, n is the *mean motion* $= k\sqrt{\mu}/a^{3/2}$, and T is, as usual, the time of perifocal passage. Often one employs the alternate form

$$M = M_0 + n(t - t_0),$$

where t_0 is some arbitrary initial time called the "epoch" and M_0 is the corresponding value of the mean anomaly. The *mean longitude*, L, is defined in terms of M by $L \triangleq M + \omega + \Omega$ (for retrograde motion, $L_r = M + \omega - \Omega$), while the *mean argument of latitude*, U, is defined by $U \triangleq M + \omega$. The U variable is particularly useful in the case of nearly circular orbits where the perifocus becomes indeterminate and the L variable is useful in orbits of small inclination where the node becomes undefined. Having obtained a, e, and T or M_0, the orientation unit vectors, which are employed to define the orbit plane in preference to the orientation angles, may be computed from Eqs. (80), (83), and (85), e.g.,

$$P_x = a_x/e,\ Q_x = b_x/e\sqrt{p},\ \text{and}\ W_x = h_x/\sqrt{p} \qquad x \to y, z.$$

A summary of the foregoing formulas is given in Chapter 8. Special formulas and techniques are required for orbits of very small eccentricity and for orbits with an eccentricity near unity. (cf. Chapter 8E in Herrick.[1]) In the case of parabolic orbits, in place of Kepler's equation we introduce *Barker's equation*, which takes the form (see derivation in the Appendix)

$$k\sqrt{\mu}\,(t - T) = qD + D^3/6. \tag{90}$$

In the case of hyperbolic orbits we employ an equation analogous to Kepler's equation by introducing F, in place of E, i.e.,

$$M_h = e \sinh F - F \tag{91}$$

where the subscript h refers to hyperbolic motion and

$$M_h = n_h(t - T)$$

and

$$n_h \triangleq k\sqrt{\mu}/(-a)^{3/2}.$$

The new universal variable $\tilde{X}$, which can replace E, D, and F, yields a more general form for Kepler's equation, i.e.,

$$\tilde{M} = \tilde{M}_0 + \tilde{n}(t - t_0), \text{ where } \tilde{n} \triangleq k\sqrt{\mu}.$$

For the ellipse, $\tilde{M} \triangleq a^{3/2}M$ for the parabola $\tilde{M} \triangleq D$, and for the hyperbola $\tilde{M} \triangleq M(-a)^{3/2}$. In general, $\tilde{M}$ is given in terms of $\tilde{X}$ by (see **26** p. 332)

$$\tilde{M} = q\tilde{X} + e\left(\frac{\tilde{X}^3}{3!} - \frac{\tilde{X}^5}{a.5!} + \frac{\tilde{X}^7}{a^2.7!} - \cdots\right).$$

Note that this system of universal variables has the disadvantage of not having a closed form expression in terms of standard trigonometric or hyperbolic functions and involve expansions about perifocal passage time.

Having considered the various forms of Kepler's Equation, we can now solve for T or M_0 (or $\tilde{M}_0$) Furthermore, we have a from Eq. (86); $e\ cos\ E$ and $e\ sin\ E$ from Eqs. (88) for the ellipse (and, hence, e since $e^2 = (e \cos E)^2 + (e \sin E)^2$); **P** from Eqs. (79) and (80) (i.e., $a_x = (\dot{D}x - D\dot{x})/\sqrt{\mu}$ and $P_x = a_x/e, x \rightarrow y, z$); **Q** from Eqs. (82) and (83) (i.e., $b_x = (\dot{H}x - H\dot{x})/\sqrt{\mu}$, $Q_x = b_x/e\sqrt{p}$); and, as has been noted previously, T (or M_0 or $\tilde{M}_0$) from Eqs. (89), (90), or (91). The orbit is, therefore, completely determined and an orbital position can be represented (i.e., predicted) for any subsequent time t_2 e.g., for an ellipse E_2 is found by solving the transcendental Kepler's Equation for E_2 at $t = t_2$; $x_{\omega 2}$ and $y_{\omega 2}$ are obtained from Eqs. (15); and the equatorial coordinates of the space vehicle at time t_2, i.e., x_2, y_2, z_2, are obtained from Eq. (22):

$$\begin{aligned} x_2 &= x_{\omega 2}P_x + y_{\omega 2}Q_x \\ y_2 &= x_{\omega 2}P_y + y_{\omega 2}Q_y \\ z_2 &= x_{\omega 2}P_z + y_{\omega 2}Q_z. \end{aligned}$$

If the observations are to be represented for a specific observation station, then **R** may be obtained from Eqs. (24) for that observatory's location and observation time; ξ, η, and ζ from Eqs. (27): ρ_2; L_{x2}, L_{y2}, L_{z2}, and finally the topocentric right ascension and declination of the space vehicle at time t_2 from Eqs. (28) and (29). It is emphasized that the utilization of the unit vectors **P** and **Q** allow for orbit determination and representation *without* the need for the cumbersome evaluation of trigonometric functions (except in Kepler's Equation), and consequently, their use is always preferred over the use of the more common orientation angles: i, Ω, and ω.

Of course, the preceding analysis assumes two-body motion. In general, unless only approximate representations are required, a more rigorous orbit computation is desirable. In this case, the position and velocity $\mathbf{r}$, $\dot{\mathbf{r}}$ or the orbital elements a, e, M_0, $\mathbf{P}$, $\mathbf{Q}$, $\mathbf{W}$ (as obtained in this section) can be utilized as the basis for the special or general perturbation of Chapters 8 and 9. The orbit, having been carried forward by either of these two methods, can serve as the basis for representations of observations, i.e., for the generation of an ephemeris, by means of Eqs. (24)–(29). A clear distinction should, therefore, be drawn at this point between orbit computation and orbit determination. Essentially, the initial conditions for the *orbit computation* (position and velocity or orbital elements) are provided by the *orbit determination* and in this sense the following methods of Gibbs, Laplace, Gauss etc., must go hand in hand with the orbit computation methods of the subsequent chapters to yield orbital predictions.

6.2. Gibbs' Method

The simplest formulation of a typical Gibbsian method can be carried out in the case of a point-to-point geocentric or ICBM trajectory. Let us suppose that the coordinates of the take-off point, the landing point, and the apogee or highest point are known. Furthermore, for simplicity, let us assume that the Earth is spherical and that the vehicle is injected onto its orbit impulsively. The steps for the orbit determination are then as follows: Given x_ω and y_ω for the take-off, B (beginning), the apogee, A, and the landing, E (ending) form

$$r_A = \sqrt{x_{\omega A}{}^2 + y_{\omega A}{}^2} = a(1 + e)$$

$$p = r_B + e x_{\omega B} = a(1 - e^2) = r_A(1 - e), \tag{92}$$

so that

$$e = (r_A - r_B)/(x_{\omega B} + r_A). \tag{93}$$

Given e and p one can solve for a, while E_B is given by

$$\sin E_B = y_{\omega B}/a\sqrt{1 - e^2}$$

and

$$\cos E_B = (x_{\omega B} + ae)/a = (a - r_B)/ae. \tag{94}$$

Kepler's equation may be formed and a value for T obtained by means of E_B, M_B, and n.

6.2.1. General Method

For more general application the Gibbsian method depends upon the condition that all radii from the focus (or force center) to the object at the three dates are coplanar, i.e.,

$$\mathbf{r}_2 = c_1\mathbf{r}_1 + c_3\mathbf{r}_3. \tag{95}$$

Equation (95) actually represents three-component equations that can be solved for the scalar constants c_1 and c_3. Since the x-component of Eq. (95) is $x_{\omega 2} = c_1 x_{\omega 1} + c_3 x_{\omega 3}$ in the $\mathbf{P}-\mathbf{Q}$ orbit-plane system and since $x_{\omega i} = (p - r_i)/e$ from the equation of a conic (14), we find that $p - r_2 = c_1(p - r_1) + c_3(p - r_3)$ or

$$p = (c_1 r_1 + c_3 r_3 - r_2)/(c_1 + c_3 - 1). \tag{96}$$

Given c_1 and c_3 from Eq. (95) and the parameter, p, from Eq. (96), $\mathbf{W}$ can next be determined from

$$\mathbf{W} = \mathbf{r}_1 \times \mathbf{r}_3/|\mathbf{r}_1 \times \mathbf{r}_3| \triangleq \mathbf{r}_1 \times \mathbf{r}_3/S. \tag{97}$$

The computation of $\mathbf{Q}$ follows from the substitution of (97) into $\mathbf{Q} = \mathbf{W} \times \mathbf{P}$, i.e., $S\mathbf{Q} = [\mathbf{r}_1 \times \mathbf{r}_3] \times \mathbf{P}$. This triple vector product can be resolved as $S\mathbf{Q} = \mathbf{r}_3(\mathbf{P} \cdot \mathbf{r}_1) - \mathbf{r}_1(\mathbf{P} \cdot \mathbf{r}_3)$, where $\mathbf{P} \cdot \mathbf{r}_i = x_{\omega i} = (p - r_i)/e$ or

$$e\mathbf{Q} = [\mathbf{r}_3(p - r_1) - \mathbf{r}_1(p - r_3)]/S. \tag{98}$$

Given $e\mathbf{Q}$, e can be obtained from

$$e^2 = (e\mathbf{Q}) \cdot (e\mathbf{Q}) = e^2Q_x^2 + e^2Q_y^2 + e^2Q_z^2$$

Given e, a may be computed as

$$a = p/(1 - e^2).$$

Of course $\mathbf{P} = \mathbf{Q} \times \mathbf{W}$ and E_i can be obtained from Eqs. (88) (given $ex_{\omega i} = p - r_i$) cf. Eqs. (144). Kepler's equation (89) can then be solved the "easy way" in order to obtain T (given $n = k\sqrt{\mu}/a^{3/2}$).

6.2.2. Herrick–Gibbs

Herrick's modification of Gibbs' method, termed here the *Herrick–Gibbs method*, involves the employment of three-position measurements to represent velocity at the central or second date. This method proceeds as follows:

Given the three observed positions $\mathbf{r}_1$, $\mathbf{r}_2$, and $\mathbf{r}_3$ and the times between these τ_{12}, τ_{23}, and τ_{13}, where $\tau_{ij} \triangleq k(t_j - t_i)$ we turn to the Herrick–Gibbs numerical differentiation formulas for velocity, (good to the fourth order or to $(r^v/5!)\tau_{ij}^5$):

if
$$d_i \triangleq G_i + H_i/r_i^3,$$

where
$$G_1 \triangleq \tau_{23}^2/\tau_{12}\tau_{23}\tau_{13},$$
$$G_3 \triangleq \tau_{12}^2/\tau_{12}\tau_{23}\tau_{13},$$

and
$$G_2 \triangleq G_1 - G_3;$$

and
$$H_1 = \mu\tau_{23}/12,$$
$$H_3 = \mu\tau_{12}/12,$$

and
$$H_2 \triangleq H_1 - H_3,$$

then
$$\dot{\mathbf{r}}_2 = -d_1\mathbf{r}_1 + d_2\mathbf{r}_2 + d_3\mathbf{r}_3. \tag{99}$$

As an example, the d coefficients of Herrick are easily derived as follows: (cf. Herrick,[68] and Van Sant, *et al.*[69]).

The differences $\mathbf{r}_1 - \mathbf{r}_2$ and $\mathbf{r}_3 - \mathbf{r}_2$ are expressed by means of the series expansions about $\mathbf{r}_2$ at τ_2

$$\mathbf{r}_1 - \mathbf{r}_2 = -\tau_{12}\dot{\mathbf{r}}_2 + \tau_{12}^2\frac{\ddot{\mathbf{r}}_2}{2} - \tau_{12}^3\frac{\dddot{\mathbf{r}}_2}{6} + \tau_{12}^4\frac{\mathbf{r}_2^{iv}}{24} - \cdots \tag{100}$$

$$\mathbf{r}_3 - \mathbf{r}_2 = \tau_{23}\dot{\mathbf{r}}_2 + \tau_{23}^2\frac{\ddot{\mathbf{r}}_2}{2} + \tau_{23}^3\frac{\dddot{\mathbf{r}}_2}{6} + \tau_{23}^4\frac{\mathbf{r}_2^{iv}}{24} + \cdots . \tag{101}$$

The second terms on the right hand side of these equations can be eliminated by multiplying by τ_{23}^2 and τ_{12}^2, respectively, and subtracting:

$$-\tau_{23}^2\mathbf{r}_1 + (\tau_{23}^2 - \tau_{12}^2)\mathbf{r}_2 + \tau_{12}^2\mathbf{r}_3 = \tau_{12}\tau_{23}\tau_{13}\left[\dot{\mathbf{r}}_2 + \tau_{12}\tau_{23}\frac{\dddot{\mathbf{r}}_2}{6} + \tau_{12}\tau_{23}(\tau_{23} - \tau_{12})\frac{\mathbf{r}_2^{iv}}{24} + \cdots\right]. \tag{102}$$

The second time derivative of $\mathbf{r}_1$, and $\mathbf{r}_3$ are then determined from Eqs. (100) and (101) by differentiating twice (with the derivatives of the constant time intervals, τ_{ij} taken as zero). By multiplying the first of the resulting expressions by τ_{23}, and the second by τ_{12} and adding, we find that $\dddot{\mathbf{r}}$ can be eliminated. Because of the definition of τ_{ij}, $\tau_{23} + \tau_{12} = \tau_{13}$, so that:

$$\tau_{23}\ddot{\mathbf{r}}_1 - \tau_{13}\ddot{\mathbf{r}}_2 + \tau_{12}\ddot{\mathbf{r}}_3 = \tau_{12}\tau_{23}\tau_{13}\left[\frac{\mathbf{r}_2{}^{iv}}{2} + \cdots\right]. \tag{103}$$

Similarly, $\mathbf{r}_2{}^{iv}$ can be eliminated between the second derivatives of Eqs. (100) and (101) by multiplying them by τ_{23}^2 and τ_{12}^2 respectively and subtracting, so that

$$-\tau_{23}^2\ddot{\mathbf{r}}_1 + (\tau_{23}^2 - \tau_{12}^2)\ddot{\mathbf{r}}_2 + \tau_{12}^2\ddot{\mathbf{r}}_3 = \tau_{12}\tau_{23}\tau_{13}[\dddot{\mathbf{r}}_2 + \ldots]. \tag{104}$$

By truncating the foregoing two equations after the fourth derivative of $\mathbf{r}_2$ and substituting the resulting expressions for $\mathbf{r}_2{}^{iv}$ and $\dddot{\mathbf{r}}_2$ from Eqs. (103) and (104) into Eq. (102) there results

$$-\tau_{23}^2\mathbf{r}_1 + (\tau_{23}^2 - \tau_{12}^2)\mathbf{r}_2 + \tau_{12}^2\mathbf{r}_3 - \tau_{12}\tau_{23}\tau_{13}\dot{\mathbf{r}}_2$$
$$= \frac{\tau_{12}\tau_{23}\tau_{13}}{12}[-\tau_{23}\ddot{\mathbf{r}}_1 + (\tau_{23} - \tau_{12})\ddot{\mathbf{r}}_2 + \tau_{12}\ddot{\mathbf{r}}_3].$$

Next the dynamical relation that

$$\ddot{\mathbf{r}}_i = -\mu\mathbf{r}_i/r_i^3$$

is introduced and the definitions of H_i, G_i, and d_i in Eqs. (99) are then determined.

We are now possessed of $\mathbf{r}_2$ and $\dot{\mathbf{r}}_2$ for the middle date, and are able to proceed with a standard set of formulas for the determination of the elements. Since the values of $\dot{\mathbf{r}}$ are often not as well known as $\mathbf{r}$, it has been suggested (cf. Van Sant *et al.*[69]) that several sets of $\mathbf{r}_1$ and $\mathbf{r}_3$ be reduced to obtain a more precise average $\dot{\mathbf{r}}_2$.

The Gibbsian method may also be employed if only two positions and the time interval are given (similar to the Gaussian development). In this case the ratios of the triangles,† denoted by c_1, and c_3, are developed from a f and g series expansion of $\mathbf{r}_1$ and $\mathbf{r}_3$ about $\mathbf{r}_2$ in the form

$$c_1\mathbf{r}_1 - \mathbf{r}_2 + c_3\mathbf{r}_3 = 0. \tag{105}$$

It should be noted that Eq. (105), which is identical to Eq. (95), cannot be solved directly for the c's, as in the pure Gibbsian procedure, because in

† See Section 6.5 for a discussion of the "ratios of the triangles."

this instance $\mathbf{r}_2$ is not given but is to be determined. The expressions for the c's as developed by Gibbs are:

$$c_i = A_i + B'_i\left(1 + \frac{B_2}{r_2^3}\right)/r_2^3 \cong A_i + B'_i/r_2^3 \tag{106}$$

$$A_1 = \tau_{23}/\tau_{13}, \qquad A_3 = \tau_{12}/\tau_{13},$$

$$B_1 = \frac{\mu}{12}(\tau_{12}^2 + \tau_{12}\tau_{23} - \tau_{23}^2), \qquad B'_1 = A_1(B_1 + B_2),$$

$$B_2 = \frac{\mu}{12}(\tau_{12}^2 + 3\tau_{12}\tau_{23} - \tau_{23}^2), \qquad B'_3 = A_3(B_3 + B_2),$$

$$B_3 = \frac{\mu}{12}(\tau_{12}^2 + \tau_{12}\tau_{23} + \tau_{23}^2),$$

and again

$$\tau_{ij} = k(t_j - t_i).^*$$

Equipped with $\mathbf{r}_2$ one could now return to the Herrick–Gibbs formula (99) and establish the velocity at the second date as well as the position. As a first approximation the B_i may be taken as zero.

6.2.3. Range-Only Gibbsian for Circular Orbits

A third variation of Gibbs' method has been devised by Baker and is utilized when range data alone are available for low-eccentricity orbits. Note that those methods that are based upon pure geometry or upon Eq. (95) are generically referred to as Gibbsian.

In standard notation the vector equation relating the vector from the geocenter to the vehicle, $\mathbf{r}$, the vector from the observer to the vehicle, $\boldsymbol{\varrho}$, and the vector *from* the observer *to* the geocenter, $\mathbf{R}$, can be formulated as

$$\boldsymbol{\varrho} = \mathbf{r} + \mathbf{R}$$

* If in Eq. (50) $i = 1, 3$ and $0 \to 2$, then

$$\begin{array}{l|l} r_1 = f_1\mathbf{r}_2 + g_1\dot{\mathbf{r}}_2 & +g_3 \\ r_3 = f_3\mathbf{r}_2 + g_3\dot{\mathbf{r}}_2 & -g_1 \end{array}$$

$$\mathbf{r}_1 g_3 - \mathbf{r}_3 g_1 = \mathbf{r}_2(f_1 g_3 - f_3 g_1) \triangleq \mathbf{r}_2 g_2,$$

and c_1 and c_3 can be associated with g_3/g_2 and g_1/g_2 respectively. Substitution of the f's and g's and series approximations will then give rise to the foregoing formulas for c_i in terms of τ_{ij} and $1/r_2^2$.

so that

$$\rho^2 = r^2 + R^2 + 2(\mathbf{R} \cdot \mathbf{r}), \tag{107}$$

where

$$\mathbf{R} = X\mathbf{I} + Y\mathbf{J} + Z\mathbf{K}$$

and

$$\mathbf{r} = r\mathbf{U}. \tag{108}$$

For orbits of zero or nearly zero eccentricity the most useful elements prove to be the components of **U** and **V** reckoned at some epoch t_0, e.g., the time of the middle observation (**P** and **Q** are indeterminate and hence are unsuitable). For zero eccentricity or circular orbits $\mathbf{U}_i$ may be represented in terms of these elements $\mathbf{U}_0$ and $\mathbf{V}_0$ by

$$\mathbf{U}_i = \mathbf{U}_0 \cos (v_i - v_0) + \mathbf{V}_0 \sin (v_i - v_0), \tag{109}$$

where, although v_i is undefined, the difference $v_i - v_0$ can still be defined by

$$n(t_i - t_0) = v_i - v_0 \text{ while } r = a$$

for a circular orbit. Consequently, at any given time, t_i, one can define $\mathbf{r}_i$ for a circular orbit by

$$\mathbf{r}_i = a[\mathbf{U}_0 \cos n\delta t_i + \mathbf{V}_0 \sin n\delta t_i] \tag{110}$$

where $n = k_e \sqrt{\mu}/a^{3/2}$ and $\delta t_i \triangleq t_i - t_0$. As was shown in Section 4.4 the components of the station position vector $\mathbf{R}_i$ (measured *from* the station *to* the geocenter) can be given by

$$\mathbf{R}_i \begin{cases} X = -x_T = -x_c \cos \theta_i = -x_c c'_i, \\ Y = -y_T = -x_c \sin \theta_i = -x_c s'_i, \\ Z = -z_T = -y_c \end{cases} \tag{111}$$

where $c'_i \triangleq \cos \theta_i$, $s_i \triangleq \sin \theta_i$, x_c and y_c are the time-constant coordinates of a single radar station measured in a meridian plane or elliptical cross-section of the reference spheroid, θ_i is the local sidereal time of the station at time t_i (see Sections 4.4 and 11.1), and $\mathbf{R}_i$ (components denoted by either X, Y, Z or $-x_T$, $-y_T$, $-z_T$) is the actual time-varying coordinates relative to the station (or "topos").

If we define $c_i \triangleq \cos n\delta t_i$ and $s_i \triangleq \sin n\delta t_i$, then at any time, t_i, for a circular orbit

$$\mathbf{r}_i \cdot \mathbf{R}_i$$
$$= -ax_c c'_i(U_{0x}c_i + V_{0x}s_i) - ax_c s'_i(U_{0y}c_i + V_{0y}s_i) - ay_c(U_{0z}c_i + V_{0z}s_i)$$

and since $R^2 = r_c^2 = x_c^2 + y_c^2$, ρ_i^2 can be represented at any time, t_i, by

$$\rho_i^2 = c_i c'_i D_1 + c_i s'_i D_2 + c_i D_3 + s_i c'_i D_4 + s_i s'_i D_5 + s_i D_6 + a^2 + r_c^2 \quad (112)$$

where

$$D_1 = -2ax_c U_{0x},$$
$$D_2 = -2ax_c U_{0y},$$
$$D_3 = -2ay_c U_{0z},$$
$$D_4 = -2ax_c V_{0x},$$
$$D_5 = -2ax_c V_{0y},$$

and

$$D_6 = -2ay_c V_{0z}.$$

Given seven observed ρ's at seven times from a single station it is then possible to eliminate algebraically the six unknown, but time constant, D's. For example, by utilizing Cramer's law one finds:*

$$\Delta\bar{\rho}_1^2 + c_1 c'_1 C_1 + c_1 s'_1 C_2 + c_1 C_3 + s_1 c'_1 C_4 + s_1 s'_1 C_5 + s_1 C_6 = 0 \quad (113)$$

where

$$\Delta \triangleq \begin{vmatrix} c_2 c'_2, & c_2 s'_2, & \cdots, & s_2, \\ c_3 c'_3, & \cdots & & \cdot \\ \cdot & & & \cdot \\ \cdot & & & \cdot \\ \cdot & & & \cdot \\ \cdot & & & \cdot \\ c_7 c'_7, & c_7 s'_7, & \cdots, & s_7, \end{vmatrix}, \qquad C_1 \triangleq \begin{vmatrix} \bar{\rho}_2^2, & c_2 s'_2, & \cdots, & s_2, \\ \bar{\rho}_3^2, & \cdots & & \cdot \\ \cdot & & & \cdot \\ \cdot & & & \cdot \\ \cdot & & & \cdot \\ \cdot & & & \cdot \\ \bar{\rho}_7^2, & c_7 s'_7, & \cdots, & s_7, \end{vmatrix},$$

$$C_2 \triangleq \begin{vmatrix} c_2 c'_2, & \bar{\rho}_2^2, & \cdots, & s_2, \\ c_3 c'_3, & \cdots & & \cdot \\ \cdot & & & \cdot \\ \cdot & & & \cdot \\ \cdot & & & \cdot \\ \cdot & & & \cdot \\ c_7 c'_7, & \bar{\rho}_7^2, & \cdots, & s_7, \end{vmatrix},$$

etc. cf. Eq. (141) and $\bar{\rho}_i^2 \triangleq r_i^2 + a^2 - \rho_i^2$.

The value of n to yield a zero value for Eq. (113) can then be found by a root solving technique since the seven values of θ_i and δt_i along with the observed ρ_i are known. Given n, the semimajor axis, a, can be immediately computed and, since the coefficients of the D's in Eq. (112) are now known, it is possible to solve for the actual value of the D's from which a determina-

* In reference 70, Eq. (113) is set down in a more concise form as simply one so-called *eliminant* determinant.

tion of $\mathbf{U}_0$ and $\mathbf{V}_0$ can be made (see Baker[70] for a more complete discussion in which observations from multiple stations and from satellite-borne stations are considered).

6.2.4. Range-Only Gibbsian for Low-Eccentricity Orbits

If the orbit is not exactly circular, two alternate procedures can be followed. The first is to utilize the assumed circular orbit as a "preliminary" orbit in the *differential correction* procedure to be discussed in Section 6.6 and in more detail with respect to rectilinear parabolic orbits in this section. In the case of differential correction the preliminary values (zeroth approximation) of U_0 and i can be obtained from

$$U_{0z} = \sin i \sin U_0$$

and

$$V_{0z} = \sin i \cos U_0, \tag{114}$$

while Ω may be obtained from

$$\mathbf{N} = \mathbf{U}_0 \cos U_0 - \mathbf{V}_0 \sin U_0$$

by the relations $N_x = \cos \Omega$, $N_y = \sin \Omega$ ($N_z = 0$). The semimajor axis is, of course, known, and for the preliminary circular orbit, a_N and a_M are zero. The second method for moderate eccentricities would be to utilize $\mathbf{P}$ and $\mathbf{Q}$ directly. In this case

$$\mathbf{r} = x_\omega \mathbf{P} + y_\omega \mathbf{Q} \tag{115}$$

so that

$$\mathbf{R} \cdot \mathbf{r} = x_\omega X P_x + x_\omega Y P_y + x_\omega Z P_z + y_\omega X Q_x + y_\omega Y Q_y + y_\omega Z Q_z. \tag{116}$$

For orbits with small eccentricity

$$x_\omega = a \cos M + \frac{ae}{2} (\cos 2M - 3) + 0\left(\frac{e^2}{2}\right)$$

and

$$y_\omega = a \sin M + \frac{ae}{2} \sin 2M + 0\left(\frac{e^2}{2}\right). \tag{117}$$

(See reference 13, p. 181, problem number six.)

Since $M = M_0 + n\delta t$, one can write

$$x_\omega = c(a \cos M_0) - s(a \sin M_0) + c_2(\tfrac{1}{2}ae \cos 2M_0) - s_2(\tfrac{1}{2}ae \sin 2M_0) - \tfrac{3}{2}ae$$

and

$$y_\omega = s(a \cos M_0) + c(a \sin M_0) + s_2(\tfrac{1}{2}ae \cos 2M_0) + c_2(\tfrac{1}{2}ae \sin 2M_0), \quad (118)$$

where $c_2 \triangleq \cos 2n\delta t$, and $s_2 \triangleq \sin 2n\delta t$. Thus,

$$\rho^2 = cc'D_1 + cs'D_2 + cD_3 + sc'D_4 + ss'D_5 + sD_6 + c_2c'D_7 + c_2s'D_8 + c_2D_9 + s_2c'D_{10} + s_2s'D_{11} + s_2D_{12} + c'D_{13} + s'D_{14} + D_{15}, \quad (119)$$

where

$$\begin{aligned}
D_1 &= -2ax_c(P_x \cos M_0 + Q_x \sin M_0),\\
D_2 &= -2ax_c(P_y \cos M_0 + Q_y \sin M_0),\\
D_3 &= -2ay_c(P_z \cos M_0 + Q_z \sin M_0) - 2a^2e \cos M_0,\\
D_4 &= +2ax_c(P_x \sin M_0 - Q_x \cos M_0),\\
D_5 &= +2ax_c(P_y \sin M_0 - Q_y \cos M_0),\\
D_6 &= +2ay_c(P_z \sin M_0 - Q_z \cos M_0) + 2a^2e \cos M_0,\\
D_7 &= -aex_c(P_x \cos 2M_0 + Q_x \sin 2M_0),\\
D_8 &= -aex_c(P_y \cos 2M_0 - Q_y \sin 2M_0),\\
D_9 &= -aey_c(P_z \cos 2M_0 + Q_z \sin 2M_0),\\
D_{10} &= +aex_c(P_x \sin 2M_0 - Q_x \cos 2M_0),\\
D_{11} &= +aex_c(P_y \sin 2M_0 - Q_y \cos 2M_0),\\
D_{12} &= +aey_c(P_z \sin 2M_0 - Q_z \cos 2M_0),\\
D_{13} &= 3P_xaex_c,\\
D_{14} &= 3P_yaex_c,
\end{aligned}$$

and

$$D_{15} = 3P_zaey_c + a^2 + r_c^2, \text{ where } r_c^2 \triangleq x_c^2 + y_c^2.$$

With 16 observations of ρ (i.e., 16 ρ's, 16 θ's, and 16 τ's given) the D's can be eliminated algebraically, i.e., the function

$$[\rho_1, \rho_2, \ldots \rho_i \ldots, \rho_{16}, s'(\tau_i), c'(\tau_i), s(n\tau_i), c(n\tau_i), s_2(n\tau_i), c_2(n\tau_i)] = 0$$

is established (cf. Eq. (113)) and a root-solving technique can be employed to determine the mean motion, n (which, of course, is a function of a). Any root ambiguity can be eliminated by representing a 17th ρ for all possible roots, (i.e., by computing a value of ρ_{17} for t_{17} by means of Eq. (119) for all ambiguous values of n) and comparing them with an observed ρ_{17}. The coefficients D_{13}, D_{14}, and D_{15} are then determined and the components of the vectorial parameter $\mathbf{a} = e\mathbf{P}$ are computed by:

$$\begin{aligned} eP_x &= D_{13}/3ax_c, \\ eP_y &= D_{14}/3ax_c, \text{ and} \\ eP_z &= [D_{15} - (a^2 + r_c^2)]/3ay_c. \end{aligned} \tag{120}$$

From which the eccentricity e is obtained by

$$e^2 = (eP_x)^2 + (eP_y)^2 + (eP_z)^2. \tag{121}$$

The other elements can be obtained in a similar fashion; however, since the perifocal and apofocal distances are often the only information required, the solution is terminated at the point when

$$\begin{aligned} q_1 &= a(1 - e) \text{ and} \\ q_2 &= a(1 + e) \end{aligned} \tag{122}$$

are computed (a is, of course, obtained directly from n).

6.2.5. Range-Only Gibbsian for Rectilinear Orbits

A similar treatment can be utilized for nearly rectilinear ellipses and hyperbolas and for any class of parabolas.[70] A particularly simple formulation is obtained for a rectilinear parabola in which $q = 0$ and Eq. (90) reduces to

$$\begin{aligned} r_i &= \tfrac{1}{2}[6k_e\sqrt{\mu}(t_i - T)]^{2/3}, \\ &= \tfrac{1}{2}[6\{\tilde{M}_0 + \tilde{n}(t_i - t_0)\}]^{2/3} \end{aligned} \tag{123}$$

while $\mathbf{r} = -r\mathbf{P} = r\mathbf{U}$ so that analogous to Eq. (119)

$$\rho_i^2 = r_i^2 + r_c^2 - 2r_i(x_c c'_i U_x + x_c s'_i U_y + y_c U_z). \tag{124}$$

with four values of ρ_i ($i = 1, 2, 3, 4$) the constants $2x_cU_x$, $2x_cU_y$, and $2y_cU_z$ can be algebraically eliminated, e.g., in determinant form by employing Cramer's law, or in this case more simply by employing

$$r_4(c_{23}E_{34} - c_{34}E_{23})(r_3F_{21}E_{23} - r_1F_{32}E_{12}) = r_1(c_{12}E_{23} - c_{23}E_{12}) \cdot (r_4F_{32}E_{34} - r_2F_{43}E_{23}), \tag{125}$$

where $c'_i \triangleq \cos\theta_i$; $c'_j \triangleq \cos\theta_j$; $s'_i \triangleq \sin\theta_j$; $c_{ij} \triangleq c'_i - c'_j$, $E_i \triangleq r_i^2 + r_c^2 - \rho_i^2$, $E_{ij} \triangleq c'_i s'_j - s'_i c'_j$, and $F_{ij} \triangleq E_i r_j c'_j - E_j r_i c'_i$. Instead of n, the time of perigee passage, T or $\tilde{M}_0$ (where $\tilde{M}_0 = t_0 - t)/\tilde{n}$), is determined by a root-solving technique. Again ambiguity can be resolved by representing an extra ρ and comparing it with the observed value. This procedure is particularly useful for the generation of a preliminary lunar or interplanetary orbit from range-only data—see Section 11.4.

6.2.6. Correction of Preliminary Orbit

As in the case of the circular orbit, the rectilinear parabolic orbit can be *corrected* by means of a subsequent observed ρ_i ($i = 5$) in this instance into a rectilinear ellipse or hyperbola. The first step in this procedure is to *represent* a computed value of ρ_5 by obtaining a computed value of r_5 from Eq. (123) (given t_5 and T), substituting it into Eq. (124) along with the known values of x_c, y_c, c'_5, s'_5, U_x, U_y, and U_z, and computing ρ_5 (note that the sidereal time of the fifth observation, θ_5, is known—hence c'_5 and s'_5 are known, whereas U_x, U_y, and U_z are obtained through a solution of Eq. (124) $i = 1, 2, 3, 4$ after having obtained T from Eq. (125) by a root-solving technique). This *computed* value of range, ρ_{c5} is then subtracted from an *observed* value of range, ρ_{05}, to form the so-called "observed-minus-computed" residual $\Delta\rho_5$.

If the orbit was truly a rectilinear parabolic orbit and if the observations of ρ_5 were perfect, then $\Delta\rho_5 = 0$. If instead the orbit was a "nearly" parabolic rectilinear orbit, i.e., either a rectilinear ellipse or a rectilinear hyperbola possessing a long but not infinite semimajor axis a, then $\Delta\rho_5 \neq 0$, and its value can be employed to gain a first approximation to $(1/a)$ (the zeroth approximation—or preliminary value—$(1/a)_0$, being zero). Such a procedure was mentioned in passing with respect to the circular orbit and will be carried through in greater detail in the following paragraphs (a more complete discussion of differential correction—particularly as it is applied to the "improvement" of orbital constants on the basis of multiple observations—is included in Section 6.6.2).

For rectilinear orbits ρ will be a function of a (or $1/a$), so that one can express a differential in ρ by a Taylor series in $(1/a)$, i.e.,

$$\Delta\rho = \frac{\partial\rho}{\partial(1/a)}\,\Delta(1/a) + \frac{\partial^2\rho}{\partial(1/a)^2}\,\Delta(1/a)^2 + \cdots$$

or

$$\Delta\rho \cong \frac{\partial\rho}{\partial(1/a)}\,\Delta(1/a)$$

for small values of $\Delta(1/a)$. In more detail

$$\Delta\rho \triangleq \rho_0 - \rho_c \cong \frac{\partial\rho}{\partial(1/a)}[(1/a)_0 - (1/a)_c] = \frac{\partial\rho}{\partial(1/a)}\Delta(1/a),$$

where $(1/a)_0$ is the value of $1/a$ giving rise to the observation of range and $(1/a)_c$ is the value of $1/a$ utilized in the computation of range. Since the computation of ρ_c assumed a rectilinear parabolic, we find that $(1/a)_c = 0$ and

$$\Delta\rho = [\partial\rho/\partial(1/a)](1/a)_0.$$

The only outstanding problem is the determination of $\partial\rho/\partial(1/a)$. Since

$$\rho^2 = r^2 + R^2 + 2(\mathbf{R}\cdot\mathbf{r})$$

and

$$\mathbf{R}\cdot\mathbf{r} = -r(x_c c' U_x + x_c s' U_y + y_c U_z),$$

$$\frac{\partial\rho}{\partial(1/a)} = \frac{1}{\rho}[r - (x_c c' U_x + x_c s' U_y + y_c U_z)]\frac{\partial r}{\partial(1/a)}.$$

In terms of certain new "universal" variables designed by Herrick[1] (which are equally applicable to all conic sections)

$$r = q + e\left\{\frac{\tilde{X}^2}{2!} - \frac{\tilde{X}^4}{a4!} + \frac{\tilde{X}^6}{a^2 6!} - \cdots\right\} \tag{126}$$

where $\tilde{X}$ can be associated with $\sqrt{a}\,E$, D, or $\sqrt{-a}\,F$ for the ellipse, parabola, and hyperbola, respectively. Thus for a rectilinear orbit of arbitrary a (or $\tilde{X}$),

$$r = \frac{\tilde{X}^2}{2!} - \frac{\tilde{X}^4}{a4!} + \frac{\tilde{X}^6}{a^2 6!} - \cdots,$$

so that

$$\frac{\partial r}{\partial(1/a)} = -\frac{\tilde{X}^4}{4!} + \frac{2\tilde{X}^6}{a6!} - \cdots + \left(\tilde{X} - \frac{4\tilde{X}^3}{a4!} + \cdots\right)\frac{\partial\tilde{X}}{\partial(1/a)}.$$

The partial derivative must be evaluated not only at the time of observation (i.e., at t_5) but also for the parabolic orbit in which $1/a = 0$ and $\tilde{X} \equiv D$. From Eq. (16) (with $q = 0$) it is clear that $D = \sqrt{2r}$ and from Eq. (123) that r is not a function of a and, therefore, $\partial\tilde{X}/\partial(1/a) = 0$. In fine

$$\frac{\partial\rho}{\partial(1/a)} = -\frac{r^2}{\rho 3!}[r - (x_c c' U_x + x_c s' U_y + y_c U_z)] \tag{127}$$

$$= -\frac{\tilde{X}^4}{\rho 4!}\left[\frac{\tilde{X}^2}{2} - (x_c c' U_x + x_c s' U_y + y_c U_z)\right]$$

and the "improved" value of $1/a$ derived from this observation is $\Delta(1/a) = (1/a)_0 = \Delta\rho/(\partial\rho/\partial(1/a))$.

By the preceding analysis we have been able to determine a rectilinear orbit from five observations of range only. The further correction of the orbit, by means of other observed ρ's, into an orbit of arbitrary eccentricity involves the use of special techniques (see reference 70) and falls outside of the scope of this introductory text.

6.3. The Laplacian Method

In the *Lagrangian method* one seeks to obtain the values of ρ at three dates and then either $\mathbf{r}$ and $\dot{\mathbf{r}}$ or $\mathbf{r}_1$ and $\mathbf{r}_3$ (as in the Gaussian procedure), or $\mathbf{r}_1$, $\mathbf{r}_2$, and $\mathbf{r}_3$ (as in the Gibbsian procedure). In the *Laplacian method,* however, the object is to obtain ρ and $\dot{\rho}$ at the middle date from the observed α and δ for the three dates. This section will be restricted to a presentation of the Laplacian method (cf. Herrick).[68]

6.3.1. General Method

Let it be assumed that topocentric right ascension, α, and declination, δ, are observed on three dates (or, alternatively, assuming that three pairs of h and A are given). If $\boldsymbol{\rho}$ is defined in terms of the unit vector $\mathbf{L}$, then $\boldsymbol{\rho} = \rho\mathbf{L}$, where the components of $\mathbf{L}$, in terms of α and δ (see Section 4.5) are

$$\begin{aligned} L_x &= \cos\delta\cos\alpha, \\ L_y &= \cos\delta\sin\alpha, \\ L_z &= \sin\delta. \end{aligned} \tag{128}$$

Let us again define $\mathbf{r}$ in terms of $\boldsymbol{\rho}$ and $\mathbf{R}$ and proceed with the first approximation by extracting the first and second derivatives, i.e.,

$$\begin{aligned} \mathbf{r} &= \rho\mathbf{L} - \mathbf{R}, \\ \dot{\mathbf{r}} &= \dot{\rho}\mathbf{L} + \rho\dot{\mathbf{L}} - \dot{\mathbf{R}}, \\ \ddot{\mathbf{r}} &= \ddot{\rho}\mathbf{L} + 2\dot{\rho}\dot{\mathbf{L}} + \rho\ddot{\mathbf{L}} - \ddot{\mathbf{R}}. \end{aligned}$$

Since

$$\ddot{\mathbf{r}} = \frac{-\mu\mathbf{r}}{r^3} = \frac{-\mu(\rho\mathbf{L} - \mathbf{R})}{r^3},$$

therefore

$$\left(\ddot{\rho} + \frac{\mu\rho}{r^3}\right)\mathbf{L} + 2\dot{\rho}\dot{\mathbf{L}} + \rho\ddot{\mathbf{L}} = \ddot{\mathbf{R}} + \frac{\mu\mathbf{R}}{r^3}. \tag{129}$$

It should be noted that this vector equation (known as the "Poincaré form") represents three component equations in four unknowns (if it is assumed that $\dot{\mathbf{L}}$ and $\ddot{\mathbf{L}}$ can, in principle, be obtained by numerical differentiation at the second date), i.e., three equations in ρ_2, $\dot{\rho}_2$, $\ddot{\rho}_2$, and r_2 if we specialize to the second date. Consequently, it is possible to reduce this system to two equations in three unknowns by first solving for ρ_2 and then for $\dot{\rho}_2$ (i.e., by first eliminating $\ddot{\rho}_2$ and $\dot{\rho}_2$.) Thus,

$$D\rho_2 = A' - \frac{B'}{r_2^3} \tag{130}$$

and if $D = 0$ (see p. 151) r_2 can still be computed by (130) or, if $D \neq 0$, and

$$A \triangleq \frac{A'}{D}, \qquad B \triangleq \frac{B'}{D}$$

then

$$\rho_2 = A - \frac{B}{r_2^3}$$

where, in determinant notation, (all determinants evaluated at the second date)

$$D \triangleq \begin{vmatrix} L_x & \dot{L}_x & \ddot{L}_x \\ L_y & \dot{L}_y & \ddot{L}_y \\ L_z & \dot{L}_z & \ddot{L}_z \end{vmatrix}$$

$$A' \triangleq \begin{vmatrix} L_x & \dot{L}_x & \ddot{X} \\ L_y & \dot{L}_y & \ddot{Y} \\ L_z & \dot{L}_z & \ddot{Z} \end{vmatrix}$$

$$B' \triangleq -\mu \begin{vmatrix} L_x & \dot{L}_x & X \\ L_y & \dot{L}_y & Y \\ L_z & \dot{L}_z & Z \end{vmatrix}$$

with X, Y, and Z being as usual the equatorial coordinates of the geocenter relative to the observer. Elimination of $\ddot{\rho}_2$ and ρ_2 yields the second equation

$$D\dot{\rho}_2 = C' - \frac{E'}{r_2^3} \tag{131}$$

where

$$C' \triangleq \frac{1}{2}\begin{vmatrix} L_x & \ddot{X} & \ddot{L}_x \\ L_y & \ddot{Y} & \ddot{L}_y \\ L_z & \ddot{Z} & \ddot{L}_z \end{vmatrix}$$

and

$$E' \triangleq \frac{-\mu}{2}\begin{vmatrix} L_x & X & \ddot{L}_x \\ L_y & Y & \ddot{L}_y \\ L_z & Z & \ddot{L}_z \end{vmatrix}.$$

In order to carry out this computation, one requires $\dot{L}_x$, $\dot{L}_y$, $\dot{L}_z$, $\dot{X}$, $\dot{Y}$, $\dot{Z}$, $\ddot{L}_x$, $\ddot{L}_y$, $\ddot{L}_z$, $\ddot{X}$, $\ddot{Y}$, and $\ddot{Z}$. In a fashion similar to the Herrick–Gibbs method, we numerically differentiate and obtain

$$\dot{X}_2 = [-\tau_{23}{}^2 X_1 + (\tau_{23}{}^2 - \tau_{12}{}^2)X_2 + \tau_{12}{}^2 X_3]/\tau_{12}\tau_{23}\tau_{13}$$

and

$$\ddot{X}_2 = 2[\tau_{23}X_1 + (\tau_{12} - \tau_{23})X_2 + \tau_{12}X_3]/\tau_{12}\tau_{23}\tau_{13} \tag{132}$$

$$X \rightarrow Y,\ Z,\ L_x,\ L_y, \text{ and } L_z \text{ (where } \tau_{21} = -\tau_{12}).$$

If the three observations are from the same observatory, then the derivatives $\mathbf{R}$ can be determined explicitly. Expressions for $\dot{X}$, $\dot{Y}$, and $\dot{Z}$ may be found in Section 4.4, while

$$\ddot{X} = \omega^2(C + H)\cos\phi\cos\theta,$$

$$\ddot{Y} = \omega^2(C + H)\cos\phi\sin\theta,$$

and

$$\ddot{Z} = 0 \tag{133}$$

where $\omega \equiv \dot{\theta}$, i.e., the rotational rate of the Earth. There are now two equations relating r_2 and ρ_2, namely,

$$\rho_2 = A - \frac{B}{r_2{}^3} \tag{134}$$

$$r_2{}^2 = \rho_2{}^2 - 2\rho_2(\mathbf{L}_2 \cdot \mathbf{R}_2) + R_2{}^2. \tag{135}$$

Equation (134) represents the dynamical constraints of the problem while Eq. (135) represents the geometrical constraints. For geocentric satellites the employment of Eqs. (132) yield very inexact results if τ_{ij}/H is not small (where τ_{ij} is expressed in the characteristic time unit, the

k_e^{-1} min, and H is expressed in Earth's equatorial radii.) For large τ_{ij}/H, A and B of Eq. (134) can be determined without recourse to the series development by Gauss' method. Such alternate forms for A and B are derived (see Herrick[1]) as follows: substitution of $\mathbf{r}_i = \rho_i\mathbf{L}_i - \mathbf{R}_i$ into Eq. (105) yields

$$c_1\rho_1\mathbf{L}_1 - \rho_2\mathbf{L}_2 + c_3\rho_3\mathbf{L}_3 - c_1\mathbf{R}_1 + \mathbf{R}_2 - c_3\mathbf{R}_3 = 0,$$

from which we wish to eliminate ρ_1 and ρ_3. This elimination is accomplished by first taking a vector cross product with $\mathbf{L}_1$, i.e.,

$$-\rho_2\mathbf{L}_2 \times \mathbf{L}_1 + c_3\rho_3\mathbf{L}_3 \times \mathbf{L}_1 - c_1\mathbf{R}_1 \times \mathbf{L}_1 + \mathbf{R}_2 \times \mathbf{L}_1 - c_3\mathbf{R}_3 \times \mathbf{L}_1 = 0$$

and then by taking the vector dot product with $\mathbf{L}_3$, i.e.,

$$-\rho_2(\mathbf{L}_2 \times \mathbf{L}_1 \cdot \mathbf{L}_3) - c_1\mathbf{R}_1 \times \mathbf{L}_1 \cdot \mathbf{L}_3 + \mathbf{R}_2 \times \mathbf{L}_1 \cdot \mathbf{L}_3 - c_3\mathbf{R}_3 \times \mathbf{L}_1 \cdot \mathbf{L}_3 = 0$$

so that

$$\rho_2 \begin{vmatrix} L_{x_2}L_{y_2}L_{z_2} \\ L_{x_1}L_{y_1}L_{z_1} \\ L_{x_3}L_{y_3}L_{z_3} \end{vmatrix} = \begin{vmatrix} X_2Y_2Z_2 \\ L_{x_1}L_{y_1}L_{z_1} \\ L_{x_3}L_{y_3}L_{z_3} \end{vmatrix} - c_1 \begin{vmatrix} X_1Y_1Z_1 \\ L_{x_1}L_{y_1}L_{z_1} \\ L_{x_3}L_{y_3}L_{z_3} \end{vmatrix} - c_3 \begin{vmatrix} X_3Y_3Z_3 \\ L_{x_1}L_{y_1}L_{z_1} \\ L_{x_3}L_{y_3}L_{z_3} \end{vmatrix}.$$

Substitution of Eq. (106) into the preceding equation yields an equation of same form as Eq. (134) but without the series developments of Eqs. (132) (but still involving the series approximations inherent in the coefficients of Eq. (106)). Consequently, we are again possessed of two equations in ρ_2 and r_2. These are solved by Newton's method of approximations to yield a first approximation as follows:

(i) A preliminary estimate is made of r_2. A value may be determined from certain preliminary rough solutions or from a graphical approximation.

(ii) After r_2 has been estimated, ρ_2 is computed from $\rho_2 = A - \dfrac{B}{r_2^3}$.

(iii) The function $f(r_2) \triangleq \rho_2^2 - 2\rho_2(\mathbf{L}_2 \cdot \mathbf{R}_2) + R_2^2 - r_2^2$ is computed. Note that $f(r_2) = 0$ for the correct value, i.e., we are looking for this root.

(iv) The derivative $\dfrac{df(r_2)}{dr_2} \triangleq f'(r_2) = 2[\rho_2 - (\mathbf{L}_2 \cdot \mathbf{R}_2)]\dfrac{d\rho_2}{dr_2} - 2r_2$ which, since $\dfrac{d\rho_2}{dr_2} = 3\dfrac{B}{r_2^4}$, is simply $f'(r_2) = 2r_2\left[\dfrac{3B}{r_2^5}(\rho_2 - \mathbf{L}_2 \cdot \mathbf{R}_2) - 1\right]$ is computed.

(v) The correction to r_2, Δr_2, is $\Delta r_2 = -\dfrac{f(r_2)}{f'(r_2)}$ (i.e., $f'(r_2) \cong [f(r_2 \text{ correct}) - f(r_2 \text{ estimate})]/\Delta r_2 = -f(r_2 \text{ estimate})/\Delta_r$).

(vi) The process is repeated, beginning with step (ii), using the second-order correction to r_2, i.e., $r_2 + \Delta r_2$. Having obtained r_2 one may next obtain $\dot{\rho}_2$ from Eq. (131) and equipped with ρ_2 and $\dot{\rho}_2$ the position and velocity at the second date (which can be employed to construct the orbital elements) can be computed from

$$\mathbf{r}_2 = \rho_2 \mathbf{L}_2 - \mathbf{R}_2$$

and

$$\dot{\mathbf{r}}_2 = \dot{\rho}_2 \mathbf{L}_2 + \rho_2 \dot{\mathbf{L}}_2 - \dot{\mathbf{R}}_2. \tag{136}$$

Usually the orbital elements resulting from the foregoing first approximation procedure do not satisfy the first and third places ($\mathbf{r}_1$ and $\mathbf{r}_3$) to the accuracy of the observations. In any case it is desirable to check the accuracy of the orbit by representing the first and third dates to ascertain whether a second approximation is necessary.

The representation is most effectively accomplished by the f and g series, or their closed form equivalents (see Section 4.6, Eq. (49)), which express the first and third positions in terms of the intermediate elements $\mathbf{r}_2$ and $\dot{\mathbf{r}}_2$, i.e., in this case we let $i = 1,3$ in

$$\mathbf{r}_i = f_i \mathbf{r}_2 + g_i \dot{\mathbf{r}}_2 \tag{137}$$

where the f_i and g_i are conveniently determined from the functions of τ already computed in e.g., Eq. (132).

The subsequent approximations can be made by the Leuschner method of differential correction which results in improved values of ρ_2 and $\dot{\mathbf{r}}_2$ (see Section 6.6.2 and Chapter 14 in Herrick).[1]

Before carrying out this second approximation (for heliocentric orbits) the observed times should be corrected for the intervals elapsed while the light traveled from the object to the observer, i.e.,

$$t = t_{\text{obs}} - \alpha^* \rho$$

where α^* is the reciprocal of the velocity of light or 0.005,772 days/a.u. Finally, given $\mathbf{r}_2$ and $\dot{\mathbf{r}}_2$, the determination of the orbital elements follows along the lines indicated in Section 6.1.

6.3.2. Range and Range–Rate Laplacian

Range, range-rate, and higher derivatives can be employed in an analogous fashion to $\mathbf{L}$, $\dot{\mathbf{L}}$, and their higher derivatives in order to generate a preliminary two-body orbit (see Baker).[70] As an illustrative example let us again consider the particularly simple problem of a rectilinear parabolic orbit (cf. Section 6.2). The basic range, ρ, range rate, $\dot{\rho}$, and higher order derivatives (obtained perhaps by numerical differentiation) are determined at some epoch, t_0, i.e.,

$$\mathbf{r} \cdot \mathbf{R} = \tfrac{1}{2}(\rho^2 - r_c^2 - r^2) \triangleq A$$

$$\mathbf{r} \cdot \dot{\mathbf{R}} + \dot{\mathbf{r}} \cdot \mathbf{R} = \rho\dot{\rho} - r\dot{r} \triangleq \dot{A}$$

$$(\text{i.e., } \rho\dot{\rho} = \boldsymbol{\varrho} \cdot \dot{\boldsymbol{\varrho}},\ \dot{\boldsymbol{\varrho}} = \dot{\mathbf{r}} + \dot{\mathbf{R}} \text{ and } \mathbf{R} \cdot \dot{\mathbf{R}} = 0)$$

$$\mathbf{r} \cdot \left(\ddot{\mathbf{R}} - \frac{\mu\mathbf{R}}{r^3}\right) + 2\dot{\mathbf{r}} \cdot \dot{\mathbf{R}} = \ddot{A} \qquad (\text{i.e., } \ddot{\mathbf{r}} = -\mu\mathbf{r}/r^3);$$

and

$$\mathbf{r} \cdot \left(\dddot{\mathbf{R}} - \frac{3\mu\dot{\mathbf{R}}}{r^3} + \frac{3\mu\dot{r}\mathbf{R}}{r^4}\right) + \dot{\mathbf{r}} \cdot \left(3\ddot{\mathbf{R}} - \frac{\mu\mathbf{R}}{r^3}\right) = \dddot{A}. \tag{138}$$

For a rectilinear parabola $\mathbf{r} = r\mathbf{U}$ and $\dot{\mathbf{r}} = \dot{r}\mathbf{U}$, while

$$\begin{aligned}
\mathbf{R} &= \mathbf{I}(-x_c c') + \mathbf{J}(-x_c s') + \mathbf{K}(-y_c),\\
\dot{\mathbf{R}} &= \mathbf{I}(+x_c s'\omega) + \mathbf{J}(-x_c c'\omega),\\
\ddot{\mathbf{R}} &= \mathbf{I}(x_c c'\omega^2) + \mathbf{J}(x_c s'\omega^2), \text{ and}\\
\dddot{\mathbf{R}} &= -\omega^2\dot{\mathbf{R}}, \text{ where } \omega = \text{the rotational rate of the Earth.}
\end{aligned} \tag{139}$$

Consequently, we find that

$$\begin{aligned}
A &= U_x B_c + U_y B_s + U_z B_r,\\
\dot{A} &= U_x B_{sc} + U_y B_{cs} + U_z B_{\dot{r}},\\
\ddot{A} &= U_x B_+ + U_y B_- + U_z B_0,\\
\text{and} \quad \dddot{A} &= U_x B_{\dot{r}-} + U_y B_{\dot{r}+} + U_z B_{\dot{r}0};
\end{aligned}$$

where $B_c \triangleq -rx_c c'$, $B_s \triangleq -rx_c s'$, $B_{\dot{r}} \triangleq -ry_c$;

$$B_{sc} \triangleq x_c(\omega r s' - \dot{r}c'),\ B_{cs} \triangleq -x_c(\omega r c' + \dot{r}s'),\ B_{\dot{r}} \triangleq -\dot{r}y_c; \tag{140}$$

$$B_+ \triangleq x_c\left(\frac{\mu c'}{r^2} + 2\dot{r}\omega s' + r\omega^2 c'\right),$$

$$B_- \triangleq x_c\left(\frac{\mu s'}{r^2} - 2\dot{r}\omega c' + r\omega^2 s'\right),\ B_0 \triangleq \mu y_c/r^2;$$

$$B_{\dot{r}-} \triangleq x_c\left(\dot{r}c'\left[3\omega^2 - \frac{2\mu}{r^3}\right] - \omega s'\left[\frac{3\mu}{r^2} + r\omega^2\right]\right),$$

$$B_{\dot{r}+} \triangleq x_c\left(\dot{r}s'\left[3\omega^2 - \frac{2\mu}{r^3}\right] + \omega c'\left[\frac{3\mu}{r^2} + r\omega^2\right]\right),$$

and $B_{\dot{r}0} \triangleq -2\mu\dot{r}y_c/r^3$.

Since all of the quantities are evaluated at the same epoch, there is no need to separate s' and c'. Algebraic elimination of the U's by Cramer's rule leads to

$$\Delta A = B_c C_1 + B_s C_2 + B_r C_3 \tag{141}$$

where

$$\Delta \triangleq \begin{vmatrix} B_{sc} & B_{cs} & B_{\dot{r}} \\ B_+ & B_- & B_0 \\ B_{\dot{r}-} & B_{\dot{r}+} & B_{\dot{r}0} \end{vmatrix}, \quad C_1 \triangleq \begin{vmatrix} \dot{A} & B_{cs} & B_{\dot{r}} \\ \ddot{A} & B_- & B_0 \\ \dddot{A} & B_{\dot{r}+} & B_{\dot{r}0} \end{vmatrix},$$

$$C_2 \triangleq \begin{vmatrix} B_{sc} & \dot{A} & B_{\dot{r}} \\ B_+ & \ddot{A} & B_0 \\ B_{\dot{r}-} & \dddot{A} & B_{\dot{r}0} \end{vmatrix}, \text{ and } C_3 \triangleq \begin{vmatrix} B_{sc} & B_{cs} & \dot{A} \\ B_+ & B_- & \ddot{A} \\ B_{\dot{r}-} & B_{\dot{r}+} & \dddot{A} \end{vmatrix}.$$

Other alternate solutions are, of course, possible depending upon the relative size of the elements (see Crout).[71] Equation (141) represents one equation in D, i.e., for the rectilinear case

$$r = D^2/2, \; \dot{r} = 2\sqrt{\mu}/D, \; D \rightarrow \tilde{X} \text{ etc.},$$

and can, therefore, be evaluated by a root-solving technique, i.e., D determined at the epoch, t_0. The value of T can then be obtained from Barker's equation (with $q = 0$ for a rectilinear orbit). Given T, Eqs. (141) can then be solved for U_x, U_y, U_z and the orbit is determined.

6.4. Gauss' Method

Gauss' "improved method of determining the orbit of a newly found planet without hypothesis as to the period or eccentricity" was based on Kepler's Law of Areas which states that the radius vector of the heliocentric ellipse sweeps over equal areas in equal intervals of time. He reasoned that an infinite number of confocal ellipses could be made to pass through two points, but there could be only one, in general, in which the time required to traverse the distance between the points would agree with the interval provided by the observations. He derived two fundamental equations, one expressing the ratio of the area of the sector formed by $\mathbf{r}_1$ and $\mathbf{r}_3$ to the area of the corresponding triangle in terms of the time interval and eccentric anomalies; the other making use of Kepler's equation relating the mean and eccentric anomalies at the first and third dates respectively. By successive approximations of his rather cumbersome equations Gauss derived a theoretical orbit that passed through the first and third observed positions but did not usually exactly represent the middle position. (See section 6.5 for a discussion of the "ratios of the triangles.")

Gauss' method finds a particularly useful application to astrodynamics in the determination of preliminary two-body lunar and interplanetary trajectories.* In both of these cases one is usually provided with the position of the vehicle at launch $\mathbf{r}_1$, the position of the vehicle at landing $\mathbf{r}_3$, and the time interval τ_{13}. A variation of the ordinary Gaussian procedure that is particularly useful in lunar trajectories, has been developed by Herrick and Liu.[72] This method is as follows:

(i) Assume a value of the parameter, p.

(ii) Compute the time interval for this assumed orbit as follows:

Let us again define S by

$$S\mathbf{W} \triangleq \mathbf{r}_1 \times \mathbf{r}_3,$$

(cf. Eq. (97)) therefore, since $\mathbf{Q} = \mathbf{W} \times \mathbf{P}$

$$S\mathbf{Q} = [S\mathbf{W}] \times \mathbf{P}$$

or

$$\begin{aligned} S\mathbf{Q} &= -\mathbf{P} \times [\mathbf{r}_1 \times \mathbf{r}_3] \\ &= -\mathbf{r}_1 x_{\omega 3} + \mathbf{r}_3 x_{\omega 1} \end{aligned}$$

where the triple vector product was utilized just as in the Gibbsian method of section 6.2.1. Recalling that $H_i = r_i - p = -ex_{\omega i}$, where $i = 1$ and 3 one obtains:

$$eS\mathbf{Q} = e(-\mathbf{r}_1 x_{\omega 3} + \mathbf{r}_3 x_{\omega 1}) = H_3 \mathbf{r}_1 - H_1 \mathbf{r}_3.$$

Taking a dot product with $\mathbf{r}_1$ yields

$$eS\mathbf{Q} \cdot \mathbf{r}_1 = eSy_{\omega 1} = H_3 r_1^2 - H_1 \mathbf{r}_1 \cdot \mathbf{r}_3 \triangleq H_3 r_1^2 - H_1 C. \; (C \triangleq \mathbf{r}_1 \cdot \mathbf{r}_3).$$

Thus

$$ey_{\omega 1} = (H_3 r_1^2 - H_1 C)/S$$

and

$$ey_{\omega 3} = (H_3 C - H_1 r_3^2)/S. \tag{142}$$

Also

$$e^2(x_{\omega 1}^2 + y_{\omega 1}^2) \equiv e^2 r_1^2, \quad 1 \to 3,$$

* Such procedures have been employed by Convair Astronautics, Aeronutronic, and the Committee on Industrial & Economic Research.

so that

$$[S^2H_1^2 + (H_3r_1^2 - H_1C)^2]/S^2 = e^2r_1^2$$

or

$$e = \frac{1}{Sr_1}\sqrt{S^2H_1^2 + (H_3r_1^2 - H_1C)^2} \qquad 1 \to 3. \tag{143}$$

Having determined e, one can solve for $x_{\omega i}$, and $y_{\omega i}$, and obtain a from $a = p/(1 - e^2)$, finally we can compute E_1 and E_3 from

$$\cos E_i = e + \frac{x_{\omega i}}{a} \qquad \text{and} \qquad \sin E_i = \frac{y_{\omega i}}{a\sqrt{1 - e^2}} \tag{144}$$

where $i = 1$ and 3.

From Kepler's equation, $M_1 = E_1 - e \sin E_1$, $1 \to 3$, so that we may compute $\tau_{13} = (M_3 - M_1)a^{3/2}$. This value of τ_{13} will, in general, be different from the given time interval, hence a residual can be obtained.

(iii) By repeating the foregoing computations, using new arbitrary values of p, the residual in the time interval can be represented numerically as a function of p. By a procedure such as Newton's approximation the value of p giving a zero residual (root) is then determined.

6.5. Olbers' Method for Determining a Parabolic Orbit

In 1797 Olbers produced the first practical method for calculating the parabolic orbit of a newly discovered comet that has stood the test of time. This method is similar to the Gaussian method but restricted to parabolic orbits. Most previous methods had been subject to large errors as the result of the basic hypothesis that the comet moved in a straight line at uniform speed during the period of observation. Still earlier methods, following Newton's example, had been purely graphical in character.

Olbers' fundamental hypothesis that the comet moves in a plane passing through the Sun's center applies to orbits of any eccentricity. It leads to three equations in the heliocentric coordinates at three dates x_i, y_i, z_i ($i = 1$, 2, 3) in which the coefficients are the well-known "ratios of the triangles" formed by the radii and chords, i.e., precisely the c_i's, given without derivation, in Eq. (105). That the c_i's can be so interpreted is easily demonstrated as follows:

(i) Taking the vector cross product of Eq. (105) with $\mathbf{r}_1$, we find that

$$\mathbf{r}_1 \times \mathbf{r}_2 = c_3\mathbf{r}_1 \times \mathbf{r}_3 \qquad (\mathbf{r}_1 \times \mathbf{r}_1 = 0)$$

(ii) The component of these cross product vectors on $\mathbf{W}$ is

$$\mathbf{r}_1 \times \mathbf{r}_2 \cdot \mathbf{W} = c_3\mathbf{r}_1 \times \mathbf{r}_3 \cdot \mathbf{W}.$$

(iii) Consequently,

$$c_3 = \mathbf{r}_1 \times \mathbf{r}_2 \cdot \mathbf{W}/\mathbf{r}_1 \times \mathbf{r}_3 \cdot \mathbf{W} = |\mathbf{r}_1 \times \mathbf{r}_2|/|\mathbf{r}_1 \times \mathbf{r}_3|.$$

(iv) Thus the ratio of the areas of the triangles formed by $\mathbf{r}_1$ and $\mathbf{r}_2$, S_{12}, to that formed by $\mathbf{r}_1$ and $\mathbf{r}_3$, S_{13}, is simply $c_3 = S_{12}/S_{13}$. A similar argument holds for $c_1 = S_{23}/S_{13}$.

According to Kepler's second law, the areas of the sectors formed by the radius vector are proportional to the respective time intervals. Olbers' assumption that the ratios of the corresponding triangles are proportional to the intervals introduces errors that may be considerable if the three observed times are not evenly spaced.

Theoretically, the three basic equations of the plane, when expressed in terms of the geocentric distances and the observed coordinates (which he referred to the ecliptic for greater convenience) can be solved directly for the ρ_1; but in practice, this leads to an indeterminacy because of small divisors. Olbers therefore eliminated ρ_2 and obtained an expression for ρ_3 in terms of ρ_1 and numerical quantities derived from the observations, of the form:

$$\rho_3 = M\rho_1. \tag{145}$$

See Herget[73] for an explicit form for M.

As a condition that the orbit should be a parabola, he next introduced Euler's relationship between the radii of the first and third dates and the chord, s, and corresponding time interval:

$$6k_s(t_3 - t_1) = (r_1 + r_3 + s)^{3/2} - (r_1 + r_3 - s)^{3/2},$$

which he expressed in terms of the geocentric distances and the ecliptic coordinates, i.e., the chord, s, between $\mathbf{r}_1$ and $\mathbf{r}_3$ is given by

$$s^2 = (\mathbf{r}_3 - \mathbf{r}_1) \cdot (\mathbf{r}_3 - \mathbf{r}_1). \tag{146}$$

Theoretically, the two equations can be solved for the unknown ρ_1 and ρ_3, In practice, however, the rationalization of Euler's equation produces an involved expression of such high degree that it is more convenient to find the numerical solution by trial and error as follows:

(i) Given $\mathbf{L}_1$ and $\mathbf{L}_3$ assume values for r_1 and r_3. For a newly discovered comet, it is usually sufficient to start with $r_1 = r_3 = 1$.

(ii) Compute the chord s by means of Euler's equation and the assumed r_i.

(iii) Compute ρ_1 from the geometrical relation between the chord and the geocentric coordinates i.e., Eq. (146) and $\mathbf{r}_i = \rho_i \mathbf{L}_i + \mathbf{R}_i$, $i = 1,3$ (from which ρ_3 has been eliminated by means of Eq. (145)).

(iv) Compute ρ_3 from Eq. (145).

(v) Compute r_1 and r_3 from the geometrical relations given by the triangles Sun–Earth–comet, i.e., from $\mathbf{r}_i = \rho_i \mathbf{L}_i + \mathbf{R}_i$ $i = 1,3$.

(vi) With these values of r_1 and r_3 repeat the entire process until the final r_i are equal to the last starting values.

The orientation elements i and Ω, the argument of latitude u, the true anomaly v, and the perihelion distance q are readily found from the heliocentric coordinates $\mathbf{r}_1$ and $\mathbf{r}_3$. The time of perihelion passage T is determined from Barker's equation (Eq. (90)).

By means of the geocentric distances derived from the preliminary orbit, corrections for parallax are applied to the observed right ascension and declination, and the times of observation corrected for the light time. In repetition of the orbit determination with the adjusted quantities, higher order terms in the ratios of the triangles may be included in order to reduce the errors of the approximations to a minimum.

6.6. Utilization of Observational Data

This subsection describes the use to which a large amount of observational data is put in an orbit-determination procedure. There are two aspects to this problem. The first is the reduction of data by the use of normal places and smoothing, and the second is the differential correction procedure. Both aspects apply to the problem of a definitive orbit in which all the useful data should be included.

6.6.1. Normal Places and Smoothing

In this context a "normal place" is defined as a combination of several observations that are grouped closely together into one single "observation" which is meant to convey all the information content of the group in a single point, for the mean of the observed times.

In the classical methods normal places are usually formed from residuals, based upon a preliminary orbit, by averaging them for a cluster of observations close together in time. Such a procedure has been employed in celestial mechanics to replace a least-squares differential correction, but it can also be employed to reduce the quantity of data prior to a differential correction. An alternative normal-place procedure is more properly termed "smoothing" and involves the fit of observations to a Taylor series, or to a smooth curve (such as a parabola).

Let the vector $\mathbf{L}$ again be defined as the unit vector from the observation point to the object, i.e., $\boldsymbol{\rho} = \rho\mathbf{L}$. Its first and second derivatives with respect to τ are denoted by $\dot{\mathbf{L}}$ and $\ddot{\mathbf{L}}$ respectively, where $\tau = k(t - t_0)$.

It is possible to determine the values of $\mathbf{L}$, $\dot{\mathbf{L}}$, and $\ddot{\mathbf{L}}$, as required for inputs to a Laplacian orbit determination, from values of $\mathbf{L}$ obtained through direct observations from a single station or a chain of adjacent stations. The computational method follows:

(i) Let the subscript i indicate an observation made at time τ_i. Furthermore let the subscript 0 denote the particular time point at which it is desired to obtain values of the vectors $\mathbf{L}_0$, $\dot{\mathbf{L}}_0$, and $\ddot{\mathbf{L}}_0$. It should be emphasized that this time need not correspond to an actual time of observation.

(ii) Utilizing this convention, it is possible to represent the values of $\mathbf{L}$ obtained through direct observations by the first three terms of a Taylor series, i.e.,

$$\mathbf{L}_i = \mathbf{L}_0 + \tau_i\dot{\mathbf{L}}_0 + \frac{\tau_i^2}{2}\ddot{\mathbf{L}}_0, \qquad i = 1, 2, \ldots, N \tag{147}$$

where N is the total number of observations. The above constitute N equations in three unknowns. Should N equal three, the desired vectors may be determined uniquely. Should N exceed three, the unknowns are overdetermined and may be obtained by a curve-fitting technique such as the method of least squares.

One obvious extension of the above formula is the determination of $\mathbf{L}$ at three distinct points, as required for inputs to a Gaussian or other orbit determination method. This is accomplished simply by successive application of the technique for obtaining $\mathbf{L}_0$. For precision orbits, $\mathbf{L}_0$ can be considered a smoothed data point.

6.6.2. Differential Correction

The single most important tool in the definitive determination of a space vehicle orbit from observations is that of the differential correction. Such procedures have been employed for the improvement of orbits since Gauss.

Differential correction is applied in astrodynamics for two conceptually different purposes. As has been shown earlier in this section we may determine a preliminary orbit on the basis of some simplified physical model (e.g., assume only two-body forces) or upon some simplified orbit (e.g., assume a rectilinear parabola, circular orbit, etc.) or we may even handle the observations in such a way that our computed preliminary orbit doesn't exactly "satisfy" them (e.g., as in Laplace's method). In any event, even given perfect observational data, our subsequent observations would not necessarily agree with what we computed them to be on the basis of our preliminary orbit. As has been demonstrated, these subsequent observations can be utilized to *correct* the preliminary orbit, with its inherent assumptions, into an improved orbit. This then is the first possible application of differential correction. A second application, to be dealt with in the following section, considers the effect of errors in the observational data themselves. Clearly, even if our preliminary orbit was complete in all respects and was based upon no assumptions, the subsequent observations would still differ from the computed ones due to random and systematic observational errors. Consequently, a differential correction procedure could be utilized to improve an orbit that was originally computed on the basis of imperfect observational data—and all new data can serve to further improve the orbit as time goes on; an example of this procedure was Rabe's correction of the orbit of Eros (see Section 5.3.2).

With regard to this last point it is often erroneously believed that such an improvement of an orbit on the basis of new observational data involves the *redetermination* of orbits from complete sets of observations called "fixes." As noted by Herrick, such a procedure is defective because it both discards all prior information (almost certainly more valuable than current information in specifying certain orbital elements) and contaminates good raw observational data with poor data in the process of establishing the fix.

Again, as has been pointed out by Herrick,[1] "The improvement of orbits by differential correction may be based upon *any* six observational data, as a minimum, or upon many more redundant data, by utilizing the method of least squares. The possibility of choosing the most accurate data,whether optical or electronic, and of averaging out errors of observation and discarding discordant observations, the assignment of weights and the inclusion of data over a longer range of time, all indicate the obvious advantages of the differential correction over the one-shot redetermination."

Differential correction is based upon the "representation" of the observations by calculating what the observations would have been if the space vehicle traveled exactly along the preliminary orbit. Because such an orbit will not be exactly correct, the observational data discussed in the foregoing subsections, e.g., the angles α, δ, h, A, or the Doppler range rate, $\dot{\rho}$, etc., will differ from the computed coordinates. (It should be noted that the uncertainty in the observation station's coordinates may also contribute to this difference.)

Residuals are then formed by subtracting the computed data (e.g., $\dot{\rho}_c$ based upon the preliminary orbit) from the observed data (e.g., $\dot{\rho}_0$). These residuals ($\Delta\dot{\rho}$) are then analytically formulated as a first order Taylor series in several variables, i.e.,

$$\Delta\dot{\rho}_1 = \left(\frac{\partial\dot{\rho}_1}{\partial p_1}\right)\Delta p_1 + \left(\frac{\partial\dot{\rho}_1}{\partial p_2}\right)\Delta p_2 + \cdots + \left(\frac{\partial\dot{\rho}_1}{\partial p_n}\right)\Delta p_n$$

$$\Delta\dot{\rho}_2 = \left(\frac{\partial\dot{\rho}_2}{\partial p_1}\right)\Delta p_1 + \left(\frac{\partial\dot{\rho}_2}{\partial p_2}\right)\Delta p_2 + \cdots + \left(\frac{\partial\dot{\rho}_2}{\Delta p_n}\right)\Delta p_n$$

$$\vdots$$

$$\Delta\dot{\rho}_N = \left(\frac{\partial\dot{\rho}_N}{\partial p_1}\right)\Delta p_1 + \left(\frac{\partial\dot{\rho}_N}{\partial p_2}\right)\Delta p_2 + \cdots + \left(\frac{\partial\dot{\rho}_N}{\partial p_n}\right)\Delta p_n, \qquad (148)$$

where $\Delta\dot{\rho}_i$ stands for any "observed-minus-computed" residual, and the p_j's represent n orbital parameters, e.g., a, e, T, . . . or $\mathbf{a}$, $\mathbf{b}$, . . . etc., or, perhaps the observation station's coordinates.* Often the coefficients of a series expansion of certain elements are utilized as parameters to take into account secular variations in period, nodal longitude, etc. Such a procedure has been employed in the case of satellite orbits by Miczaika and Curtis of Air Force Cambridge Research Center. In the case of missile orbits, x, y, z at burnout are often well determined and only $\dot{x}$, $\dot{y}$, $\dot{z}$ at burnout need be differentially corrected. This latter procedure has been em-

* The geodetic applications of precision orbit work is now manifest. The basic problem is the determination of the distance (usually a *geodesic* or shortest distance between two points on a mathematically defined reference surface, e.g., a spheroid) between two stations. Several classical methods, e.g., star occultations, flare triangulation, geodimeter, and certain new methods such as the tellurometer, Raydist equipment, Shoran, and Hiran are in use today (see reference[74] for a discussion of these methods). Hiran, consisting of an airplane flying at a constant altitude crosswise between two transponder stations and measuring transmission–reception time delays, appears to yield the most accurate distances. Yet, by the differential correction of the coordinates of a station through observation of a well-known satellite, a three-dimensional fix can be obtained that promises to yield a more accurate station fix than Hiran. Note that triangulation is completely inferior to the differential correction technique which utilizes station coordinates as the p_i's.

ployed effectively by Speer at Army Ballistic Missile Agency (he corrected two angles and a speed rather than the rectangular components of velocity).

Eqs. (148) can be inverted and solved for the values of $\Delta p_1, \ldots \Delta p_j, \ldots \Delta p_n$, to be added to the original values of the parameters (or station coordinates) $p_1, \ldots p_j, \ldots p_n$, thereby yielding an improved set (provided the number of residuals, N, equals or exceeds the number of parameters, n, and there are no singularities in the inversion). If N exceeds n, the most probable values of the Δp_j are found by least squares from which the standard deviation of the elements can be obtained.

There is no way to avoid the inversion process in establishing general analytical expressions for corrections to the elements. If one wishes to avoid inversion, the redetermination of the orbit may be used, perhaps based on a minimum number of normal points, but the disadvantages of redetermination remain. In short, it is preferable to treat the problem as dynamic and continuing rather than as a static redetermination process.

The inverse problem, of obtaining a station's coordinates from photographs made *from* the vehicle itself, can be treated in a similar fashion. Having a precise estimation of the orientation of the camera axis (see Section 11.3.3) and a definitive orbit for the vehicle, it is possible to compute the expected positions of some localized feature, e.g., a road intersection or a stable river fork that can be identified or associated with available cartographic material. (The definitive orbit for the space vehicle can be obtained by precise observation prior and subsequent to the photography.) By subtracting the computed and observed positions of the localized features (i.e., obtaining $\Delta \rho_i$'s) and by numerically determining the appropriate partial derivatives Eqs. (148) can be entered and improved station coordinates (and even certain camera orientation parameters) can be obtained (i.e., improved p_i's obtained). Equipped with these improved coordinates of check points it is then possible to relate the cartographic maps to a single datum and achieve a geodetic tie-in. It should be recognized that the determination of a definitive orbit is of critical importance in achieving an accurate tie-in.

The inversion of Eqs. (148) requires a knowledge of all the partial derivatives, $\partial \dot{\rho}_i / \partial p_j$. In classical celestial mechanics, these have customarily been obtained by analytical differentiation of the "representation" formulas. However, the needs of modern automatic machine calculation are often best served if, instead, they are obtained numerically directly from the formulas themselves. All that is required is to introduce a small variation, δp_j to each p_j in turn. That is, for a variation in the jth parameter, two numerical representations of $\dot{\rho}_i$ (at the time of the ith observation) are subtracted:

$$\frac{\partial \dot{\rho}_i}{\partial p_j} \cong \frac{\delta \dot{\rho}_i}{\delta p_j} = \frac{\dot{\rho}_i(p_1, \ldots p_i + \delta p_j, \ldots p_n) - \dot{\rho}_i(p_1, \ldots p_j, \ldots p_n)}{\delta p_j}. \tag{149}$$

(The choice of a proper numerical value for δp_j is usually made on a trial and error basis.)

For certain specific circumstances, such as in the case of a slightly perturbed, satellite, certain analytical partials are preferable in that their employment would reduce the computational burden of numerically evaluating the partials (involving at least six numerical integrations of variant orbits). In particular, as has been shown by Herrick and Walters[75] if the elements U_0, a, $e \cos \omega (\triangleq a_N)$, $e \sin \omega (\triangleq a_M)$, Ω, and i are utilized for low-eccentricity orbits, then the partials in the case of range ρ, range rate $\dot{\rho}$, and α and δ, can be derived and are listed in Table XI (the elements $\mathbf{U}_0$ and $\mathbf{V}_0$ may prove to have even greater utility).

The first two columns of Table XI give coefficients that are especially designed for low eccentricity orbits. The last two columns are quite general, but ordinarily the residuals are expressed in terms of components of $\mathbf{L}$, i.e., ΔL_x, ΔL_y, and ΔL_z rather than in α and δ (cf. Chapter 14, in Herrick).[1] Table XII lists the vector components, and Table XIII the coefficients to be employed in computing the partials given in Table XI.

Such analytical partials are also useful in understanding the observational problem. For example, the coefficients of ΔU_0 and Δa_N are identical when the object crosses the meridian at the northern antinode. Thus, a southern-hemisphere observation of a satellite would be necessary in order to remove the ambiguity.

Over small intervals (less than a radian or two) it is possible to expand the position and velocity of the vehicle in a power series in time (the f and g series). Analytical partial derivatives can also be developed for α and δ or $\mathbf{L}$ in this manner, and employed in the differential correction. Such a procedure was devised by Leuschner and is based upon the relationships

$$\mathbf{r}_i = \rho_i \mathbf{L}_i - \mathbf{R}_i = f_i \mathbf{r}_2 + g_i \dot{\mathbf{r}}_2$$

or for $i = 1, 3$

$$x_1 = \rho_1 L_{x1} - X_1 = f_1 x_2 + g_1 \dot{x}_2,$$

$$x_3 = \rho_3 L_{x3} - X_3 = f_3 x_2 + g_3 \dot{x}_2 \qquad x \rightarrow y, z, \tag{150}$$

and

$$\mathbf{r}_2 \cdot \mathbf{r}_2 = (\boldsymbol{\varrho}_2 - \mathbf{R}_2) \cdot (\boldsymbol{\varrho}_2 - \mathbf{R}_2) = r_2^2 = \rho_2^2 - 2\rho_2 R_2 \cos \psi_2 + R_2^2 \tag{151}$$

$$x \rightarrow y, z,$$

TABLE XI. ANALYTICAL PARTIALS

partial of: / with respect to:	ρ	$\dot{\rho}$ (Analysis carried out by R. Gersten)
U_0	$a(\mathbf{R}\cdot\mathbf{V})/\rho$	$[-a\dot{u}\boldsymbol{\varrho}\cdot(\mathbf{N}\cos u+\mathbf{M}\sin u)$ $+\,a\dot{\boldsymbol{\varrho}}\cdot(\mathbf{M}\cos u-\mathbf{N}\sin u)-\dot{\rho}a(\mathbf{R}\cdot\mathbf{V})/\rho]/\rho$
a	$[a+\mathbf{R}\cdot\mathbf{V}-\frac{3}{2}(u-U_0)$ $(\mathbf{R}\cdot\mathbf{V})]/a\rho$	$[\boldsymbol{\varrho}\cdot(\mathbf{N}\dot{u}\{\frac{1}{2}\sin u+\frac{3}{2}(u-U_0)\cos u\}+\mathbf{M}\dot{u}\{\frac{3}{2}(u-U_0)$ $\sin u-\frac{1}{2}\cos u\})+\dot{\boldsymbol{\varrho}}\cdot(\mathbf{M}\{\sin u-\frac{3}{2}(u-U_0)$ $\cos u\}+\mathbf{N}\{\cos u+\frac{3}{2}(u-U_0)\sin u\})-\dot{\rho}\{a$ $+\,\mathbf{R}\cdot\mathbf{U}-\frac{3}{2}(u-U_0)\mathbf{R}\cdot\mathbf{V}\}/\rho]/\rho$
a_N	$a[(\mathbf{R}\cdot\mathbf{V})\sin u-\boldsymbol{\varrho}\cdot\mathbf{N}]/\rho$	$[a\dot{u}\rho\cdot(\mathbf{M}\{\cos^2 u-\sin^2 u\}-\mathbf{N}\,2\sin u\cos u)$ $-\,a\dot{\boldsymbol{\varrho}}\cdot(\mathbf{N}\{1+\sin^2 u\}+\mathbf{M}\sin u\cos u)$ $-\dot{\rho}a(\mathbf{R}\cdot\mathbf{V}\sin u-\boldsymbol{\varrho}\cdot\mathbf{N})/\rho]/\rho$
a_M	$-a[(\mathbf{R}\cdot\mathbf{V})\cos u$ $+\,\boldsymbol{\varrho}\cdot\mathbf{M}]/\rho$	$[a\dot{u}\boldsymbol{\varrho}\cdot(\mathbf{N}\{\cos^2 u-\sin^2 u\}+\mathbf{M}\,2\sin u\cos u)$ $+\,a\dot{\boldsymbol{\varrho}}\cdot(\mathbf{N}\sin u\cos u-\mathbf{M}\{1+\cos^2 u\}$ $+\,\dot{\rho}a(\mathbf{R}\cdot\mathbf{V}\cos u-\rho\cdot\mathbf{M})/\rho]/\rho$
Ω	$a[(\mathbf{R}\cdot\mathbf{V})\cos i-$ $(\mathbf{R}\cdot\mathbf{W})\cos u\sin i]/\rho$	$[-\boldsymbol{\varrho}\cdot(\mathbf{N}\cos i\sqrt{\mu/\rho}\{\cos u+e\cos\omega\}+\mathbf{M}\cos i$ $\sqrt{\mu/\rho}\{\sin u+e\sin\omega\}-\mathbf{W}\sin i\sqrt{\mu/\rho}\{\sin u$ $+\,e\sin\omega\})+\dot{\rho}\cdot(\mathbf{M}r\cos u\cos i-\mathbf{N}r\sin u\cos i$ $-\,\mathbf{W}r\cos u\sin i)-\dot{\rho}a\mathbf{R}\cdot(\mathbf{V}\cos i-$ $-\,\mathbf{W}\cos u\sin i)/\rho]/\rho$
i	$a[(\mathbf{R}\cdot\mathbf{V})\sin u]/\rho$	$[\boldsymbol{\varrho}\cdot\mathbf{W}\sqrt{\mu/\rho}\{\cos u+e\cos\omega\}+\dot{\boldsymbol{\varrho}}\cdot\mathbf{W}r\sin u$ $-\,\dot{\rho}a(\mathbf{R}\cdot\mathbf{W})(\sin u)/\rho]/\rho$

partial of: / with respect to:	α (topocentric)	δ (topocentric)
U_0	$\mathbf{A}\cdot(\mathbf{U}R_n+\mathbf{V}V_n)U_0/\rho\cos\delta$	$\mathbf{D}\cdot(\mathbf{U}R_n+\mathbf{V}V_n)U_0/\rho$
a	$\mathbf{A}\cdot(\mathbf{U}R_a+\mathbf{V}U_a)/a\rho\cos\delta$	$\mathbf{D}\cdot(\mathbf{U}R_a+\mathbf{V}U_a)/a\rho$
a_N	$\mathbf{A}\cdot(\mathbf{U}R_{xn}+\mathbf{V}U_{xn})/\rho\cos\delta$	$\mathbf{D}\cdot(\mathbf{U}R_{xn}+\mathbf{V}U_{xn})/\rho$
a_M	$\mathbf{A}\cdot(\mathbf{U}R_{yn}+\mathbf{V}U_{yn})/\rho\cos\delta$	$\mathbf{D}\cdot(\mathbf{U}R_{yn}+\mathbf{V}U_{yn})/\rho$
Ω	$\mathbf{A}\cdot(\mathbf{V}r\cos i-\mathbf{W}r\sin i\cos u)/\rho\cos\delta$	$\mathbf{D}\cdot(\mathbf{V}r\cos i-\mathbf{W}ri\sin i\cos u)/\rho$
i	$\mathbf{A}\cdot\mathbf{W}r\sin u/\rho\cos\delta$	$\mathbf{D}\cdot\mathbf{W}r\sin u/\rho$

TABLE XII. VECTOR COMPONENTS

Component \ Vector	$\mathbf{R}$	$\mathbf{r}$	$\mathbf{U}$	$\mathbf{A}$	$\mathbf{D}$	$\mathbf{h}$	$\mathbf{W}$
x	X	x	x/r	$\frac{-(y-Y)}{\sqrt{(x-X)^2+(y-Y)^2}}$	$\frac{-A_y(z-Z)}{(r-R)}$	$\frac{(y\dot{z}-z\dot{y})}{\sqrt{\mu}}$	$h_x/\sqrt{p}$
y	Y	y	y/r	$\frac{(x-X)}{\sqrt{(x-X)^2+(y-Y)^2}}$	$\frac{A_x(z-Z)}{(r-R)}$	$\frac{(z\dot{x}-xz)}{\sqrt{\mu}}$	$h_y/\sqrt{p}$
z	Z	z	z/r	0	$\frac{\sqrt{(x-X)^2-(y-Y)^2}}{(r-R)}$	$\frac{(x\dot{y}-y\dot{x})}{\sqrt{\mu}}$	$h_z/\sqrt{p}$

$\mathbf{V} = \mathbf{W} \times \mathbf{U}$; $\mathbf{N} = \mathbf{U} \cos u - \mathbf{V} \sin u$; $\mathbf{M} = \mathbf{U} \sin u + \mathbf{V} \cos u$.

TABLE XIII. COEFFICIENTS

Sub: \ Quantity:	R	U
u	$a^2e \sin E/r$	$a^2 \sqrt{1-e^2}/r$
a	$r/a - \frac{3}{2}(u - U_0)R_u/a$	$-\frac{3}{2}(u - U_0)U_u/a$
x_N	$a^2[e \cos \omega -$ $e \cos (E + \omega)]/r$	$a^2[2 \sin (E + \omega) + \sin E \cos \omega(\sqrt{1-e^2}$ $\{1 + r/p\} - 2) - e \sin \omega(1/\{1 + \sqrt{1-e^2}\}$ $+ \cos^2 E)]/r$
y_N	$a^2[e \sin \omega -$ $\sin (E + \omega)]/r$	$a^2[-2 \cos (E + \omega) + \sin E \sin \omega(\sqrt{1-e^2}\{1 +$ $r/p\} - 2) + e \cos \omega(1/\{1 + \sqrt{1-e^2}\} +$ $\cos^2 E)]/r$

where $\boldsymbol{\rho}_2 \cdot \mathbf{R}_2 \equiv \rho_2 R_2 \cos \psi_2$ and ψ_2 is called the *angle of elongation*. From these equations, partial derivatives are extracted and combined until finally the following six equations are obtained (see Chapter 14 in Herrick[1] for more details)

$$\begin{aligned} \rho_1 \Delta L_{x1} + L_{x1}\Delta\rho_1 &= (L_{x2}f_1 + x_2 a_1 + \dot{x}_2 b_1)\Delta\rho_2 + g_1\Delta\dot{x}_2 \\ \rho_3 \Delta L_{x3} + L_{x3}\Delta\rho_3 &= (L_{x2}f_3 + x_2 a_3 + \dot{x}_2 b_3)\Delta\rho_2 + g_3\Delta\dot{x}_2 \end{aligned} \tag{152}$$

where

$$a_i \triangleq \left(\frac{3\tau_i^2}{2r_2^5} - 2\tau_i^3 \frac{\dot{r}_2}{r_2^6}\right)(\rho_2 - R_2 \cos \psi_2)$$

and

$$b_i \triangleq \left(\frac{\tau_i^2}{2r_2^5}\right)(\rho_2 - R_2 \cos \psi_2)$$

where τ_i is the time difference in k_e^{-1} mins between the ith observation and the second observation i.e., the observation "at the second date."

(In the foregoing reduction $\Delta\mathbf{L}_2$ is assumed to be zero.) From Eqs. (152) $\Delta\rho_1$ and $\Delta\rho_3$ are algebraically eliminated leaving four equations to be solved for the four unknowns $\Delta\dot{x}_2$, $\Delta\dot{y}_2$, $\Delta\dot{z}_2$, and $\Delta\rho_2$ (note that ΔL_{x1} and ΔL_{x3} are the known observed-minus-computed residuals). Such a procedure is well tailored to the correction of a preliminary Laplacian orbit in which the observed and computed $\mathbf{L}$ at the middle date are identical (i.e., $\Delta\mathbf{L}_2 = 0$) while the observed values of $\mathbf{L}$ at the first and third date do not quite fit the computed ones. The improved set of $\dot{x}_2 + \Delta\dot{x}_2$, $\dot{y}_2 + \Delta\dot{y}_2$, $\dot{z}_2 + \Delta\dot{z}_2$, and $\rho_2 + \Delta\rho_2$ (where $\dot{x}_2$, $\dot{y}_2$, $\dot{z}_2$, ρ_2, etc. were obtained from the preliminary

Laplacian method) will now allow a fit of the observed and computed **L** at the first and third date (but not necessarily at the second any longer).

For error analysis, of course, one would obtain the mean square error of a prediction from the mean square errors of the parameters, $\epsilon_{p_j}{}^2$ from Eqs. (148) modified by the theory of propagation of errors to

$$\epsilon_{\rho_i}{}^2 = \left(\frac{\partial \dot{\rho}_i}{\partial p_1}\right)^2 \epsilon_{p_1}{}^2 + \left(\frac{\partial \dot{\rho}_i}{\partial p_2}\right)^2 \epsilon_{p_2}{}^2 + \cdots + \left(\frac{\partial \dot{\rho}_i}{\partial p_n}\right)^2 \epsilon_{p_n}{}^2. \tag{153}$$

The mean square errors or standard deviation of the parameters or elements, ϵ_{p_j}, are obtained as a by-product from the inversion of Eqs. (148) by a standard least-squares procedure (assuming that the number of observations is greater than the number of parameters).

6.6.3. Ambiguous Solutions for Orbits

There are extensive regions surrounding the Sun and intersecting at the Earth within which a two-body heliocentric orbit has two unrelated or ambiguous solutions for the geocentric distance ρ (cf. Eq. (129)). In an investigation of the possibility of double solutions in the general orbit problem, C. V. L. Charlier[167] deduced a simple criterion for determining whether or not there are two real values for the geocentric distance, ρ, in a given situation, by deriving the bipolar coordinates of the limiting curve separating the regions of double from those of unique solutions in the plane through the Earth, Sun, and object (cf. pp. 215 to 218 of Moulton[13]). If the expression

$$1 + 3m \cos \psi$$

is zero, the object is on the boundary surface; if it is positive there are two distinct orbits possible; if negative, there is a unique solution. The angle ψ in Charlier's criterion is the *elongation* of the object from the Sun; m is found from

$$m \triangleq \left(\frac{\kappa}{\cos \delta}\right) \frac{1}{R^4}$$

where κ is the constant found in Lambert's equation for the apparent orbit which is

$$\frac{\kappa}{\cos \delta} = \frac{\rho}{\left(\dfrac{1}{R^3} - \dfrac{1}{r^3}\right)}.$$

In the Laplacian methods, κ is a function of the observed spherical coordinates and their velocities and accelerations (cf. Eqs. (132)). In the Gaussian methods it is a function of the ratios of the triangles (i.e., the c's of Eq. (105)). Crommelin[168] believed that Comet 1927f (Gale) was in the region of double solutions. An investigation by Makemson[169], however, proved that the comet was outside the two-solution zone and that the indeterminacy found by Crommelin arose from the very slow convergence of the f and g series. When two solutions for the geocentric distance exist, both are found in the tables with argument $1/m$ and ψ published by Leuschner[170]. To distinguish between them further observations must be represented. Residuals from the spurious orbit will show a rapidly increasing systematic error.

Another related class of nearly indeterminate orbit solutions would exist for orbits determined from angle data only (i.e., $\mathbf{L}$ only) if the track of the object across the celestial sphere nearly follows a great circle. In this case the observer himself would be in the orbit plane. Specifically, as noted by Moulton (p. 223[13]), if the derivatives of $\mathbf{L}$ that enter into the determinant D are generated from three observations that lie on a great circle, then $D = 0$ and the solution is indeterminate. Similarly, the "24-hr" equatorial or stationary satellites present indeterminable problems for orbit determination based upon terrestrial observations, while range and/or range-rate data taken near the nodes or antinodes of orbits can lead to ambiguous solutions. More specifically, except for the case of observations taken from an exactly equatorial or polar station, there exists no actual ambiguity for range and range-rate observations made from a terrestrial station. Because of the Earth's rotation a station (other than one established exactly on the North or South Pole) effectively traces out a baseline in space as it is carried around by the Earth. Thus, space vehicles moving in different directions but with the same dimensional orbital elements and distances of closest approach to the station will exhibit different range and range-rate data. The data received by an equatorial station would, on the other hand, be the same for two vehicles proceeding on identical orbits but with inclinations of opposite sign.

In the application of the differential correction procedure, indeterminacy problems arise because the represented or computed observational data differ too greatly from the actually observed data. This difficulty can be remedied in two different ways: (i) a better preliminary orbit can be achieved, e.g., by utilizing the low-eccentricity orbit of Eq. (119) instead of the zero-eccentricity orbit of Eq. (113); or (ii) a more selective choice can be made of the data upon which to base the differential correction. In this latter case it may be necessary to somehow transfer to geocentric

7 THE N-BODY PROBLEM

There exist but ten integrals of the equations of motion for an arbitrary system of n bodies (for $n > 2$). Six of these integrals show that the center of mass or barycenter exhibits rectilinear motion at constant speed; three more state that the angular momentum of the system is constant, and the tenth is simply an expression of the conservation of kinetic and potential energy. As was proved by Bruns and Poincaré there exist no other algebraic integrals of the n-body problem; consequently, a general solution can be found only for the two-body problem in which six integrals or constants are required.

The following section discusses the three-body problem; generalized equations of motion for the n-body problem; the perturbative function; and certain equations for including other forces, which we class with the n-body forces, such as those forces occasioned by the asphericity of the Earth, drag, and lift (the equations to be employed for the inclusion of thrust are discussed in Chapter 10).

Before embarking upon our discussion of the three-body problem it might prove useful to consider very briefly some recent research of Klemperer who has treated a more general problem: the plane configurations of a number of mutually gravitating bodies that revolve about their mass center in dynamic equilibrium. Klemperer in a Douglas Aircraft Company report (SM-37458) has found solutions for a rhombic configuration, i.e., for a configuration in which the masses are at the vertices and center of an equilateral parallelogram having oblique angles. Solutions are also given for hexagonal and octagonal rosettes, i.e., for equilateral polygons in which every other vertex (occupied by a mass m_1) is at some constant distance

r_1 from the center; while the vertices in between (occupied by a mass m_2) are at a different constant distance r_2 from the center.*

As Klemperer points out "it would be possible to arrange four or more bodies in such a dynamic equilibrium constellation, provided that certain conditions of symmetry are fulfilled." Clearly the initial positions and velocities and the masses of the bodies comprising the configuration must be chosen such that their mutual gravitational attraction carries them around their mutual mass center in the same orbit every period. Furthermore, the orbital angular velocity at which this is possible must be the same for all bodies (except for the central one, of course). Consequently, the orbits must all be circular, the motion planar, and the size of the masses chosen so as to retain this state of affairs.

7.1. The Three-Body Problem

Although a general solution to the three-body problem (which requires 12 arbitrary constants or integrals) is not possible, certain special solutions can be found. These were originally studied in Lagrange's prize work[76] in 1772 and have recently been reconsidered by Klemperer and Benedikt[77] and, in connection with orbit computation techniques, in Baker.[78] There are three special solutions (the two nontrivial solutions are described in Moulton,[13] Finlay-Freundlich,[79] and in other texts): the three bodies at the vertices of an equilateral triangle, three bodies in a straight line, and the trivial case of the three bodies all at one point.†

7.1.1. The Straight Line Solutions

As an example, let us consider a libration (or oscillation) point, i.e., a stable point, of the three-body problem in the Earth–Moon system, and introduce a "synodic" satellite after Klemperer. Since the general three-body solution is very complex, the following simplifying assumptions are made: (i), zero mass for the satellite; (ii), neglect of all perturbations except those due to the Moon; and (iii), a circular orbit for the Moon. Of the five possible orbits, the straight line solution in which the satellite is at inferior conjunction, i.e., between the Earth and Moon on their line of centers, is selected; as an example (see Fig. 25).

* The specification of this distance is exceedingly sensitive. Very slight departures from these points are, nevertheless, still possible and stable oscillations could be achieved.

† There also exists a solution involving a physically meaningless system of *fixed* masses, due to Euler (Whittaker[80]).

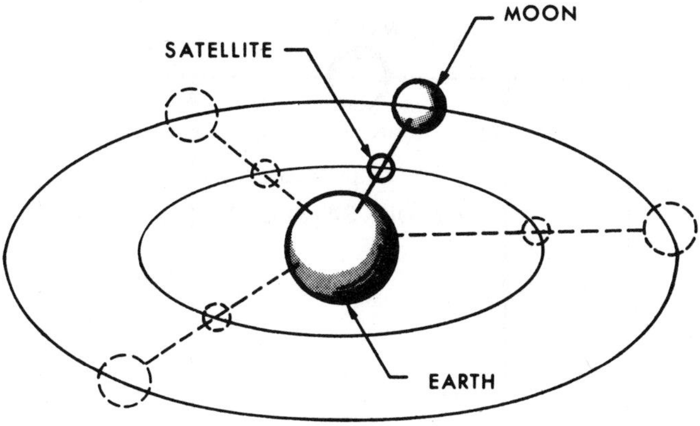

FIG. 25. Synodic satellite.

The relative position of the satellite with respect to the Earth–Moon system, as well as the distances, is shown in Fig. 26 where

1 is the distance from the Earth-center to the Moon-center (unit distance for $a_☾$ is assumed);

ϵ is the relative distance from the barycenter of the Earth–Moon system to the Earth-center;

λ is the relative distance from the barycenter to the Moon-center;

η is the relative distance from the Earth-center to the satellite; and

ξ is the relative distance from the Moon-center to the satellite.

One sees from Fig. 26 that

$$\epsilon + \lambda = 1 \tag{154}$$

and

$$\epsilon/\lambda = \frac{\text{Moon Mass}}{\text{Earth Mass}} = 0.012{,}288{,}800$$

by the definition of a barycenter.*

In order to expedite the analysis a rotating coordinate system is chosen. The equati›n of motion takes the form:

$$\frac{k_e^2 m_\Delta m_\oplus}{\eta^2} = \frac{k_e^2 m_\Delta m_☾}{(1-\eta)^2} + \omega_☾^2 m_\Delta(\eta - \epsilon)$$

* The actual mass of the Moon is not known to this many figures, nevertheless, it is convenient to choose a hypothetical lunar mass for consistency in the computations as they were employed in reference 78.

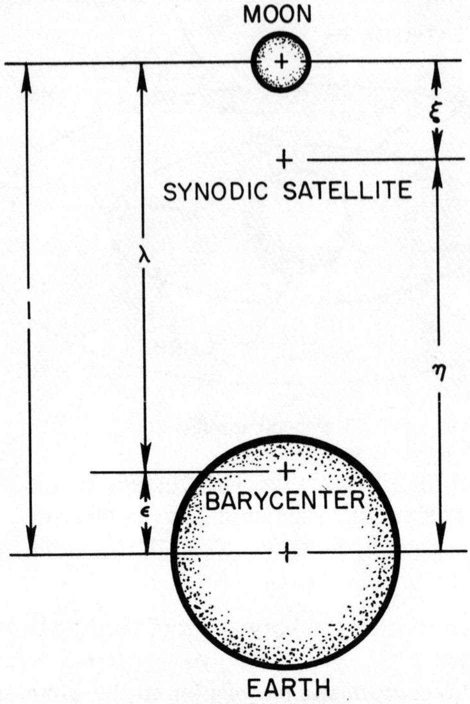

FIG. 26. Relative distances.

where

$$\omega_{☾}^2 = \frac{k_e^2(m_\oplus + m_{☾})}{\lambda + \epsilon} = \frac{k_e^2 m_\oplus}{\lambda}$$

and m_Δ = mass of the synodic satellite vehicle.

Hence,

$$\frac{k_e^2 m_\oplus}{\eta^2} = \frac{k_e^2 m_{☾}}{(1-\eta)^2} + \frac{k_e^2 m_\oplus}{\lambda}(\eta - \epsilon),$$

so that

$$\frac{1}{\eta^2} = \frac{\epsilon}{\lambda}\frac{1}{(1-\eta)^2} + \frac{\eta - \epsilon}{\lambda}.$$

From this latter relation one finds that

$$\lambda(1-\eta)^2 = \epsilon\eta^2 + (\eta - \epsilon)(1-\eta)^2\eta^2$$

or

$$\eta^5 - (\epsilon + 2)\eta^4 + (1 + 2\epsilon)\eta^3 - \lambda\eta^2 + 2\lambda\eta - \lambda = 0. \tag{155}$$

Given Eq. (154) and the ratio ϵ/λ we may solve Eq. (155) for η (for the inferior conjunction point) and find:

$$\eta = 0.849{,}108{,}70.$$

The period of the satellite can be determined from Kepler's third law

$$P_{☾} = \frac{2\pi a_{☾}^{3/2}}{k_e \sqrt{\mu}}. \tag{156}$$

The constants for the above equation are taken from Chapter 5:

$$\begin{aligned} a_{☾} &= 60.268{,}18 \quad \text{Earth radii,} \\ k_e &= 0.074{,}365{,}74, \text{ and} \\ \mu_{\oplus ☾} &= m_{\oplus} + m_{☾} = 1 + 0.012{,}288{,}8. \end{aligned}$$

The mean motion or angular velocity is given by

$$n = \frac{2\pi}{P_{☾}}. \tag{157}$$

Substituting Eq. (156) into Eq. (157) the latter becomes

$$n = \frac{k_e \sqrt{\mu}}{a_{☾}^{3/2}} = 0.000{,}159{,}916{,}40 \, \frac{\text{rad}}{\text{min}}.$$

The tangential velocity of the satellite is

$$\dot{s} = \frac{\eta a_{☾} n}{k_e} = \frac{\eta \sqrt{\mu}}{\sqrt{a_{☾}}}. \tag{158}$$

The initial values of position and velocity, which are also the values at the end of every period, will be:

$$\begin{aligned} x &= a_{☾}\eta = 51.174{,}236 \text{ Earth radii,} & \dot{x} &= 0 \\ y &= 0, & \dot{y} &= \frac{\eta\sqrt{\mu}}{\sqrt{a_{☾}}} \\ & & &= 0.110{,}045{,}20 \\ z &= 0, & \dot{z} &= 0. \end{aligned}$$

For more than three bodies, certain regular polyhedra formed by the mass points (e.g., for the four-body problem a tetrahedric configuration) are the counterparts of Lagrange's solution for three bodies. Such configurations have been mentioned qualitatively in the introduction to the Chapter and no further detail will be given.

7.1.2. The Equilateral Triangle Solutions

Nature has actually provided us with an example of the triangle solution in the Trojan group of minor planets. There are two points in the plane passing through the Sun and Jupiter that form equilateral triangles with the two large bodies, being distant 5.2 a.u. from each. According to the particular solution of the three-body problem found by Lagrange in 1772, an infinitesimal body placed at either of these points will pursue a stable orbit around the Sun in the same period as Jupiter, i.e., 11.86 years. If given a slight displacement from the equilibrium point, the particle would oscillate about it in a period of several hundred years depending on its distance from the point.

Lagrange's brilliant mathematical deduction was prophetic. In 1906, Wolf discovered a small planet that proved to be situated near the equilateral triangle point 60° preceding Jupiter. The planet was named for the Greek hero, Achilles, and the group became known eventually as the Trojan asteroids. The second Trojan, 617 Patroclus, was discovered in October of the same year; and was followed by Hector and Nestor in 1907 and 1908. There are 14 known members (in 1959) about evenly distributed between the two equilateral points, the latest one having been discovered in 1957 and not yet having received a permanent number. Many orbits were computed by a variety of methods and many articles were written about Achilles. Theories of general perturbations for planets with mean motions of 300″ were devised by Linders, Wilkens, E. W. Brown, and others, some inclusive of Saturn perturbations.[14] Brown's tables were revised by Brouwer after they began to show large deviations from the observed positions.

In 1954, Rabe made an analytical investigation of Kuiper's suggestion that the Trojans were former satellites of Jupiter that escaped during the long interval when the mass of the original "protoplanet," which became Jupiter, slowly diminished by evaporation to about $1/20$ of its initial value.[81] Rabe proved, by means of an osculating Jacobi integral (or energy of an object moving in a rotating coordinate system, see page 281 in Moulton[13]) associated with a variable mass, that a general orbital development from satellite to Trojan will result from any systematic decrease in Jupiter's mass. Under special initial conditions the same satellite escaping from the diminishing gravitational attraction of the great planet may become a "hidalgo," i.e., a planet which revolves outside the orbit of Jupiter. The minor planet 944 Hidalgo, discovered in 1920, is a unique case. With an eccentricity of 0.65 and an inclination of 43°, Hidalgo requires 13 years to complete an orbit that carries it from within 2.0 a.u. of the Sun at perihelion to 9.4 at aphelion.

Both Kuiper and Rabe arrived, by entirely independent methods at a mass for the protoplanet equal to 20 times the present mass of Jupiter and $\frac{1}{50}$ the present mass of the Sun. Kuiper's conclusions were based on the dynamical stability of the protoplanet in consideration of its chemical composition and development, whereas Rabe's value represents "the best estimate for the minimum original mass of the protoplanet which permits us to explain the actual Trojans as escaped satellites of Jupiter." Rabe found that while the satellite's jovicentric (Jupiter-centered) distance increases at a rate proportional to $d\mu/\mu$ where μ is in units of the Sun's mass and $d\mu$ is the rate of change of mass, the orbit of Jupiter also expands but at a much slower rate proportional to $d\mu$.

7.2. Generalized Equations of Motion for the *n*-body Problem

Just as was done in the case of two-body motion it is useful to formulate the equations of n-body motion in relative form. This is done, even though we recognize that no general solution is possible, in order to provide a basis for the perturbational techniques to be discussed in the following section (in particular for "special perturbations").

The forces acting on the ith-body occasioned by the attraction of the other n-1 bodies (cf. Chapter 15 in Herrick),[1] is given in inertial coordinates by

$$m_i \frac{d^2\mathbf{r}_i}{dt^2} = k^2 \sum_{\substack{j=1 \\ (j \neq i)}}^{n} m_i m_j \frac{\mathbf{r}_{ij}}{r_{ij}^3} + k^2 m_i \mathbf{P}_i$$

for $i = 1, 2, \ldots, n$, i.e., the x-component would be

$$m_i \frac{d^2x_i}{dt^2} = k^2 \sum_{\substack{j=1 \\ (j \neq i)}}^{n} m_i m_j \frac{x_{ij}}{r_{ij}^3} + k^2 m_i P_{xi}, \qquad x \to y, z, \tag{159}$$

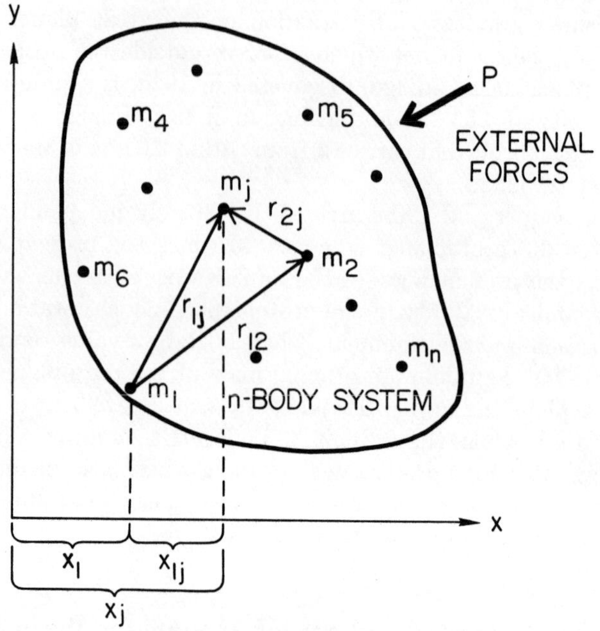

FIG. 27. n-body problem.

where $\mathbf{P}_i$ represents the perturbative accelerations of m_i *aside* from the attraction of the other $(n - 1)$ bodies, e.g., drag, electromagnetic radiation, etc. (See Fig. 27). The convention is adopted that

$$x_{ij} = x_j - x_i \qquad x \to y,\, z \tag{160}$$

and, consequently,

$$r_{ij}^2 = x_{ij}^2 + y_{ij}^2 + z_{ij}^2.$$

Given these equations it is then possible to derive the ten integrals of the n-body problem as is done by Herrick.[1]

It is next useful to determine the equations of motion in relative form. Following the two-body presentation, we essentially translate the origin from the barycenter to one of the bodies, namely m_1. From Eq. (160)

$$\frac{d^2x_{ij}}{dt^2} = \frac{d^2x_j}{dt^2} - \frac{d^2x_i}{dt^2} \qquad x \to y,\, z.$$

Thus, for $i = 1$ and 2:

$$m_1 \frac{d^2x_1}{dt^2} = k^2 \sum_{j=2}^{n} m_1 m_j \frac{x_{1j}}{r_{1j}^3} + k^2 m_1 P_{x1}$$

$$m_2 \frac{d^2x_2}{dt^2} = k^2 \sum_{\substack{j=1 \\ (j \neq 2)}}^{n} m_2 m_j \frac{x_{2j}}{r_{2j}^3} + k^2 m_2 P_{x2} \qquad x \to y,\, z.$$

Therefore,

$$\frac{d^2x_{12}}{dt^2} = \frac{d^2x_2}{dt^2} - \frac{d^2x_1}{dt^2} = k^2 \sum_{\substack{j=1 \\ (j \neq 2)}}^{n} \frac{m_j x_{2j}}{r_{2j}^3} - k^2 \sum_{j=2}^{n} \frac{m_j x_{1j}}{r_{1j}^3} + k^2(P_{x_2} - P_{x_1}). \tag{161}$$

If the two-body accelerations between m_1 and m_2 are isolated from the rest, then, with the incorporation of Newton's third law

$$\frac{d^2x_{12}}{dt^2} = -k^2(m_1 + m_2)\frac{x_{12}}{r_{12}^3} + k^2 \sum_{j=3}^{n} m_j \left(\frac{x_{2j}}{r_{2j}^3} - \frac{x_{1j}}{r_{1j}^3}\right) + k^2(P_{x_2} - P_{x_1}),$$

$$x \to y,\, z, \tag{162}$$

which are the equations of *relative motion* in component form.

At this point it should be noted that the perturbations enter only as differences between the perturbative (or, in this case, non-two-body) accelerations acting on the origin (mass m_1) and on the object (mass m_2). It should become clear why, even though the absolute value of the acceleration on the Moon caused by the Sun is greater than that caused by the Earth, the Moon remains on a geocentric orbit. If the value for the Sun's attraction on the Earth (center of coordinates, m_1) is subtracted from the Sun's attraction on the Moon (m_2), then it can be shown that the second and the third terms on the right of Eq. (162) are small compared to the first and, consequently, the first "two-body" term dominates in the Earth–Moon orbit.

The equations of motion of the n-body problem can also be phrased in barycentric, stellar, and other coordinate systems, as is done by Herrick.[1] For certain problems such equations are valuable.

It is again useful to define

$$\tau \triangleq k(t - t_0) \text{ and } \mu_{1,2} \triangleq (m_1 + m_2).$$

Thus,

$$\frac{d^2x_{12}}{d\tau^2} = -\mu_{1,2}\frac{x_{12}}{r_{12}^3} + \sum_{j=3}^{n} m_j\left(\frac{x_{2j}}{r_{2j}^3} - \frac{x_{1j}}{r_{1j}^3}\right) + P_{x_2} - P_{x_1}. \tag{163}$$

As will be shown in Chapter 8, it is convenient to separate the accelerations that produce the reference motion (in this case two-body motion) from the remaining perturbative forces. In keeping with this we define

$$\ddot{x} \triangleq -\frac{\mu_{1,2}x_{12}}{r_{12}^3} \triangleq -\mu x/r^3$$

and

$$\dot{x}' \triangleq \sum_{j=3}^{n} m_j\left(\frac{x_{2j}}{r_{2j}^3} - \frac{x_{1j}}{r_{1j}^3}\right) + P_{x_2} - P_{x_1}, \quad x \to y,z$$

so that

$$\frac{d^2x}{d\tau^2} = \ddot{x} + \dot{x}'. \tag{164}$$

7.3. The Perturbative Function

In the case of three or more bodies it is often useful to define the *perturbative function*, R, which is analogous to the *potential function*, Φ, that was developed to represent the perturbative forces resulting from the asphericity of the Earth (see Chapter 5). In Chapter 9 the perturbative function is employed advantageously in dealing with general perturbations. Let us define R for a third body (e.g., the Sun or Moon) by

$$R \triangleq k_e^2\frac{m_3}{r_3}\left(\frac{r_3}{r_{23}} - \frac{\mathbf{r}\cdot\mathbf{r}_3}{r_3^2}\right) = k_e^2\frac{m_3}{r_3}\left(\frac{r_3}{|\mathbf{r}_3 - \mathbf{r}_2|} - \frac{r}{r_3}C\right), \tag{165}$$

where

$$C \triangleq \frac{\mathbf{r}\cdot\mathbf{r}_3}{rr_3} \equiv \cos(\angle\mathbf{r}, \mathbf{r}_3) \equiv \mathbf{U}\cdot\mathbf{U}_3;$$

m_3 = the mass of the third body; and
$\mathbf{r}_3$ = the radius vector from the dynamical center to the third body.

It should be noted that like Φ, R is the negative of the potential per unit mass (occasioned by the third body) and hence its partial derivatives yield accelerations. Let us proceed by recognizing that

$$(\mathbf{r}_3 - \mathbf{r})^2 = (\mathbf{r}_3 - \mathbf{r}) \cdot (\mathbf{r}_3 - \mathbf{r}) = r_3^2 - 2\mathbf{r} \cdot \mathbf{r}_3 + r^2,$$

while

$$\frac{(\mathbf{r}_3 - \mathbf{r})^2}{r_3^2} = 1 - \frac{2\mathbf{r} \cdot \mathbf{r}_3}{r_3^2} + \frac{r^2}{r_3^2} = 1 - 2\frac{r}{r_3}C + \left(\frac{r}{r_3}\right)^2.$$

Consequently, one can expand R as follows:

$$\begin{aligned} R &= k_e^2 \frac{m_3}{r_3}\left[\left(1 - 2\frac{r}{r_3}C + \frac{r^2}{r_3^2}\right)^{-1/2} - \frac{r}{r_3}C\right] \\ &= k_e^2 \frac{m_3}{r_3}\left[P_0(C) + \left(\frac{r}{r_3}\right)P_1(C) + \left(\frac{r}{r_3}\right)^2 P_2(C) + \cdots - \left(\frac{r}{r_3}\right)C\right] \\ &= k_e^2 \frac{m_3}{r_3}\left[1 + \left(\frac{r}{r_3}\right)C + \left(\frac{r}{r_3}\right)^2\left(\frac{3}{2}C^2 - \frac{1}{2}\right) + \cdots - \left(\frac{r}{r_3}\right)C\right]. \end{aligned} \tag{166}$$

The computation of C depends upon $\mathbf{U}$, the latter having the components

$$\begin{aligned} U_x &= \cos u \cos \Omega - \sin u \sin \Omega \cos i \\ U_y &= \cos u \sin \Omega + \sin u \cos \Omega \cos i \\ U_z &= \sin u \sin i \end{aligned}$$

or

$$\begin{aligned} U_x &= \cos (u + \Omega) + \sin u \sin \Omega(1 - \cos i) \\ &= \cos (u + \Omega) + 2 \sin u \sin \Omega \sin^2 \frac{i}{2} \\ U_y &= \sin (u + \Omega) - \sin u \cos \Omega(1 - \cos i) \\ &= \sin (u + \Omega) - 2 \sin u \cos \Omega \sin^2 \frac{i}{2} \\ U_z &= \sin u \sin i. \end{aligned}$$

In light of the foregoing C can be explicitly determined by

$$\begin{aligned} C = \mathbf{U} \cdot \mathbf{U}_3 &= \cos (u + \Omega) \cos (u_3 + \Omega_3) + \sin (u + \Omega) \sin (u_3 + \Omega_3) \\ &\quad + 4 \sin u \sin u_3 \sin^2 \frac{i}{2} \sin^2 \frac{i_3}{2} (\sin \Omega \sin \Omega_3 + \cos \Omega \cos \Omega_3) \\ &\quad + 2 \sin u \sin^2 \frac{i}{2} [\cos (u_3 + \Omega_3) \sin \Omega - \sin (u_3 + \Omega_3) \cos \Omega] \\ &\quad + 2 \sin u_3 \sin^2 \frac{i_3}{2} [\cos (u + \Omega) \sin \Omega_3 - \sin (u + \Omega) \cos \Omega_3] \\ &\quad + \sin u \sin u_3 \sin i \sin i_3 \end{aligned}$$

$$= \cos(u + \Omega - u_3 - \Omega_3) + 4 \sin u \sin u_3 \sin^2 \frac{i_3}{2} \sin^2 \frac{i}{2} \cos(\Omega - \Omega_3)$$

$$-2 \sin u \sin^2 \frac{i}{2} \sin(u_3 + \Omega_3 - \Omega) - 2 \sin u_3 \sin^2 \frac{i_3}{2} \sin(u + \Omega - \Omega_3)$$

$$+ \sin u \sin u_3 \sin i \sin i_3. \qquad (167)$$

The application of these relationships will be discussed in Chapter 9.

7.4. Aspherical Earth and Moon, Drag, and Lift Forces

Aside from these strictly n-body forces, there exist non-two-body forces resulting from the perturbative influence of the Earth's and Moon's asphericity, from drag, and from lift.

Taking x, y, and z partial derivatives of the potential function, Φ, given in Chapter 5 (see Section 9.2.2.1) we find that the accelerations of the vehicle resulting from the Earth's asphericity are:

$$\ddot{x} + \dot{x}' = \partial\Phi/\partial x = \frac{-m_\oplus x}{r^3} - \frac{x}{r_5} Jm_\oplus(1 - 5U_z^2) + \frac{xz}{r^7}(7U_z^2 - 3)Hm_\oplus$$

$$- \frac{x}{6r^7} Km_\oplus(3 - 42U_z^2 + 63U_z^4) + \cdots,$$

$$\ddot{y} + \dot{y}' = \partial\Phi/\partial y = \frac{-m_\oplus y}{r^3} + \frac{y}{x}\dot{x}', \text{ and}$$

$$\ddot{z} + \dot{z}' = \partial\Phi/\partial z = \frac{-m_\oplus z}{r^3}$$

$$- \frac{z}{r^5} Jm_\oplus(3 - 5U_z^2) + \frac{3}{5r^5} Hm_\oplus\left((1 - 10U_z^2 + \frac{35}{3} U_z^4\right)$$

$$- \frac{z}{6r^7} Km_\oplus(15 - 70U_z^2 + 63U_z^4) + \cdots, \qquad (168)$$

where $\ddot{x}$, $\ddot{y}$, and $\ddot{z}$ are associated (as in Eq. (164)) with the strictly two-body accelerations, i.e., with the first terms on the right of the second equal signs; $m_\oplus = 1$; and $U_z = \sin \delta$.

Similarly for the triaxial Moon ($m_{☾} = 1$ and $k_m = 0.057{,}929$)

$$\ddot{x} + \dot{x}' = \frac{\partial\Phi}{\partial x}$$

$$= -\frac{m_{☾} x}{r^3} - \frac{3U_x C}{2r^4}\left[\frac{(B - A)}{C}(1 - 5U_y^2) + \frac{(C - A)}{C}(1 - 5U_z^2)\right]$$

$$\ddot{y} + \dot{y}^{\backprime} = \frac{\partial \Phi}{\partial y}$$
$$= -\frac{m_{☾} y}{r^3} - \frac{3U_y C}{2r^4}\left[\frac{(B-A)}{C}(3 - 5U_y^2) + \frac{(C-A)}{C}(1 - 5U_z^2)\right]$$
$$\ddot{z} + \dot{z}^{\backprime} = \frac{\partial \Phi}{\partial z}$$
$$= -\frac{m_{☾} z}{r^3} - \frac{3U_z C}{2r^4}\left[\frac{(B-A)}{C}(1 - 5U_y^2) + \frac{(C-A)}{C}(3 - 5U_z^2)\right] \tag{169}$$

where Φ is given by Eq. (63), $\mathbf{U} \triangleq \mathbf{r}/r$, A, B, C are defined in Section 5.3.3, and x, y, z are referred to a *noninertial* selenographic coordinate system defined in Section 4.4.2 which is defined by the rotating and librating mean center of the Moon. The units of both Eqs. (168) and (169) are τ (hence the k_e^2 or k_m^2 is cancelled out), Earth or Moon radii, and Earth or Moon masses.

It should be noted that the partials of R (given by Eqs. (166)) with respect to x, y, and z would also yield *an approximation* to the x, y, and z components of three-body acceleration. Since, however, Eqs. (163) yield *exact* values of these components, such a procedure is not employed.

When lift and drag forces are important, it is necessary to generate

$$\dot{\mathbf{r}}^{\backprime}_D = -D_0^2 \mu \alpha \gamma \sigma v \mathbf{v}, \tag{170}$$

where

$\dot{\mathbf{r}}^{\backprime}_D$ = the drag deceleration (with components $\dot{x}^{\backprime}$, $\dot{y}^{\backprime}$, $\dot{z}^{\backprime}$);
$D_0^2 \triangleq C_{D_0} A_0 \rho_0 V_{c0}^2 / 2g_0 m_0$;
$\mu^* \triangleq m_0/m$ (an alternate definition of μ^*);
$\alpha^* \triangleq A/A_0$ (an alternate definition of α^*);
$\gamma = C_{D_0}/C_D$ = the drag-coefficient variation in the transitional regime denoted by $\gamma(\sigma)$ and in the supersonic regime denoted by $\gamma(\nu)$;
$\sigma \triangleq \dfrac{\rho}{\rho_0}$;
$\mathbf{v}$ = the velocity of the space vehicle with respect to a rotating atmosphere (in units of surface circular-satellite speed, V_{c0});
C_{D_0} = the reference value of the drag coefficient;
A = the projected frontal area of the vehicle (in m^2);
ρ_0 = the "sea-level" atmospheric density (1.225 kg/m^3);
V_{c0} = the surface circular-satellite speed (7,905.258 m/sec);
g_0 = the acceleration of gravity at unit distance (9.780,320 m/sec^2);
m = the mass of the space vehicle (in kg); and
C_D = the drag coefficient.

The factors μ^* and α^* vary as a result of ablation, configuration change, fuel consumption, etc. γ will vary as a function of the transitional parameter, $B(\sigma)$ denoted by $\gamma(\sigma)$ and the Mach number $M(\nu)$ denoted by $\gamma(\nu)$ etc. (see Chapter 10). The density ratio, σ, should be obtained by exponential interpolation of a realistic atmosphere table (see Section 5.5).

The determination of the velocity of the vehicle relative to a rotating atmosphere involves the influence of winds. If $\dot{x}$, $\dot{y}$, and $\dot{z}$ are the components of the velocity of the vehicle in equatorial coordinates, q is the speed of the cross wind measured in a framework rotating with the Earth's angular rate, (all speeds in units of surface circular-satellite speed) $\omega =$ 0.058,834,470 (the Earth's angular rotational rate in radians per k_e^{-1} min), ϕ' is the geocentric latitude of the "subvehicle point,"* ($\phi' = \sin^{-1} z/r$), α is the right ascension of the satellite ($\sin\alpha = y/\sqrt{x^2+y^2}$ and $\cos\alpha = x/\sqrt{x^2+y^2}$), and A is the azimuth *from* which the wind is coming (A and q are to be obtained by linear interpolation of wind tables with argument height, H, cf. e.g., Sissenwine[82]); then,

$$\mathbf{v}\begin{cases} \nu_x = \dot{x} + y\omega + q(\cos\alpha\sin\phi'\cos A + \sin\alpha\sin A), \\ \nu_y = \dot{y} - x\omega + q(\sin\alpha\sin\phi'\cos A - \cos\alpha\sin A), \text{ and} \\ \nu_z = \dot{z} + q\cos\phi'\cos A. \end{cases} \tag{171}$$

Clearly, H must be measured above the spheroid, i.e.,

$$H = r - 1 + f\sin^2\phi' + \tfrac{3}{8}f^2\sin^2 2\phi' + \cdots, \tag{172}$$

where f is the Earth's flattening.

It should be noted that this "height" is measured along the geocentric radius vector from the surface of the spheroid to the vehicle and not along a normal from the spheroid. Such a discrepancy is not serious and only amounts to a few feet at most, i.e.,

$$\phi - \phi' = 11'35''.64\sin 2\phi - 1''.17\sin 4\phi + \cdots$$

and has a maximum value of 11′35″.64 at 45° latitude. A more nearly cor-

* Defined herein as the point where the radius vector to the vehicle, $\mathbf{r}$, intersects the surface of the spheroid.

The geodetic latitude, ϕ_g, of the "geodetic" subvehicle point, i.e., of the point where a normal from the surface of the geoid or spheroid passes through the position of the vehicle, is given by

$$\sin(\phi_g - \phi') = \frac{f}{r}\sin 2\phi' + \frac{f^2}{4r}\left(\frac{4}{r} - 1\right)\sin 4\phi' - \cdots.$$

This equation was derived by Herrick and Gersten.

rect height could be computed as equal to

$$H = r - 1 + f \sin^2 \phi' + \frac{f^2}{2}\left(\frac{1}{r} - \frac{1}{4}\right) \sin^2 2\phi' + \cdots.$$

The lifting acceleration, $\dot{\mathbf{r}}'_L$, has the following form:

$$\dot{\mathbf{r}}'_L = D_0{}^2\mu^*\alpha^*\gamma\sigma\nu^2(C_L/C_D)\left\{\frac{\mathbf{U} \times \mathbf{v}}{\nu} \sin \xi + \frac{\mathbf{v} \times (\mathbf{U} \times \mathbf{v})}{\nu^2} \cos \xi\right\} \tag{173}$$

where ξ = the *bank angle* and C_L = the *lift coefficient.* This angle is defined as follows (see Fig. 28): consider a plane perpendicular to the velocity of the vehicle relative to the atmosphere, $\mathbf{v}$. A unit vector in this perpendicular plane that is also perpendicular to $\mathbf{r}$ is $\mathbf{U} \times \mathbf{v}/\nu$ (note that $\mathbf{r} = \mathbf{U}r$). A unit vector orthogonal to $\mathbf{r} \times \mathbf{v}$ that is also in the plane perpendicular to $\mathbf{v}$ is

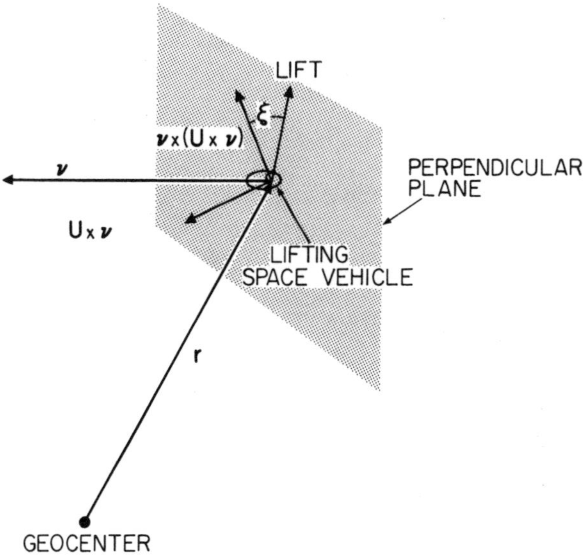

FIG. 28. Bank angle.

$\mathbf{v} \times (\mathbf{U} \times \mathbf{v})/\nu^2$. The bank angle, ξ, is then measured from this latter unit vector to the lift acceleration vector, which, by definition, is also in the plane perpendicular to $\mathbf{v}$. The $\sin \xi$ and $\cos \xi$ terms, therefore, indicate the resolution of the lift accelerations in the $\mathbf{U} \times \mathbf{v}/\nu$ and $\mathbf{v} \times (\mathbf{U} \times \mathbf{v}/\nu^2)$ directions.

Other perturbative influences are discussed in Chapter 10 and similar expressions for their inclusion can be derived (e.g., the low-thrust accelerations are explicitly presented in the referenced Chapter).

8 SPECIAL PERTURBATIONS

Orbits obtained from simple two-body computations are often useful for feasibility calculations. When a precise definitive orbit is required, however, recourse should be taken to the more sophisticated perturbation procedures outlined in the following two sections. There is no particular effort made in these sections to derive formulas from first principles and the work is presented in summary form. This is particularly true of the variation-of-parameters discussion. For a more detailed development the reader's attention is directed to the two references (Chapter 17, in Herrick[1] and Baker[9]).

The term *special perturbations* refers to the determination of an orbit by numerical integration so as to include the effect of various perturbative forces that cause the trajectory to depart from the Keplerian form. Special perturbations are particularly useful for orbits having only a limited duration, e.g., lunar and interplanetary trajectories, but they are also used for comet orbits and for the five outer planets. The initial conditions for these trajectories could in fact be obtained from the orbit determination procedures discussed in Chapter 6. Because of the number of integration steps and the fact that the accumulated error increases with the number of steps, special perturbations are not well suited to the long-term prediction of lunar motion or to the long-term prediction of the orbits of the inner planets, for which excellent tables of general perturbations are available. From a variety of methods for the numerical integration of the perturbative accelerations of an object we select Cowell's, Encke's, and the variation-of-parameters methods for detailed discussion in Chapter 8. An explanation of other methods may be found in *Planetary Coordinates*,[83] as, for example, a method due to Hansen that is similar to Encke's method (cf. Herget[73] and Hansen[84]) but with coordinates referred to rotating axes which move so as to keep pace with the object on its orbit.

It should be recognized that the choice of the numerical integration technique that is to be employed, whether that of Runge-Kutta, Milne, Gauss-Jackson, or Adams, etc., is entirely independent of the perturbation method to be adopted.

8.1. Cowell's Method

Cowell's method includes the direct step-by-step integration of the total acceleration, central as well as perturbative, of a vehicle. It is interesting to note that this simple, rather straightforward method was developed later than the more refined techniques such as Encke's method. The first problem to which Cowell's method was applied was the determination of the orbit of the eighth satellite of Jupiter. The necessity of carrying a large number of significant figures due to the large central force term is an obvious disadvantage of this method. The necessary decrease in the size of the integration step, particularly in the region of a large central force, makes the method tedious for hand calculations.

The advent of the high-speed machine is responsible for a considerable revival of Cowell's method. The coordinates of the five outer planets, for example, were determined at the Watson Laboratories by this method. The Themis Code, developed at the University of California Radiation Laboratory, is an IBM 704 program of Cowell's method for interplanetary orbits.[85] For precision orbit work, round-off error tends to limit the usefulness of programs based upon Cowell's method. Even with "double precision programs" accuracy is lost, since tabular information such as the coordinates of the planets is not available to more than seven or eight significant figures. The interpolations (even with a series of dummy digits added to the tabulations) will always involve random interpolation and rounding errors for further entries into the tables.

With regard to the amount of time spent in actual numerical computations by Cowell's method (be it by hand or electronically) the analysis of reference 78 has shown that in most instances the Cowell procedure requires ten times more time than the other perturbational methods. This result has been amply confirmed by independent researchers at Convair Astronautics, Republic Aviation Co., Systems Corporation of America, and Aeronutronic. In spite of the time-consuming computations and less accurate results, Cowell's procedure does exhibit the great virtue of simplicity. Furthermore, it can be applied most generally to a great variety of problems (the development of more general perturbational methods is, however, under investigation by V. Szebehely of General Electric, S. Herrick of UCLA, and others).

In Cowell's method, (cf. Herrick[1] and Herget[73,86]) the equations of motion, which must be integrated twice to obtain position coordinates, are:

$$\frac{d^2x}{d\tau^2} = \ddot{x} + \dot{x}^{\backprime}, \qquad x \rightarrow y, z. \tag{174}$$

The central force term in the x-direction, $\ddot{x}$, is defined by $-\mu x/r^3$. The total perturbative term in the x-direction due to bulge, drag, thrust, and the attraction of other bodies, etc., is $\dot{x}^{\backprime}$ e.g., see Eqs. (168), (170), (254), and (164) respectively.

8.2. Encke's Method

Over a hundred years ago, the German astronomer, J. F. Encke, proposed a method of handling special perturbations that has proved to be well suited to slightly perturbed orbits such as ballistic lunar-trajectories. Encke's method differs from Cowell's in that differential accelerations or the deviations from a two-body reference orbit rather than the total accelerations are integrated. (For a more comprehensive treatment of Encke's method, cf. Chapter 16 in Herrick,[1] pages 91, 96–98 in Herget.[73]) Figure 29 shows the relationship between the reference orbit and the actual path of the vehicle. Note that at the point of tangency or "osculation" both the true and the reference orbit exhibit the same position and velocity.*

Let x, y, z denote the actual position of the object; x_e, y_e, z_e the position of a hypothetical object (moving without perturbations) at the same time on the reference orbit; and ξ, η, ζ the difference between the true coordinates and those of the reference orbit, i.e., (initially at osculation $\xi, \eta, \zeta = 0$)

$$\xi \triangleq x - x_e \qquad x \rightarrow y, z; \qquad \xi \rightarrow \eta, \zeta. \tag{175}$$

The differential accelerations between actual and reference-orbit positions of the rocket are (x_e, y_e, z_e being computed as in Section 6.1 or pp. 176–178)

$$\frac{d^2\xi}{d\tau^2} = \mu\left[-\frac{x}{r^3} + \frac{x_e}{r_e^{\,3}}\right] + \dot{x}^{\backprime} = (\ddot{x} - \ddot{x}_e) + \dot{x}^{\backprime};\ \xi = \iint \frac{d^2\xi}{d\tau^2}\, d\tau^2.$$

$$x \rightarrow y, z; \qquad \xi \rightarrow \eta, \zeta. \tag{176}$$

* The term "osculating orbit" implies both a tangency and the same velocity, while the term "intermediary orbit" only implies tangency.

The first parenthesis on the right-hand side is obviously the difference between the accelerations on the reference orbit and on the actual path, and $\dot{x}'$ represents the total perturbational component. Time need not always be utilized as independent variable in Eq. (176) of Encke's method. If E

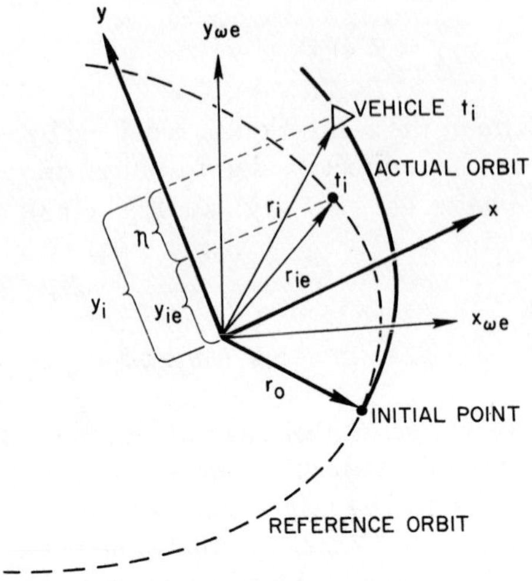

FIG. 29. Deviation from reference orbit.

(or F for hyperbolic orbits) is utilized, one is able to circumvent the solution of the transcendental Kepler's equation at each point of the reference orbit when the computation of x_e, y_e, z_e, and r_e is required. Such a procedure is outlined in Section III of Baker.[2]

One of the purposes of Encke's method is to reduce the number of significant figures carried in the calculations. Taking the differences of the nearly equal accelerations, $\ddot{x} - \ddot{x}_e$, would only increase the number required. The difficulty is resolved by expanding $\ddot{x} - \ddot{x}_e$ as follows,

$$\ddot{x} - \ddot{x}_e = \frac{\mu}{r_e^3}(fqx - \xi), \tag{177}$$

where

$$fq \triangleq 3q - \frac{3 \cdot 5}{2!} q^2 + \frac{3 \cdot 5 \cdot 7}{3!} q^3 - \cdots \tag{178}$$

and

$$q \triangleq \frac{1}{r_e^2}\left[\xi\left(x_e + \frac{1}{2}\xi\right) + \eta\left(y_e + \frac{1}{2}\eta\right) + \zeta\left(z_e + \frac{1}{2}\zeta\right)\right]; \tag{179}$$

so that the individual terms $\ddot{x}$ and $\ddot{x}_e$ need never be computed explicitly.

In contrast to Cowell's method, therefore, only the differential *accelerations* due to perturbations are integrated to obtain the actual position of the vehicle. Taking advantage of this fact, it is found that longer intervals can be chosen in the step-by-step integration process. A careful choice of the reference orbit is necessary in order to make the method more effective.

If the true orbit differs too greatly from the reference orbit, a new "osculating" reference orbit must be taken as a new starting point. This process is called "rectification" (again initially $x = x_e$ and $\xi = 0$ etc.).

The Encke philosophy can also be applied to the computation of a number of orbits (termed "variant orbits") that lie very close to some standard, i.e., orbits that differ only slightly in initial conditions. In this case the reference orbit would be the standard orbit about which can be computed an envelope of variant orbits. Such a procedure is particularly useful in sensitivity or guidance error computations.

8.3. The Variation-of-Parameters Method

The "variation of parameters" or "variation of elements" method differs from that of Encke in that there is a continuous rectification of the reference orbit (cf. Herrick[1,88,17] and Stracke.[90]) The reference motion of the object

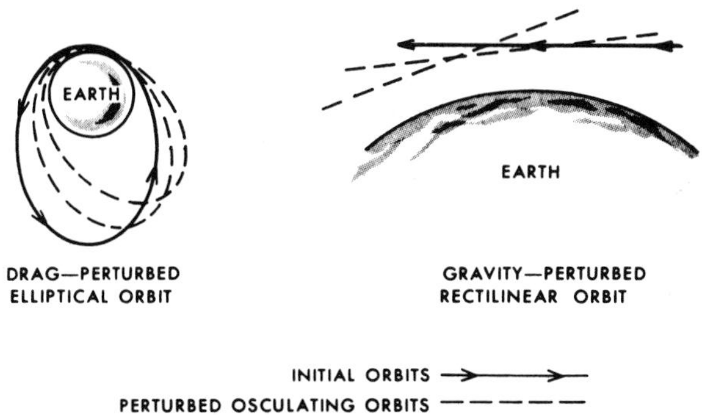

Fig. 30. Variation of parameters technique.

in question is represented by a set of parameters that, in the absence of perturbative forces, would remain constant with the time. As an example, astronomers often employ elements specifying the elliptical two-body motion of an object as the reference orbit. (See the left side of Fig. 30 for such an orbit perturbed by drag.) They then integrate the variation of some of these parameters, such as a, e, the time of perifocal passage, T, (or, more commonly, $M_0 = n(t_0 - T)$), and the orientation angles of the orbit plane i, Ω, and ω, etc. Often, certain vectorial parameters are integrated as proposed by Herrick,[88] rather than these conventional elements, e.g., **a**, **b**, **h**, etc., also see Musen.[91] Perturbative forces will then cause the parameters to vary, and the differential equations of motion are formulated in terms of the orbit elements or functions thereof.

8.3.1. Perturbative Derivatives

It should be noted that the "grave" notation for perturbative accelerations introduced in the discussion of the n-body problem has a more general signification in the variation-of-parameters procedure. More rigorously one may define, for any function, f, of a set of parameters, p,

$$\frac{df}{d\tau}(p_1, p_2 \; . \; . \; . \; p_i \; . \; . \; . \; p_{n,}\tau) = \frac{\partial f}{\partial \tau} + \sum_{i=1}^{n} \left(\frac{\partial f}{\partial p_i} \frac{dp_i}{d\tau} \right) \triangleq \dot{f} + f^{\backprime}. \tag{180}$$

Certain variables have only a "dot" variation (e.g., $\dot{r}$, $\dot{x}$, $\dot{y}$, $\dot{z}$) as there is no perturbative variation in position at the point of tangency where the osculating ellipse has the same coordinates as the two-body orbit, i.e., instantaneously a change in rate but *not* a change in position in inertial space is possible, or, in other words, a perturbative acceleration gives rise to a rate of change of velocity *not* position. Other elements have only a "grave" or perturbative variation (since there is no two-body variation in these elements), e.g., in terms of the radial, $\dot{r}^{\backprime}$; transverse $r\dot{v}^{\backprime}$ (or $r\dot{l}^{\backprime}$); and normal, $r\dot{b}^{\backprime}$; components of acceleration caused by perturbative forces, we find that

$$a^{\backprime} = 2a^2\dot{\mathbf{r}} \cdot \dot{\mathbf{r}}^{\backprime}/\mu; \tag{181}$$

$$e^{\backprime} = \frac{r\dot{r}^{\backprime}}{\sqrt{\mu a}} \sin E + \frac{1}{2}\frac{a^{\backprime}}{a}\left[\left(\frac{r}{a} + 1\right)\cos E - e\right] \tag{182}$$

or

$$e^{\backprime} = \frac{r\dot{r}^{\backprime}}{\sqrt{\mu p}}\left(\frac{p}{r}\sin v\right) + \frac{r^2\dot{v}^{\backprime}}{\sqrt{\mu p}}\left[\left(\frac{p}{r} + 1\right)\cos v + e\right]; \tag{183}$$

$$ev^{\backprime} = \frac{r\dot{r}^{\backprime}}{\sqrt{\mu p}}\left(\frac{p}{r}\cos v\right) - \frac{r^2\dot{v}^{\backprime}}{\sqrt{\mu p}}\left(\frac{p}{r} + 1\right)\sin v; \tag{184}$$

$$i^{\backprime} = r^2\dot{b}^{\backprime}\cos u/\sqrt{\mu p}; \tag{185}$$

$$\Omega^{\backprime} = r^2 \dot{b}^{\backprime} \sin u / \sqrt{\mu p} \sin i; \tag{186}$$

$$l^{\backprime} = \Omega^{\backprime}(1 - \cos i); \text{ etc.} \tag{187}$$

The first of the foregoing equations can be immediately obtained from differentiation of the *vis-viva* integral, if one treats the constant a as a "variable" and the variable r as a "constant." Thus,

$$2\dot{s}\dot{s}^{\backprime} = \mu a^{\backprime}/a^2$$

with

$$r^{\backprime} = 0 \text{ and } \dot{s}\dot{s}^{\backprime} \equiv \dot{\mathbf{r}} \cdot \dot{\mathbf{r}}^{\backprime}.$$

The $e^{\backprime}$ and $v^{\backprime}$ relations can be obtained by a similar differentiation of

$$e \cos v = \frac{p}{r} - 1 = \frac{r^3 \dot{v}^2}{\mu} - 1$$

(see the bottom of p. 113) and

$$e \sin v = \dot{r} \sqrt{p/\mu} = \frac{r^2 \dot{r} \dot{v}}{\mu}.$$

(see the bottom of p. 116). Thus,

$$e^{\backprime} \cos v - e v^{\backprime} \sin v = \frac{2r^3 \dot{v} \dot{v}^{\backprime}}{\mu} = \frac{2r^2 \dot{v}^{\backprime}}{\sqrt{\mu p}} \left(\frac{p}{r}\right)$$

and

$$e^{\backprime} \sin v + e v^{\backprime} \cos v = \frac{r \dot{r}^{\backprime}}{\sqrt{\mu p}} \left(\frac{p}{r}\right) + \frac{r^2 \dot{v}^{\backprime}}{\sqrt{\mu p}} e \sin v.$$

Multiplying the first expression by $\cos v$ and the second by $\sin v$ and adding, one obtains Eq. (183) and multiplying the first expression by $\sin v$ and the second by $\cos v$ and subtracting, one obtains Eq. (184). The derivation of the other relationships can be found in Chapter 17 of Herrick.[1]

Still other quantities exhibit both two-body and perturbative variations because they are referred to a perturbed origin, e.g., the anomalies:

$$\frac{dv}{d\tau} = \dot{v} + v^{\backprime}: \quad \dot{v} = \sqrt{\mu p}/r^2 \quad \text{and} \quad v^{\backprime} = -\mathbf{Q} \cdot \mathbf{a}^{\backprime}/e; \tag{188}$$

$$\frac{dE}{d\tau} = \dot{E} + E^{\backprime}: \dot{E} = \sqrt{\mu/a}/r \text{ and } E^{\backprime} = v^{\backprime} \sqrt{1 - e^2} - \frac{r \dot{r}^{\backprime}}{\sqrt{\mu a}} - \frac{1}{2} \frac{a^{\backprime}}{a} e \sin E; \tag{189}$$

$$\frac{dM}{d\tau} = \dot{M} + M^{\backprime}: \dot{M} = n/k_e \text{ and } M^{\backprime} = v^{\backprime} \sqrt{1 - e^2} - 2r\dot{r}^{\backprime}/\sqrt{\mu a}; \tag{190}$$

$$\frac{dL}{d\tau} = \mathring{L} + L^{\backprime}: \mathring{L} = \dot{M} \text{ and } L^{\backprime} = l^{\backprime} - \frac{2r\dot{r}^{\backprime}}{\sqrt{\mu a}} - \frac{e^2 v^{\backprime}}{1 + \sqrt{1 - e^2}}; \text{ etc.} \quad (191)$$

Although the relationships involved in the variation-of-parameters technique are considerably more complex than Cowell's procedure, as was mentioned previously it has been shown that they offer a much greater accuracy and a ten-to-one decrease in computational time (cf. Baker).[78] Hence, the additional effort spent in programming them on digital computers is quickly written off by their exceptional efficiency. Unfortunately, however, the variation-of-parameters method is not a panacea since a "universal" set of parameters that are equally applicable to all orbit problems has not yet been fully developed. Hence, a different set of parameters is required for different types of orbits (e.g., different for $e = 0$ and $e = 1$ orbits), i.e., for each class of orbit the parameters that vary more slowly in response to perturbative forces are selected. Such a restriction together with the complexity inherent in the formulas discourages many engineers from the use of the variation-of-parameters method.

8.3.2. Moderate and Low–Eccentricity Formulas

The fundamental formulas employed in the computations of the method of variation-of-parameters are derived in Chapter 18 of Herrick[1] and are listed in the following. On the left-hand side of the list are equations that are useful for moderate eccentricities and on the right-hand side are listed equations that are particularly useful for low eccentricities. The derivation of this latter method is also presented by Walters.[69] (One might alternately choose $\mathbf{U}_0$ and $\mathbf{V}_0$, reckoned at some epoch, as parameters for low-eccentricity orbits.) Both methods begin with initial values of $\mathbf{r}$ and $\dot{\mathbf{r}}$.

The formulas for obtaining initial values of the parameters $\mathbf{a}$, $\mathbf{b}$, M_0, and n_0 (for moderate eccentricity orbits) and $\mathbf{a}$, $\mathbf{h}$, L_0, and n_0 (for low-eccentricity orbits) are given in Chapter 6 and are summarized and extended to low-eccentricity orbits as follows:

$$D \triangleq \frac{\mathbf{r} \cdot \dot{\mathbf{r}}}{\sqrt{\mu}},$$

$$\dot{D} = \frac{1}{\sqrt{\mu}}\left(\dot{s}^2 - \frac{\mu}{r}\right),$$

$$H \triangleq r - p = D^2 - \frac{r^2 \dot{D}}{\sqrt{\mu}},$$

$$\dot{H} = \dot{r}.$$

Moderate e

$$a_x = \frac{\dot{D}x - D\dot{x}}{\sqrt{\mu}} \quad x \to y, z$$

$$b_x = \frac{\dot{H}x - H\dot{x}}{\sqrt{\mu}} \quad x \to y, z,$$

$$e^2 = a_x^2 + a_y^2 + a_z^2,$$

$$p = \frac{b_x^2 + b_y^2 + b_z^2}{e^2},$$

$$P_x = \frac{a_x}{e}, \quad x \to y, z,$$

$$Q_x = \frac{b_x}{e\sqrt{p}} \quad x \to y, z,$$

$a = p/(1 - e^2)$ (Note $a \neq |\mathbf{a}|$),

(all of the two-body or reference-orbit elements except M_0 are now known and can be used to find x_e, y_e, z_e at any step of the Encke integration)

$$n = k_e\sqrt{\mu}/a^{3/2},$$

$$\cos E = \frac{\mathbf{r} \cdot \mathbf{P}}{a} + e,$$

$$\sin E = \frac{\mathbf{r} \cdot \mathbf{Q}}{a\sqrt{1 - e^2}},$$

which yields the initial value of E (or the value of E at any new time of rectification).

Low e

$$h_x = (y\dot{z} - z\dot{y})/\sqrt{\mu} \quad x \to y \to z \to x$$

(cyclical change),

$$p = h_x^2 + h_y^2 + h_z^2,$$

$$W_x = h_x/\sqrt{p} \quad x \to y, z$$

$$U_x = x/r \quad x \to y, z$$

$$\mathbf{V} = \mathbf{W} \times \mathbf{U}$$

$$e \sin v = \dot{r}\sqrt{\frac{p}{\mu}},$$

$$e \cos v = \frac{p}{r} - 1,$$

$$e = \sqrt{(e \cos v)^2 + (e \sin v)^2},$$

$a = p/(1 - e^2)$, (Note $a \neq |\mathbf{a}|$)

$$l_0 = \tan^{-1}\left(\frac{U_y - V_x}{U_x + V_y}\right),$$

where the quadrant of l_0 is determined by inspection of both numerator and denominator.

$$n = k_e\sqrt{\mu}/a^{3/2}$$

$$a_x = U_x e \cos v - V_x e \sin v \quad x \to y, z$$

$$\sin(v - E) = +\frac{r}{p}\left(\frac{(e \sin v)(e \cos v)}{1 + \sqrt{1 - e^2}} + e \sin v\right)$$

$$\cos(v - E) = \frac{r}{p}\left(1 - \frac{(e \sin v)^2}{1 + \sqrt{1 - e^2}} + e \cos v\right)$$

$$(v - E) = \tan^{-1}\left(\frac{\sin(v - E)}{\cos(v - E)}\right)$$

Finally, the initial value of M is found from:

$$M = E - e \sin E \rightarrow M_0,$$

(i.e., the M determined is the initial M_0 and all subsequent M's can be obtained from $M = M_0 + n(t - t_0)$, where t_0 is the initial time or epoch. Thus, for example, at any step of the integration (e.g., time t) in either Encke's or the variation-of-parameters' method, the value of E can be determined by iteration from the transcendental Kepler's Equation* $E - e \sin E = M = M_0 + n(t - t_0)$. Equipped with E the values of x_ω and y_ω and, finally, position and velocity on the reference orbit, $\mathbf{r}$ and $\dot{\mathbf{r}}$, can be obtained.)

$$e \sin E = \frac{r}{p} \sqrt{1 - e^2} e \sin v$$

$$(v - M) = (v - E) + e \sin E$$

$$L_0 = L = l_0 - (v - M).$$

$$P_x = a_x/e \quad x \rightarrow y, z \quad \mathbf{Q} = \mathbf{W} \times \mathbf{P}$$

The longitude of perigee, $\pi \triangleq \omega + \Omega$ is then computed as follows:

For direct motion:

$$\pi = \tan^{-1}\left(\frac{P_y - Q_x}{P_x + Q_y}\right);$$

or for retrograde motion:

$$\pi_r = \tan^{-1}\left\{\frac{-P_y - Q_x}{P_x - Q_y}\right\}$$

and the quadrant of π is determined by inspecting the signs of both numerator and denominator.

The eccentric anomaly, E, is then computed by iteration:

$$E_{n+1} = E_n + \frac{E_n - L + \pi - e \sin E_n}{e \cos E_n - 1}$$

For any time

$$x_\omega = a(\cos E - e), \qquad y_\omega = a(1 - e^2)^{1/2} \sin E,$$

$$\mathbf{r} = x_\omega \mathbf{P} + y_\omega \mathbf{Q},$$

$$\dot{x}_\omega = -(\mu a)^{1/2} \sin E/r, \qquad \dot{y}_\omega = [\mu a(1 - e^2)]^{1/2} \cos E/r, \text{ and}$$

$$\dot{\mathbf{r}} = \dot{x}_\omega \mathbf{P} + \dot{y}_\omega \mathbf{Q}.$$

It should be noted that these $\mathbf{r}$, $\dot{\mathbf{r}}$ values serve as a check upon the input position and velocity quantities if t is taken at the initial time.

At this juncture the accelerations, $\ddot{\mathbf{r}}$, occasioned by perturbative forces

* As mentioned in the discussion of Encke's method, in order to circumvent the solution of the transcendental Kepler's equation it has often been suggested that the eccentric anomaly be employed as independent variable instead of time. Such a procedure was first utilized by Oppolzer who computed the perturbations of Comet Pons-Winnecke for the nine revolutions from 1819 through 1869. Tross at Aeronutronic successfully applied[87] this same idea to the computation of lunar trajectories while Samoilova-Iakhontova[89] recently re-examined the use of other anomalies as independent variable.

are calculated. The x, y, z perturbative components listed in Chapter 7 are utilized to obtain the required integrands as follows:

$$r\dot{r}' = x\dot{x}' + y\dot{y}' + z\dot{z}',$$
$$\dot{s}\dot{s}' = \dot{x}\dot{x}' + \dot{y}\dot{y}' + \dot{z}\dot{z}',$$
$$D' = \frac{r\dot{r}'}{\sqrt{\mu}},$$
$$\dot{D}' = \frac{2}{\sqrt{\mu}}\,\dot{s}\dot{s}',$$
$$n' = -\frac{3}{2}\,na\,\frac{\dot{D}'}{\sqrt{\mu}}$$

Moderate e

$$H' = 2DD' - \frac{r^2\dot{D}'}{\sqrt{\mu}},$$
$$\dot{H}' = \mathbf{r}\cdot\dot{\mathbf{r}}'$$
$$a_x' = \frac{\dot{D}'x - D'\dot{x} - D\dot{x}'}{\sqrt{\mu}} \quad x \to y,\ z,$$
$$b_x' = \frac{\dot{H}'x - H'\dot{x} - H\dot{x}'}{\sqrt{\mu}} \quad x \to y,\ z,$$
$$\sqrt{p}v' = \frac{\mathbf{a}\cdot\mathbf{b}'}{e^2},$$
$$M' = \frac{(\sqrt{p}v' - 2D')}{\sqrt{a}},$$

Low e

$$r\dot{b}' = W_x\dot{x}' + W_y\dot{y}' + W_z\dot{z}',$$
$$l' \triangleq \frac{z(r\dot{b}')}{(1 + W_z)\sqrt{\mu p}},$$
$$a'_x = \frac{\dot{D}'x - D'\dot{x} - D\dot{x}'}{\sqrt{\mu}} \quad x \to y,\ z,$$
$$-ev' = Q_x a_x' + Q_y a_y' + Q_z a_z',$$
$$h'_x = (y\dot{z}' - z\dot{y}')/\sqrt{\mu} \quad x \to y, \searrow z \swarrow$$
$$L' = l' - \frac{2D'}{\sqrt{a}} - \frac{e^2 v'}{1 + \sqrt{1 - e^2}}.$$

Finally, the following integrations are carried out. (It should be noted that eight quantities are integrated, including the six components of **a** and **b** or **a** and **h**, instead of the minimum six, in order to provide checks and to avoid complications in the evaluation of some of the parameters.)

Moderate e:

$$n = n_0 + k_e \int_{t_0}^{t} n'\, dt,$$
$$M = M_0 + k_e \iint_{t_0}^{t} n'\, dt^2 + k_e \int_{t_0}^{t} M'\, dt + n_0(t - t_0).$$
$$a_x = a_{x_0} + k_e \int_{t_0}^{t} a'_x\, dt \quad x \to y,\ z$$
$$b_x = b_{x_0} + k_e \int_{t_0}^{t} b'_x\, dt \quad x \to y,\ z$$

Low e:

$$n = n_0 + k_e \int_{t_0}^{t} n'\, dt,$$
$$L = L_0 + n_0(t - t_0) + k_e \int_{t_0}^{t}\int_{t_0}^{t} n'\, dt^2 + k_e \int_{t_0}^{t} L'\, dt,$$
$$a_x = a_{x_0} + k_e \int_{t_0}^{t} a'_x\, dt \quad x \to y,\ z$$
$$h_x = h_{x_0} + k_e \int_{t_0}^{t} h'_x\, dt \quad x \to y,\ z.$$

After the integrations have been completed the program calculates the values of e, a, E, $\mathbf{P}$, $\mathbf{Q}$, (or L, $\mathbf{U}$, $\mathbf{V}$, $\mathbf{W}$), $\mathbf{r}$, and $\dot{\mathbf{r}}$ for the next time. These new values of position and velocity are utilized to generate new perturbative accelerations. Once these have been computed, the program proceeds as above until the trajectory is completed.

8.3.3. Alternate Schemes

An alternate variation-of-parameters scheme has recently been proposed by Hoelker,[92] which utilizes as a parameter a continually moving principal focus. For example, in the case of a lunar trajectory, the focus of the reference ellipse is at first located at the Earth's center and then moves towards the Moon during the flight until it nearly coincides with the Moon's center at the time of landing on the Moon. Thus, a continual variation from a geocentric to a lunicentric (*Moon-centered*) orbit is automatically achieved.

Alternatively, it is possible to choose a different form for the reference motion. One might, for example, include part of the perturbative forces caused by the aspherical shape of the Earth and employ for the reference motion a solution found by Garfinkel.[7] When drag force predominates, as in the case of entry, it is sensible to discard entirely a gravitational reference motion and employ instead a rectilinear gravity-free-drag-orbit as was done by Baker.[9] See a comparison of such a gravity perturbed orbit with the conventional drag perturbed elliptical orbit in Fig. 30.

In this case new vectorial elements $\mathbf{a} \triangleq x_\omega \mathbf{P}$ and $\mathbf{b} \triangleq \mathbf{Q}$ are integrated with y_ω as independent variable instead of the time. (Such a procedure should be employed as soon as drag acceleration exceeds gravitational acceleration.)

The entry or gravity-free variation-of-parameters technique begins by obtaining the initial values of the parameters $\mathbf{a}$ and $\mathbf{b}$. In case they are found to be necessary, alternate formulas for integration with the time as independent variable are included on the left-hand side. The procedure is as follows: Given initial position and velocity $\mathbf{r}_0$ and $\dot{\mathbf{r}}_0$, and $\mathbf{Q}_0 = \dot{\mathbf{r}}_0/\dot{s}_0$, form

$$
\begin{aligned}
W_{x_0} &= (\mathbf{r}_0 \times \dot{\mathbf{r}}_0)_x / r_0^2 \dot{v}_0, \ P_{x_0} = (\mathbf{Q}_0 \times \mathbf{W}_0)_x, \qquad x \to y,\, z \\
y_{\omega_0} &= \mathbf{Q}_0 \cdot \mathbf{r}_0 \text{ (note that } y_{\omega_0} \text{ will be negative for entry)}, \\
\dot{y}_{\omega_0} &= \dot{s}_0 = (\dot{x}_0^2 + \dot{y}_0^2 + \dot{z}_0^2)^{1/2}, \\
x_{\omega_0} &= \mathbf{P}_0 \cdot \mathbf{r}_0, \text{ by definition} \\
\dot{x}_{\omega_0} &= 0,
\end{aligned}
$$

$$a_{x_0} = x_{\omega_0} P_{x_0}, \text{ and}$$
$$b_{x_0} = Q_{x_0} \qquad x \to y, z.$$

Again it should be noted that these initial values serve as a check upon the input quantities, i.e.,

$$x_\omega^2 + y_\omega^2 \stackrel{?}{=} x^2 + y^2 + z^2.$$

At this point the perturbative influence of gravitation and lift (including unaccounted-for drag) are employed to obtain the required integrands:

$$\dot{r}' = [\dot{\mathbf{r}}_\oplus' + \dot{\mathbf{r}}_D'] \cdot \mathbf{U}, \text{ (radial component);}$$
$$r\dot{v}' = [\dot{\mathbf{r}}_\oplus' + \dot{\mathbf{r}}_D'] \cdot \mathbf{V}, \text{ (transverse component);}$$
$$r\dot{b}' = [\dot{\mathbf{r}}_\oplus' + \dot{\mathbf{r}}_D'] \cdot \mathbf{W}, \text{ (orthogonal or normal component); and}$$
$$\dot{s}' = [\dot{\mathbf{r}}_\oplus' + \dot{\mathbf{r}}_D'] \cdot \mathbf{Q}.$$

The components of $\dot{\mathbf{r}}_\oplus'$ are given by $\dot{x}_\oplus' = \partial\Phi/\partial x$ where $\partial\Phi/\partial x$ is the total bulge acceleration listed in Section 7.4 ($x \to y, z$), and the components of $\dot{\mathbf{r}}_D'$ by

$$\dot{x}_D' = -D_0^2\dot{s}^2 \left\{ \left[\mu^*\gamma(\nu)\sigma(H)\gamma(\sigma)\frac{\nu v_x}{\dot{s}^2} - \mu^*\left(A + \frac{B}{\dot{s}}\right)\left(\sum_{i=-n}^{i=n} C_i r^i\right) Q_x \right] \right.$$
$$\left. -\mu^*\gamma(\nu)\sigma(H)\gamma(\sigma)\frac{\nu^2}{\dot{s}^2}\frac{C_L}{C_{D_0}}\left[\left(\frac{\mathbf{U}\times\mathbf{v}}{\nu}\right)_x \sin\xi + \frac{\mathbf{v}}{\nu}\times\left(\frac{\mathbf{U}\times\mathbf{v}}{\nu}\right)_x \cos\xi\right] \right.$$
$$x \to y, z$$

(for low altitudes the size of $\dot{r}_D'$ can be greatly reduced by switching over to a rotating coordinate system, i.e., set $\theta = 0$ in Eq. (171) and add in coriolis and centrifugal terms).

The coefficients of $\sum C_i r^i$ are fitted to the local variation of $\sigma\gamma(\sigma)$ with the geocentric radius r (since σ depends on the altitude, $(r - r_c)$, and r_c is dependent on latitude, i.e., r_c = the local radius to the Earth's surface, the fit is dependent upon the latitude of the re-entry area); $A + B/\dot{s}$ is fitted to the Mach number drag variation; and the other symbols are defined in Chapter 7. With regard to $\sigma\gamma(\sigma)$, it often proves to be more efficient to fit its variation to the bilinear function

$$(1 - br^2)/(fr^2 - c)$$

over limited ranges of the atmosphere (see reference 9 for a more complete discussion).

It is assumed that γ can be separated into two factors, one of which reflects its Mach number variation, $\gamma(\nu)$, and the other the transitional variation, $\gamma(\sigma)$. An analytical expression for $\gamma(\sigma)$ is included in Chapter 10. If $r\dot{b}`$ is a perturbative acceleration directed normally to the orbit plane, then,

$$\mathbf{P}` = \mathbf{Q}\overline{w}` - \mathbf{W}\overline{q}` \quad \text{and}$$
$$\mathbf{Q}` = \mathbf{W}\overline{p}` - \mathbf{P}\overline{w}`; \quad \text{with}$$
$$\overline{p}` \triangleq \frac{r\dot{b}`}{\dot{s}},$$
$$\overline{q}` \triangleq \frac{y_\omega}{x_\omega \dot{s}} r\dot{b}`, \text{ and}$$
$$\overline{w}` \triangleq -v` = \omega`.$$

Also

$$x_\omega` = -\left\{\frac{x_\omega y_\omega}{\dot{s}r}\right\}\dot{r}` + \left\{\frac{y_\omega^2}{\dot{s}r}\right\} r\dot{v}`,$$

while

$$\omega` = x_\omega`/y_\omega.$$

τ as independent variable	y_ω as independent variable
$\mathbf{a}` = x_\omega\mathbf{P}` + x`_\omega\mathbf{P}$	$\mathbf{a}' = \mathbf{a}`/(\dot{y}_\omega + y`_\omega)$
$\mathbf{b}` = \mathbf{Q}`$	$\mathbf{b}' = \mathbf{b}`/(\dot{y}_\omega + y`_\omega)$
$P_1` = \left\{\frac{\dot{y}_\omega`}{A\dot{y}_\omega + B} + y`_\omega \mu_0 D_0^2 \sum_{i=-n}^{i=n} C_i r_0^i - \left[\mu_0^* D_0^2 \sum C_i(r_0^i - r^i)\right](\dot{y} + y`)\right\}$	$P'_1 = P`_1/(\dot{y}_\omega + y`_\omega)$

where

$$y_\omega` = \left\{\frac{x_\omega^2}{\dot{s}r}\right\}\dot{r}` - \left\{\frac{x_\omega y_\omega}{\dot{s}r}\right\} r\dot{v}`,\ r_0^2 \triangleq x_{\omega 0}^2 + y_\omega^2,$$

$$\dot{s} \equiv \dot{y}_\omega = \left[\dot{s}_0 + \frac{B}{A}\right]\exp\left\{-A\mu_0^* D_0^2 \sum_{i=-n}^{i=n} Y_i + AP_1\right\} - \frac{B}{A},$$

and

$$\dot{s}` \equiv \dot{y}_\omega` = (\dot{\mathbf{r}}_D` - \dot{\mathbf{r}}_\oplus`)\cdot\mathbf{Q},$$

where

$$Y_{-2} \triangleq C_{-2} \int_{y_{\omega 0}}^{y_\omega} \frac{dy_\omega}{r_0^2} = C_{-2} \int_{y_{\omega 0}}^{y_\omega} \frac{dy_\omega}{(x_{\omega 0}^2 + y_\omega^2)}$$

$$= \frac{C_{-2}}{x_{\omega 0}} [\tan^{-1}(y_\omega/x_{\omega 0}) - \tan^{-1}(y_{\omega 0}/x_{\omega 0})],$$

$$Y_{-1} \triangleq C_{-1} \int_{y_{\omega 0}}^{y_\omega} \frac{dy_\omega}{\sqrt{x_{\omega 0}^2 + y_\omega^2}}$$

$$= C_{-1} \left[\log_e \left\{ \frac{y_\omega + \sqrt{x_{\omega 0}^2 + y_\omega^2}}{y_{\omega 0} + \sqrt{x_{\omega 0}^2 + y_{\omega 0}^2}} \right\} \right],$$

$$Y_0 \triangleq C_0 \int_{y_{\omega 0}}^{y_\omega} dy_\omega = C_0[y_\omega - y_{\omega 0}],$$

etc.; or, if the bilinear form for $\sigma\gamma(\sigma)$ is employed, one replaces $\sum_{i=-n}^{i=n} Y_i$ by

$$\int_{y_{\omega 0}}^{y_\omega} \{(1 - br_0^2)/(fr_0^2 - c)\}\, dy_\omega$$

$$= \frac{(1 - bc/f)}{2G} \log_e [(G^2/f + y_\omega G)/(G^2/f - y_\omega G)] - by_\omega/f \Big|_{y_{\omega 0}}^{y_\omega}$$

for $f(fx_{\omega 0}^2 - c) < 0$, or

$$= \frac{(1 + bc/f)}{G} \tan^{-1} [y_\omega f/G] - by_\omega/f \Big|_{y_{\omega 0}}^{y_\omega}$$

for $f(fx_{\omega 0}^2 - c) > 0$, where

$$G^2 \triangleq f(f_{\omega 0}^2 - c) \text{ and } G \triangleq +\sqrt{|G|}.$$

These last two relations are to be evaluated between y_ω and $y_{\omega 0}$.

Finally, the following integrations are carried out:

$$\mathbf{a} = \mathbf{a}_0 + \int_{\tau_0}^{\tau} \mathbf{a}^{\backprime}\, d\tau, \qquad \mathbf{a} = \mathbf{a}_0 + \int_{y_{\omega 0}}^{y_\omega} \mathbf{a}'\, dy_\omega,$$

$$\mathbf{b} = \mathbf{b}_0 + \int_{\tau_0}^{\tau} \mathbf{b}^{\backprime}\, d\tau, \qquad \mathbf{b} = \mathbf{b}_0 + \int_{y_{\omega 0}}^{y_\omega} \mathbf{b}'\, dy_\omega,$$

$$P_1 = \int_{\tau_0}^{\tau} P^{\backprime}_1\, d\tau, \text{ and} \qquad P_1 = \int_{y_{\omega 0}}^{y_\omega} P'_1\, dy_\omega, \text{ and}$$

(initially P_1 is zero),

$$y_\omega = y_{\omega 0} + \int_{\tau_0}^{\tau} (\dot{y}_\omega + y^{\backprime}_\omega)\, d\tau. \qquad \tau = \tau_0 + \int_{y_{\omega 0}}^{y_\omega} \frac{dy_\omega}{(\dot{y} + y^{\backprime}_\omega)}.$$

Note that the C_i coefficients (and, hence, the Y_i) may need to be changed from level to level in order to achieve a better fit, i.e., $\sigma\gamma(\sigma) = \cdots + C_{-1/r} + C_0 + C_1 r + C_2 r^2 + \cdots$ can only be fitted to the atmosphere over limited levels, i.e., over about one "scale height."

Although singularities in the foregoing formulas do not arise in either ascent or descent drag orbits, they will emerge if one attempts to reproduce a drag-free gravity orbit. In this case it becomes clear, after a little thought, that $\dot{y}_\omega + y_\omega^\backprime$ (being the speed of the object relative to the perturbed x_ω-axis) will pass through zero twice during a complete revolution on an elliptical Keplerian orbit. Consequently, when $\dot{y}_\omega + y_\omega^\backprime$ becomes small it is necessary to switch over to the alternate formulas that have τ as independent variable.

Under certain circumstances (of low inertial speed $\dot{y}_\omega$ or high lift), $\dot{y}_\omega + y_\omega^\backprime$ may be negative. In this case the object is receding from the x_ω-axis and the integration should be carried in the negative direction. The upper limit on the integrals should, therefore, be set after an inspection of the sign of $\dot{y}_\omega + y_\omega^\backprime$.

Although the gravity-free orbit procedure has been found to be advantageous in the integration of high-speed meteorite, grazing braking ellipse, and high mass/area quotient entry orbits, it has not been found to be particularly efficient for the computation of entry from satellite orbits of low mass/area vehicles.

8.4. Determination of Latitude, Longitude, and Entry Angle

From special perturbation procedures, such as the foregoing, it is possible to represent observations (as mentioned in Chapter 4) or to determine such quantities as latitude, longitude, and entry angle at each step of the integration, i.e., given the right ascension, α, in radians of the vehicle from $\sin\alpha = y/\sqrt{x^2 + y^2}$ and $\cos\alpha = x/\sqrt{x^2 + y^2}$; and the time, t, in minutes from

$$t = \tau(13.447{,}052) \text{ min},$$

the longitude of the "subvehicle point" measured eastward from the Greenwich meridian, λ_E, is given by

$$\lambda_E = \alpha(57.295{,}779) - 15\theta_{g_0} - (0.250{,}684{,}48)(t - t_0) \qquad (192)$$

in degrees and decimals. It should be noted that negative angles found in this last equation are to be interpreted as positive fourth quadrant angles.

θ_{g_0} is the initial Greenwich sidereal time measured in hours and decimals of an hour (see Chapter 11).

The geodetic latitude (measured positive in the northern hemisphere) is computed from the geocentric latitude ϕ' and the flattening, f, by:

$$\phi = \left[\tan^{-1}\left\{\frac{1}{(1-f)^2}\tan\phi'\right\}\right] 57.295{,}779 \tag{193}$$

in decimals and degrees where $\phi' = \sin^{-1} z/r$ or more precisely the geodetic subvehicle point may be computed as shown in the footnote on page 166.

If ζ is the *entry angle* between the velocity vector of the vehicle relative to the atmosphere, $\mathbf{v}$, and the local vertical,* $\mathbf{Z}$; then

$$\cos\zeta = \mathbf{v}\cdot\mathbf{Z}/v. \tag{194}$$

The components in an equatorial system of the unit vector $\mathbf{Z}$ are:

$$Z_x = \frac{x\cos\phi}{r\cos\phi'},$$

$$Z_y = \frac{y\cos\phi}{r\cos\phi'}$$

and

$$Z_z = \sin\phi.$$

* Strictly speaking, $\mathbf{Z}$ is here defined as the local *geodetic* vertical reckoned at the geocentric "subvehicle point."

9 GENERAL PERTURBATIONS

General perturbations or the analytical integration of series expansions of the perturbative accelerations are particularly useful in the computation of orbits extending over many periods, e.g., in the case of Earth satellites, the Moon, lunar satellites, and planetary trajectories.

As noted by F. Kierstead, general perturbations also allow for a clearer interpretation of the *sources* of the perturbative force, i.e., the systematic divergence between observation and computation cannot easily be explained in special perturbations where only tabular data appear. On the other hand, in the case of general perturbations an observed harmonic deviation or anomaly can be rather easily associated with its source. An example of this is discussed in Section 9.2.4.1 where the remarkable discovery of the Earth's "pear" shape by J. A. O'Keefe and A. Eckels was made possible through the analysis of long period general perturbation terms in orbital eccentricity. The famous discovery of Neptune by Adams and independently by Leverrier represents another epochal achievement of general perturbations in which the anomalous motions of Uranus were traced to the new planet—leading subsequently to its initial observation.

The following chapter dwells briefly on the historical aspects of general perturbations, and then discusses the formulation of this technique through an illustrative example of a geocentric satellite. This analysis includes consideration of perturbations resulting from the asphericity of the Earth, drag, and the Sun and Moon. Although Hamiltonian mechanics is often used to advantage in general perturbations, it will not be introduced here.

9.1. History

During the 18th century the Moon had provided a useful laboratory for trying out theories and analytical methods of perturbations supplementing and completing the pioneer geometrical methods of Newton.* The brilliant success of Clairaut, d'Alembert, Lagrange, Laplace, and Euler in explaining the large deviations of the Moon from an elliptic orbit due to the solar attraction laid a solid foundation for solving the varied problems of minor planet orbits in the 19th century. In 1747 Clairaut and d'Alembert had integrated the equations of motion of the three-body system in series (general perturbations). In the next few years Euler investigated and developed the perturbative function, and began the development of the method of variation of parameters. Lagrange extended the latter in 1762, but he followed Euler in leaving the major axis and time of perihelion passage constant. He completed the method in 1782. Laplace and Lagrange in 1773 and 1774 investigated the stability of the solar system and found that a and n have no secular perturbations up to second-order terms in the eccentricity. Lagrange proved that this was true for all powers of e for first order perturbations in respect to the ratio of the masses. In 1809, Poisson demonstrated the absence of secular terms in a and n as far as terms of the second order in respect to the ratio of the masses. In 1878, however, Haretu proved that there *are* secular terms in n and a, when the third-order terms in the ratio of the masses are taken into account. More recently general perturbations have been utilized for planetary orbits and the theory extended by Eckert, Brouwer, and Clemence.

Delaunay's method of general perturbations has aroused much interest of late (see Brown[93] for a full discussion), and a full series is being developed at Yale by Brouwer and by Kovalevsky[94] at the University of Paris. Delaunay's theory is considered better than the Hill–Brown theory in handling the problem of small divisors, as for example division by the frequency of long-period terms, such as the motion of the node in the case of an Earth satellite when $i = 63°26'$ or when the node regresses in step with the annual motion of the Sun or in the computation of the perturbations of Saturn or Jupiter whose orbits are nearly commensurable. In this latter case, Jupiter's period is a little more than $\frac{5}{2}$ Saturn's. Hence, at every tenth successive conjunction they will be at about the same point in inertial space. When conjunctions frequently occur near the same point very large

* Newton indicated the true explanation of the Moon's variation, parallactic inequality, annual equation, variations in e and i and regression of the nodes, but his theory accounted for only one-half of the motion of the Moon's perigee. Clairaut in 1749 was on the point of substituting a new law of gravitation of the form $a = (\mu/r^2) + (\nu/r^3)$ for the Newtonian law when he found that the second order perturbations removed the discrepancy between the observed and theoretical values. Over a century later an unpublished manuscript of Newton's was examined and found to contain the full explanation of the motion of the Moon's perigee.

"long period" (period being the time between conjunctions) perturbations are produced. An example of this phenomenon in the case of Kirkwood's gaps is discussed in Section 2.2.1. Specifically, Delaunay's theory of the Moon employs an "intermediate" orbit that includes the effect of one of the prominent perturbations of the Moon caused by the Sun, i.e., the "variation," which is a lengthening of the lunar orbit along a line perpendicular to the direction to the Sun.

9.2. Geocentric Satellite Acted Upon by the Asphericity of the Earth and Drag

9.2.1. Perturbative Expressions

The method of general perturbations will be developed in a cursory fashion by means of an illustrative example of a geocentric satellite acted upon by perturbations caused by the Earth's asphericity and atmospheric drag. Such a problem has met with extensive analysis by Roberson, O'Keefe, Blitzer, Kraus, King-Hele, and Kozai to name but a few.

As a first step it is necessary to represent the variation of the appropriate orbital elements as a function of the radial, $\dot{r}^{\backprime}$, orthogonal, $r\dot{v}^{\backprime}$ (or $r\dot{l}^{\backprime}$), and normal, $r\dot{b}^{\backprime}$, perturbative components. This can be done in terms of either v or E, and the perturbative variation of a, e, v, i, Ω, and l are listed in Chapter 8. One may extend this list to include

$$\frac{n^{\backprime}}{n} = -\frac{3}{\sqrt{\mu p}}\frac{a}{r}\, e \sin v[r\dot{r}^{\backprime}] - \frac{3}{\sqrt{\mu p}}\left(\frac{ap}{r^2}\right)[r^2\dot{v}^{\backprime}], \tag{195}$$

$$\omega^{\backprime} = -\Omega^{\backprime}\cos i - \frac{[(p/r)\cos v]}{e\sqrt{\mu p}}[r\dot{r}^{\backprime}] + \left(\frac{p}{r}+1\right)\frac{\sin v}{e\sqrt{\mu p}}[r^2\dot{v}^{\backprime}], \tag{196}$$

$$L^{\backprime} = M^{\backprime} + \Omega^{\backprime} + \omega^{\backprime} = \Omega^{\backprime}(1-\cos i) - \frac{e^2 v^{\backprime}}{1+\sqrt{1-e^2}} - \frac{2r\dot{r}^{\backprime}}{\sqrt{\mu a}}, \text{ and} \tag{197}$$

$$\pi^{\backprime} = \omega^{\backprime} + \Omega^{\backprime} = l^{\backprime} - v^{\backprime}. \tag{198}$$

9.2.2. Perturbative Components

9.2.2.1. Asphericity of the Earth

It is next necessary to generate the accelerations $r^2\dot{b}^{\backprime}$, $r\dot{r}^{\backprime}$, and $r^2\dot{v}^{\backprime}$ (or $r^2\dot{l}^{\backprime}$). In the case of perturbations resulting from the asphericity of the Earth a partial differentiation of the potential function, Φ, given in Chapter 5 is carried out (cf. Herrick[95]), i.e., from Eq. (59) with $\sin\delta \equiv U_z$ cf. Eq. (168),

$$\frac{\partial\Phi}{\partial r} = -\frac{k_e^2 m}{r^2}\left[1 + \frac{J}{r^2}(1 - 3U_z^2) + \frac{4H}{5r^3}U_z(3 - 5U_z^2) + \frac{K}{6r^4}(3 - 30U_z^2 + 35U_z^4) + \cdots\right],$$

$$\frac{1}{r}\frac{\partial\Phi}{\partial l} = \frac{k_e^2 m}{r^2}V_z\left[-\frac{2J}{r^2}U_z + \frac{3H}{5r^3}(1 - 5U_z^2) - K\frac{U_z}{6r^4}(12 - 28U_z^2) + \cdots\right],$$

and

$$\frac{1}{r}\frac{\partial\Phi}{\partial b} = \frac{k_e^2 m}{r^2}W_z\left[-\frac{2J}{r^2}U_z + \frac{3H}{5r^3}(1 - 5U_z^2) - K\frac{U_z}{6r^4}(12 - 28U_z^2) + \cdots\right]. \quad (199)$$

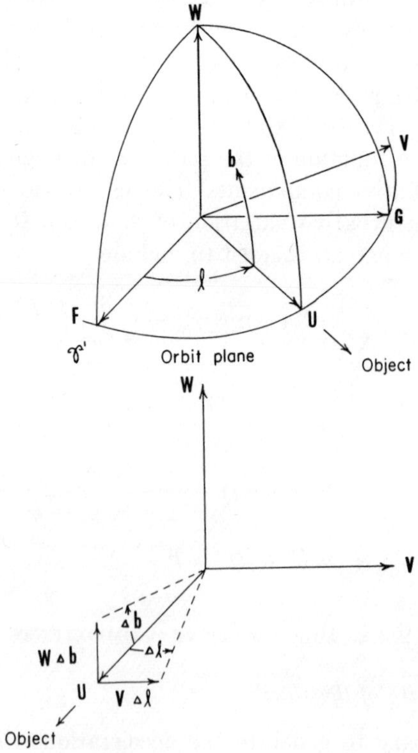

FIG. 31. Partial incremental change in **U** with respect to l and b.

This form is obtained if it is recognized that $\Delta\mathbf{U} = \Delta l\mathbf{V}$ and $\Delta\mathbf{U} = \Delta b\mathbf{W}$, so that $\partial U_z/\partial l = V_z$ and $\partial U_z/\partial b = W_z$. See Table III, Figs. 20 and 31. Furthermore, it should be noted that $\partial r/\partial r = 1$, $\partial r/\partial l = 0$, $\partial U_z/\partial r = 0$, and $\partial r/\partial b = 0$.

If the z components of $\mathbf{U}$, $\mathbf{V}$, and $\mathbf{W}$ are expressed in terms of $u = v + \omega$, i.e., (see Fig. 32)

$$\begin{aligned} U_z &= \sin i \sin u \\ V_z &= \sin i \cos u \\ W_z &= \cos i \\ U_z^2 &= \tfrac{1}{2} \sin^2 i(1 - \cos 2u) \\ U_zV_z &= \tfrac{1}{2} \sin^2 i \sin 2u \\ U_zW_z &= \sin i \cos i \sin u \\ U_z^2V_z &= \tfrac{1}{4} \sin^3 i(\cos u - \cos 3u) \\ U_z^3 &= \tfrac{1}{4} \sin^3 i(3 \sin u - \sin 3u) \\ U_z^4 &= \tfrac{1}{8} \sin^4 i(3 - 4 \cos 2u + \cos 4u), \end{aligned}$$

then Eqs. (199) become (after introducing the components of acceleration along and perpendicular to the radius vector in terms of r, l, and b e.g., see p. 13 Eq. (19) of Moulton[13])

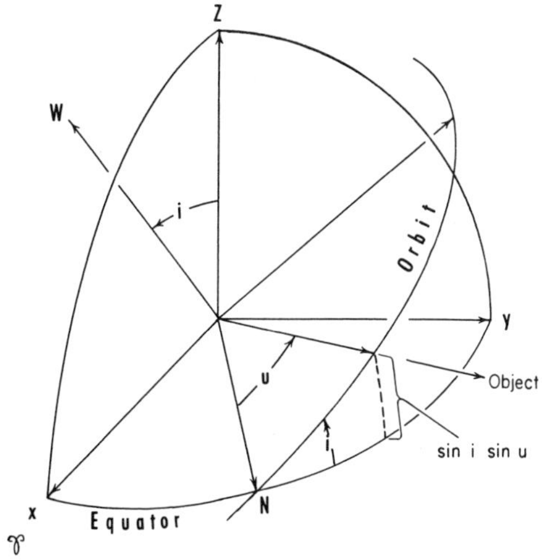

FIG. 32. Components of **U**.

$$\frac{\partial\Phi}{\partial r} = \frac{d^2r}{dt^2} - r\left(\frac{dl}{dt}\right)^2 = -\frac{k_e{}^2m}{r^2}\left\{1 + \frac{J}{r^2}\left[1 - \frac{3}{2}\sin^2 i(1 - \cos 2u)\right]\right.$$
$$+ \frac{4H}{5r^3}\sin i\left[3\left(1 - \frac{5}{4}\sin^2 i\right)\sin u + \frac{5}{4}\sin^2 i \sin 3u\right]$$
$$+ \frac{K}{r^4}\left[\frac{1}{2}\left(1 - 5\sin^2 i + \frac{35}{8}\sin^4 i\right) + \frac{5}{2}\cos 2u \sin^2 i\left(1 - \frac{7}{6}\sin^2 i\right)\right.$$
$$\left.\left. + \frac{35}{48}\cos 4u \sin^4 i\right] + \cdots\right\},$$

$$\frac{1}{r}\frac{\partial\Phi}{\partial l} = r\frac{d^2l}{dt^2} + 2\frac{dr}{dt}\frac{dl}{dt} = \frac{k_e{}^2m}{r^2}\left\{-\frac{J}{r^2}\sin^2 i \sin 2u\right.$$
$$+ \frac{3H}{5r^3}\sin i\left[\left(1 - \frac{5}{4}\sin^2 i\right)\cos u + \frac{5}{4}\sin^2 i \cos 3u\right]$$
$$\left. - \frac{K}{r^4}\sin^2 i\left[\sin 2u\left(1 - \frac{7}{6}\sin^2 i\right) + \frac{7}{12}\sin^2 i \sin 4u\right] + \cdots\right\},$$

and

$$\frac{1}{r}\frac{\partial\Phi}{\partial b} = r\frac{d^2b}{dt^2} = \frac{k_e{}^2m}{r^2}\left\{-\frac{2J}{r^2}\sin i \cos i \sin u\right.$$
$$+ \frac{3H}{5r^3}\cos i\left[1 - \frac{5}{2}\sin^2 i(1 - \cos 2u)\right]$$
$$\left. - \frac{K}{r^4}\sin i \cos i\left[2\sin u\left(1 - \frac{7}{4}\sin^2 i\right) + \frac{7}{6}\sin^2 i \sin 3u\right] + \cdots\right\}. \quad (200)$$

In order to obtain explicit perturbative components, the following relationships are derived:

$$\frac{\partial\Phi}{\partial r} = \frac{d^2r}{d\tau^2} - r\dot{l}^2 = \ddot{r} + \dot{r}^{\backprime} - r\dot{l}^2, \text{ but } \ddot{r} - r\dot{l}^2 = -\frac{\mu}{r^2}$$

(i.e., recall from Section 1.5 that $\ddot{r} = -\frac{\mu}{r^2} + r\dot{v}^2$ and since $l = \Omega + \omega + v$ and $\dot{\Omega}$ and $\dot{\omega} = 0$, then $\dot{v} = \dot{l}$; also by extension of Eq. (164) it is clear that $\left.\frac{d^2r}{d\tau^2} = \ddot{r} + \dot{r}^{\backprime}\right)$, thus

$$\dot{r}^{\backprime} = \frac{\partial\Phi}{\partial r} + \frac{\mu}{r^2}.$$

Also

$$\frac{1}{r}\frac{\partial\Phi}{\partial l} = r\frac{d^2l}{d\tau^2} + 2\dot{r}\dot{l}, \text{ but } r\ddot{l} + 2\dot{r}\dot{l} = 0$$

(since this is the value for the two-body acceleration perpendicular to **r**, which is zero), thus

$$r\dot{l}^{\backprime} = r\dot{v}^{\backprime} = \frac{1}{r}\frac{\partial\Phi}{\partial l}.$$

Lastly,

$$\frac{1}{r}\frac{\partial\Phi}{\partial b} = r\frac{d^2b}{d\tau^2} = r[\ddot{b} + \dot{b}^{\backprime}], \text{ but } \ddot{b} = 0$$

thus,

$$r\dot{b}^{\backprime} = \frac{1}{r}\frac{\partial\Phi}{\partial b}.$$

In fine, then

$$\begin{aligned}\dot{r}^{\backprime} = \frac{-\mu}{r^2}\Bigg\{&\frac{J}{r^2}\left[1 - \frac{3}{2}\sin^2 i(1 - \cos 2u)\right]\\ &+ \frac{4H}{5r^3}\sin i\left[3\left(1 - \frac{5}{4}\sin^2 i\right)\sin u + \frac{5}{4}\sin^2 i \sin 3u\right]\\ &+ \frac{K}{r^4}\left[\frac{1}{2}\left(1 - 5\sin^2 i + \frac{35}{8}\sin^4 i\right) + \frac{5}{2}\cos 2u \sin^2 i\left(1 - \frac{7}{6}\sin^2 i\right)\right.\\ &\left.+ \frac{35}{48}\cos 4u \sin^4 i\right] + \cdots\Bigg\},\end{aligned}$$

$$\begin{aligned}r\dot{v}^{\backprime} = r\dot{l}^{\backprime} = \frac{\mu}{r^2}\Bigg\{&-\frac{J}{r^2}\sin^2 i \sin 2u\\ &+ \frac{3H}{5r^3}\sin i\left[\left(1 - \frac{5}{4}\sin^2 i\right)\cos u + \frac{5}{4}\sin^2 i \cos 3u\right]\\ &- \frac{K}{r^4}\sin^2 i\left[\sin 2u\left(1 - \frac{7}{6}\sin^2 i\right) + \frac{7}{12}\sin^2 i \sin 4u\right] + \cdots\Bigg\},\end{aligned}$$

and

$$\begin{aligned}r\dot{b}^{\backprime} = \frac{\mu}{r^2}\Bigg\{&-\frac{2J}{r^2}\sin i \cos i \sin u + \frac{3H}{5r^3}\cos i\left[1 - \frac{5}{2}\sin^2 i(1 - \cos 2u)\right]\\ &- \frac{K}{r^4}\sin i \cos i\left[2\sin u\left(1 - \frac{7}{4}\sin^2 i\right) + \frac{7}{6}\sin^2 i \sin 3u\right] + \cdots\Bigg\}. \quad (201)\end{aligned}$$

9.2.2.2. Drag

In the case of perturbations resulting from drag encountered near perigee, a number of analysts have suggested differing approaches, e.g., Sterne,[96,8]

Nonweiler,[97] Rowell and Smith,[98] and Vinti.[99] The technique employed here has been developed by Baker and may offer advantages over those suggested heretofore, since it accounts for the variation in scale-height and drag-coefficient over different levels of the Earth's atmosphere.

The components of drag acceleration in a *nonrotating* atmosphere are

$$\begin{aligned} \dot{r}^{\backprime} &= -D_0^2\mu\alpha\gamma\sigma\dot{s}^2\left(\frac{\dot{r}}{\dot{s}}\right), \\ r\dot{v}^{\backprime} = r\dot{l}^{\backprime} &= -D_0^2\mu\alpha\gamma\sigma\dot{s}^2\left(\frac{r\dot{v}}{\dot{s}}\right), \text{ and} \\ r\dot{b}^{\backprime} &= 0; \end{aligned} \tag{202}$$

where D_0^2, μ^*, α^*, γ, and σ are defined as they were in Section 7.4. Let it be assumed that $\mu^* = 1$ (where this quantity refers to the mass of the vehicle m_0/m), $\alpha^* = 1$ (where this quantity refers to the area of the vehicle, A/A_0), and that

$$\begin{aligned} \gamma(\sigma)\sigma &= \gamma(\sigma_1)\sigma_1 \exp\left[-(r - r_1)/H_1\right] \quad \text{for } r_1 - H_1/2 < r < r_1 + H_1/2 \\ \gamma(\sigma)\sigma &= \gamma(\sigma_2)\sigma_2 \exp\left[-(r - r_2)/H_2\right] \quad \text{for } r_2 - H_2/2 < r < r_2 + H_2/2 \\ &\text{etc.} \end{aligned} \tag{203}$$

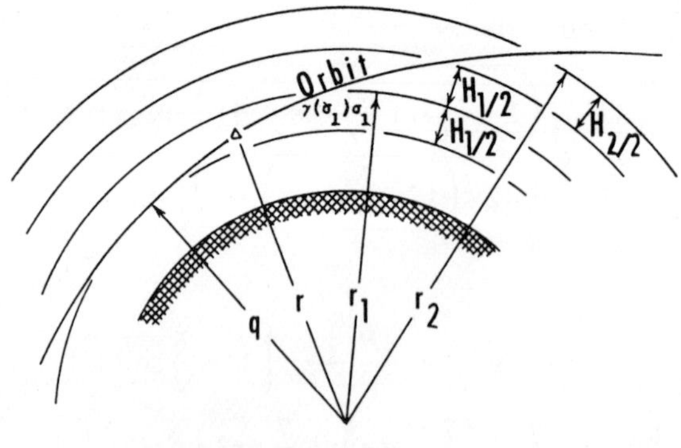

FIG. 33. Atmospheric levels.

where $\gamma(\sigma_1)$ is the transitional value of C_D/C_{D0} at r_1, σ_1 is the density ratio at r_1 and H_1 is the scale height at r_1, $1 \rightarrow 2$, . . . (see Fig. 33). It is assumed that there is no significant Mach number variation in γ. Usually $r_1 - H_1/2$

$= q$ and $r_1 + H_1/2 = r_2 - H_2/2$. Thus $r_2 = q + H_1 + H_2/2$ and

$$r_n = q + \sum_{i=1}^{n-1} H_i + \frac{H_n}{2}. \tag{204}$$

The procedure should not be limited to this definition of r_n as it might prove more accurate to expand not about the center of a level but about some lower point.

In terms of v, from the equation of a conic and from the bottom of p. 116,

$$r = p/(1 + e \cos v),$$
$$\dot{r} = \sqrt{\mu/p}e \sin v,$$

(note that in this instance μ refers to $m_1 + m_2 = m_\oplus + 0 \cong 1$)

$$r\dot{v} = \sqrt{\mu/p}(1 + e \cos v), \text{ and}$$
$$\dot{s} = \sqrt{\mu/p}\sqrt{1 + 2e \cos v + e^2}; \tag{205}$$

consequently,

$$\dot{s}\dot{r} = \frac{\mu}{p} e \sin v \sqrt{1 + 2e \cos v + e^2}, \text{ and}$$

$$\dot{s}r\dot{v} = \frac{\mu}{p}(1 + e \cos v)\sqrt{1 + 2e \cos v + e^2}. \tag{206}$$

9.2.3. Series Expressions

9.2.3.1. Asphericity of the Earth

In order to integrate the foregoing expressions analytically, it is necessary to express them in series in M or v. In the case of perturbations due to the Earth's asphericity, the perturbative forces are present continuously during the orbital period and an expansion in M (for $e < 1$) is indicated. On the other hand, in the case of drag the perturbative forces are only effective near perigee and an expansion in v itself is indicated.

The following series (expanded about $e = 0$) are useful in dealing with perturbations occasioned by the asphericity of the Earth:

$$(p/r)^n = (1 + e \cos v)^n = 1 + ne \cos v + \cdots,$$
$$(p/r)^n \sin v = (1 + e \cos v)^n \sin v = \sin v + (n/2)e \sin 2v + \cdots,$$

and

$$(p/r)^n \cos v = (1 + e \cos v)^n \cos v = (n/2)e + \cos v + (n/2)e \cos 2v + \cdots. \tag{207}$$

But, in terms of M,

$$\sin nv = -ne \sin [(n-1)M] + \sin nM + ne \sin [(n+1)M] + \cdots$$
$$\cos nv = -ne \cos [(n-1)M] + \cos nM + ne \cos [(n+1)M] + \cdots.$$

By combining expressions appropriately, the following useful forms emerge:

$$(p/r)^n = 1 + ne \cos M + \cdots$$
$$(p/r)^n \sin v = \sin M + [(n/2) + 1]e \sin 2M + \cdots$$
$$(p/r)^n \cos v = [(n/2) - 1]e + \cos M + [(n/2) + 1]e \cos 2M + \cdots.$$

By use of appropriate trigonometric identities, one finds that

$$\begin{aligned}\cos 2u = \cos (2v + 2\omega) &= \cos 2v \cos 2\omega - \sin 2v \sin 2\omega \\ &= [-2e \cos M + \cos 2M + 2e \cos 3M + \cdots] \cos 2\omega \\ &\quad -[-2e \sin M + \sin 2M + 2e \sin 3M + \cdots] \sin 2\omega;\end{aligned}$$

but

$$\cos M \cos 2\omega = \tfrac{1}{2} \cos (M + 2\omega) + \tfrac{1}{2} \cos (M - 2\omega)$$
$$\sin M \sin 2\omega = -\tfrac{1}{2} \cos (M + 2\omega) + \tfrac{1}{2} \cos (M - 2\omega)$$

etc.; consequently,

$$\begin{aligned}(p/r)^3 \cos 2u &= [1 + 3e \cos M + \cdots][-2e \sin (M + 2\omega) \\ &\quad + \sin (2M + 2\omega) + 2e \sin (3M + 2\omega) + \cdots] \\ &= -\tfrac{1}{2}e \cos (M + 2\omega) + \cos (2M + 2\omega) + \tfrac{7}{2}e \cos (3M + 2\omega) + \cdots.\end{aligned}$$

Thus, e.g.,

$$\begin{aligned}r\dot{r}' = -\frac{\mu J}{p^3}\Bigg\{&\left(1 - \frac{3}{2}\sin^2 i\right)(1 + 3e \cos M + \cdots) \\ &+ \frac{3}{2}\sin^2 i\left[-\frac{1}{2}e \cos (M + 2\omega) + \cos (2M + 2\omega)\right. \\ &\left.+ \frac{7}{2}e \cos (3M + 2\omega) + \cdots\right]\Bigg\}. \end{aligned} \tag{208}$$

Considering only the variation of e in detail, it follows from Eq. (183) that

$$e' = \frac{r\dot{r}'}{\sqrt{\mu p}}\left(\frac{p}{r}\sin v\right) + \frac{r^2\dot{v}'}{\sqrt{\mu p}}\left[\left(\frac{p}{r}+1\right)\cos v + e\right], \tag{209}$$

which, after considerable manipulation, yields

$$\begin{aligned} e' = &-\sqrt{\mu/p}\,\frac{J}{p^3}\left\{\left(1-\frac{3}{2}\sin^2 i\right)[\sin M + 3e\sin 2M]\right.\\ &+\sin^2 i\left[\frac{1}{4}\sin(M+2\omega) - \frac{1}{2}e\sin(2M+2\omega)\right.\\ &\left.\left.+\frac{7}{4}\sin(3M+2\omega) + \frac{17}{2}e\sin(4M+2\omega)\right]\right\}\\ &+\sqrt{\mu/p}\,\frac{H}{5p^4}\sin i\left\{\left(1-\frac{5}{4}\sin^2 i\right)\left[-\frac{33}{4}e\cos(-M+\omega) - 3\cos\omega\right.\right.\\ &\left.-\frac{3}{2}e\cos(M+\omega) + 9\cos(2M+\omega) + \frac{159}{4}e\cos(3M+\omega)\right]\\ &+\frac{5}{4}\sin^2 i\left[-\frac{1}{4}e\cos(M+3\omega) + \cos(2M+3\omega)\right.\\ &\left.\left.-\frac{3}{2}e\cos(3M+3\omega) + 5\cos(4M+3\omega) + \frac{127}{4}e\cos(5M+3\omega)\right]\right\} + \cdots . \end{aligned} \tag{210}$$

In a similar fashion it can be shown that for the second harmonic terms:

$$\begin{aligned} e\pi' = &-\frac{J}{p^3}\sqrt{\frac{\mu}{p}}\left\{\cos i\,(1-\cos i)[e - e\cos(2M+2\omega) + \cdots]\right.\\ &+\left(1-\frac{3}{2}\sin^2 i\right)[e + \cos M + 3e\cos 2M]\\ &+\sin^2 i\left[\frac{3}{2}e\cos 2\omega\,\frac{7}{4}\cos(M+2\omega) + \frac{11}{2}e\cos(2M+2\omega)\right.\\ &\left.\left.-\frac{1}{4}\cos(3M+2\omega) - e\cos(4M+2\omega)\right]\right\} \end{aligned} \tag{211}$$

$$L^{\backprime} = -\frac{J}{p^3}\sqrt{\frac{\mu}{p}}\left\{\cos i\,(1-\cos i)\left[1 + 3e\cos M + \frac{1}{2}e\cos(M+2\omega) - \cos(2M+2\omega) - \frac{7}{2}e\cos(3M+2\omega) + \cdots\right] + \left(1 - \frac{3}{2}\sin^2 i\right)[1 + 2e\cos M] + \sin^2 i\left[\frac{5}{4}e\cos(M+2\omega) + \cos(2M+2\omega) + \frac{13}{4}e\cos(3M+2\omega) + \cdots\right]\right\} \quad (212)$$

$$n^{\backprime} = 3n\frac{J}{p^3}\sqrt{\frac{\mu}{p}}\left\{\left(1 - \frac{3}{2}\sin^2 i\right)(3e\sin M + \cdots) + \sin^2 i\left[\frac{3}{4}e\sin(M+2\omega) - 3\sin(2M+2\omega) + \frac{63}{4}e\sin(3M+2\omega) + \cdots\right]\right\} \quad (213)$$

etc.

9.2.3.2. *Drag*

In the case of drag, the following series, expanded in terms of v (about $v = 0$) are useful. (Alternately, an expansion in terms of e (about $e = 0$) could be integrated in terms of Bessel functions; see King-Hele *et al.*[172])

$$\exp[-(r - r_1)/H_1] = 1 - (r - r_1)/H_1 + (r - r_1)^2/2H_1^2 - \cdots; \quad (214)$$

but

$$(r - r_1)/H_1 = (r - q)/H_1 - \frac{1}{2} = \frac{p}{H_1}[1/(1 + e\cos v) - 1/(1 + e)] - \frac{1}{2},$$

and since, $\cos v \cong 1 - v^2/2 + 0(v^4)$

$$(r - r_1)/H_1 \cong \frac{q}{2(1+e)}[ev^2/H_1] - \frac{1}{2} + 0(v^4);$$

so that

$$\exp[-(r - r_1)/H_1] \cong \left(1 + \frac{1}{2} + \frac{1}{4\cdot 2} + \cdots\right)[1 - qev^2/2H_1(1 + e)]$$
$$\cong 1.6487[1 - qev^2/2H_1(1 + e) + 0(v^4)] + 0(v^4). \quad (215)$$

In a similar fashion

$$\exp\,[-(r - r_n)/H_n] = \exp\left(\frac{1}{2} + \frac{\sum_{i=1}^{n-1} H_i}{H_n}\right)[1 - qev^2/2H_n(1 + e)]. \quad (216)$$

Considering only the variation of n due to drag, it is clear that only the tangential, $\dot{s}`$, is influential, hence

$$n` = -3na\frac{\dot{s}\dot{s}`}{\mu} = +\frac{3na}{\mu}D_0^2\gamma\sigma\dot{s}^3, \quad (217)$$

where $\mu = m_\oplus \cong 1$* and $\dot{s}^3$ is obtained as follows:

$$\dot{s} = \sqrt{\frac{\mu}{p}}(1 + e)\left[1 + \frac{1}{2}\frac{ev^2}{(1 + e)^2} + \cdots\right] \text{ since from Eqs. (13) and (14)}$$

$$\dot{s}^2 = \frac{\mu}{p}[(1 + e)^2 - 2e(1 - \cos v)] = \frac{\mu}{p}(1 + e)^2\left[1 + \frac{ev^2}{(1 + e)^2} + \cdots\right]$$

$$\dot{s}^3 = \left(\frac{\mu}{p}\right)^{3/2}(1 + e)^3\left[1 + \frac{3ev^2}{2(1 + e)^2} + \cdots\right]. \quad (218)$$

Thus,

$$\begin{aligned}
n` &= +\frac{3na}{\mu}D_0^2\gamma(\sigma_1)\sigma_1\,1.6487\left[1 - \frac{qev^2}{2H_1(1 + e)} + \cdots\right]\left(\frac{\mu}{p}\right)^{3/2}(1 + e)^3\Bigg[1 \\
&\qquad + \frac{3ev^2}{2(1 + e)} + \cdots\Bigg] \\
&= +3n\sqrt{\frac{\mu}{p}}\frac{(1 + e)^3}{1 - e^2}D_0^2\gamma(\sigma_1)\sigma_1\,1.6487\Bigg\{1 - ev^2\Bigg[\frac{1.5}{(1 + e)^2} \\
&\qquad - \frac{q}{2H_1(1 + e)}\Bigg] + \cdots\Bigg\} \\
&= +3n\sqrt{\frac{\mu}{p}}D_0^2\gamma(\sigma_1)\sigma_1\,1.6487\Bigg\{\frac{(1 + e)^2}{1 - e} - ev^2\left[\frac{1.5}{1 - e} + \frac{a(1 + e)}{2H_1}\right] \\
&\qquad + \cdots\Bigg\} \quad (219)
\end{aligned}$$

or

$$\frac{n`}{n} = \Psi\sqrt{\frac{\mu}{p}}\left\{\frac{(1 + e)^2}{1 - e} - ev^2\left[\frac{1.5}{1 - e} + \frac{a(1 + e)}{2H_1}\right]\right\} \quad (220)$$

* One might let μ differ slightly from one in order to partially account for the equatorial bulge at perigee. Such a modified μ would be a function of the vehicle sublatitude at perigee, ϕ_p, and might be computed from Eq. (59), i.e., $\mu = 1 + \frac{J}{3}\frac{1}{q^2}(1 - 3\sin^2\phi_p)$.

where

$$\Psi \triangleq 4.9461 D_0{}^2 \gamma(\sigma_1)\sigma_1. \tag{221}$$

It is interesting to note from Eq. (217) the paradox that as a satellite encounters drag it *speeds up*, i.e., the mean motion tends to increase. This is, of course, a logical consequence of Kepler's third law for as the semimajor axis is decreased by drag the orbital speed increases. Such an *acceleration* will continue until drag forces begin to exceed gravitational forces.

9.2.4. Analytical Integration

9.2.4.1. Asphericity of the Earth

In the case of the gravitational perturbations due to the Earth's asphericity, there exist integrals of the form

$$\left.\begin{aligned} C_{ij} \int_{\tau 0}^{\tau} \cos\,(iM + j\omega)\, d\tau \\ S_{ij} \int_{\tau 0}^{\tau} \sin\,(iM + j\omega)\, d\tau \end{aligned}\right\} \quad \begin{aligned} j &= 0, 2 \\ i &= -1, 0, 1, 2, \end{aligned} \tag{222}$$

so that their integration is simply

$$C_{ij} \int_{\tau 0}^{\tau} \cos\,(iM + j\omega)\, d\tau = C_{ij} \left[\frac{\sin\,(iM + j\omega)}{i(dM/d\tau) + j(d\omega/d\tau)} \right]_{\tau 0}^{\tau}$$

and

$$S_{ij} \int_{\tau 0}^{\tau} \cos\,(iM + j\omega)\, d\tau = -S_{ij} \left[\frac{\cos\,(iM + j\omega)}{i(dM/d\tau) + j(d\omega/d\tau)} \right]_{\tau 0}^{\tau} \tag{223}$$

i.e.,

$$\frac{d}{d\tau}\,[\sin\,(iM + j\omega)] = \cos\,(iM + j\omega) \left[i\,\frac{dM}{d\tau} + j\,\frac{d\omega}{d\tau} \right].$$

Since

$$M = L - \Omega - \omega,$$

$$\frac{dM}{d\tau} = \frac{dL}{d\tau} - \frac{d\Omega}{d\tau} - \frac{d\omega}{d\tau} = \frac{n}{k_e} + \bar{n}_s{}'\tau + L_s{}' - \Omega_s{}' - \omega_s{}'$$

$d\omega/d\tau = \omega_s{}'$; so that

$$i\,\frac{dM}{d\tau} + j\,\frac{d\omega}{d\tau} = i\,\frac{n}{k_e} + i\bar{n}_s{}'\tau + iL_s{}' - i\Omega_s{}' + (j - i)\omega_s{}',$$

where the s subscript denotes secular or nonperiodic, monotonic variations of the variable, e.g., $\bar{n}_s'$ is the average value over one period. From Eq. (212) (with the e^2 terms not shown in (212) added) the secular terms can be picked out as

$$L_s' = -\sqrt{\frac{\mu}{p}}\frac{J}{p^3}\left[\cos i(1-\cos i)\left(1-\frac{3}{2}e^2\right)+\left(1-\frac{3}{2}\sin^2 i\right)\left(2-\frac{9}{2}e^2\right) + \cdots\right], \tag{224}$$

whereas a similar analysis carried out for ω and Ω by Kozai and others yields

$$\omega_s' = \sqrt{\frac{\mu}{p}}\frac{J}{p^3}\left[\left(2-\frac{5}{2}\sin^2 i\right)-e^2\left(3-\frac{15}{4}\sin^2 i\right)+\cdots\right] \tag{225}$$

and

$$\Omega_s' = -\sqrt{\frac{\mu}{p}}\frac{J}{p^3}\cos i\left[\left(1-\frac{3}{2}e^2\right)+\cdots\right]. \tag{226}$$

Often it may be legitimately assumed that $\bar{n}_s'$, L_s', Ω_s', and ω_s' are all negligibly small when compared to n/k_e.

As an interesting example we again choose the eccentricity, and invoke the preceding assumption concerning the neglect of $\bar{n}_s'$, L_s', Ω_s', and ω_s'.

$$\begin{aligned} e - e_0 = \int_0^\tau e'\,d\tau = &+\frac{J}{n}\sqrt{\frac{\mu}{p}}\frac{k_e}{p^3}\left\{\left(1-\frac{3}{2}\sin^2 i\right)\left[\cos M + \frac{3e}{2}\cos 2M\right]\right. \\ &+\frac{1}{2}\sin^2 i\left[\frac{1}{2}\cos(M+2\omega)-\frac{e}{2}\cos(2M+2\omega)+\frac{7}{6}\cos(3M+2\omega)\right. \\ &\left.\left.+\frac{17}{4}e\cos(4M+2\omega)\right]\right\} \\ &+\frac{H}{5}\sqrt{\frac{\mu}{p}}\frac{k_e}{np^4}\sin i\left\{\left(1-\frac{5}{4}\sin^2 i\right)\left[\frac{33e}{4}\sin(-M+\omega)\right.\right. \\ &-\frac{3n}{\omega_s'}\sin\omega-\frac{3}{2}e\sin(M+\omega)+\frac{9}{2}\sin(2M+\omega) \\ &\left.+\frac{53}{4}e\sin(3M+\omega)\right]+\frac{5}{4}\sin^2 i\left[-\frac{e}{4}\sin(M+3\omega)\right. \\ &+\frac{1}{2}\sin(2M+3\omega)-\frac{e}{2}\sin(3M+3\omega)+\frac{5}{4}\sin(4M+3\omega) \\ &\left.\left.+\frac{127}{20}e\sin(5M+3\omega)\right]\right\}+\cdots. \end{aligned} \tag{227}$$

It should be noted in passing that the foregoing expression has been employed inversely by Walters and Herrick to identify the third harmonic or H term of the Earth's gravitational potential from satellite data, e.g., for satellite $1958\beta_2$ (cf. Herrick[95] and O'Keefe and Eckels[100]) $i = 34.^\circ 255$, $\omega_s` = 0.71756 \times 10^{-3}$ radians/k_e^{-1} min, $e = 0.19018$, and $a = 1.36185$. The one dominant long period term in the $e - e_0$ variation is clearly

$$-\frac{3H}{5p^4}\sqrt{\frac{\mu}{p}}\frac{k_e}{\omega_s`}\sin i\left(1 - \frac{5}{4}\sin^2 i\right)\sin\omega, \quad \text{i.e., } n/\omega_s` \text{ is a large quantity.}$$

From an analysis of the satellite data for $1958\beta_2$ the maximum amplitude of this long period term could be isolated. Given that this amplitude, $e_{\max} - e_0 \cong 5 \times 10^{-4}$, and given the orbital elements, it can be shown that $H \cong 6 \times 10^{-6}$ (cf. Herrick and Walters[95]).

9.2.4.2. Drag

In the case of drag, since $r\dot{b}` = 0$, only $n`$ (or $a`$), $e`$, and $\omega`$ are nonzero. Furthermore, in the case of $\omega`$, an inspection of the formula shows that at perigee $\omega`$ will be zero, i.e., $r\dot{r}` = 0$ and $\sin v = 0$ at perigee. Thus, as Nonweiler[97] points out, the variation of ω may be neglected.

The variation in n per perigee passage can be obtained by an integration of $n`$ in the neighborhood of perigee. Let us assume that the atmosphere is important only for a distance of two scale heights above the perigee altitude; consequently, the integration limits on r will be from $r = r_2 + H_2/2$ to $r = q$ (or to $r = r_1 - H_1/2$). If it is assumed that the orbit is symmetrical about perigee, the integrals, in terms of τ, have the following form:

$$n - n_0 = 2\int_{\tau \text{ at } r_2+H_2/2}^{\tau \text{ at } r_2-H_2/2} n`\,d\tau + 2\int_{\tau \text{ at } r_2-H_2/2=r_1+H_1/2}^{\tau \text{ at } q=r_1-H_1/2} n`\,d\tau; \qquad (228)$$

where $n \rightarrow a$ and e and the extension to more than two scale heights is straightforward.

Transformation to v as independent variable will be expedited by recognizing that

$$\int \frac{v^n}{r^2}\,d\tau = \int \frac{v^n}{r^2}\frac{dv}{(\dot{v} + v_s`)},$$

where

$$v_s` = -J\sqrt{\frac{\mu}{p}}\frac{1}{p^3}\left(1 - \frac{3}{2}\sin^2 i\right) + \cdots \text{ and}$$

$$\dot{v} = \sqrt{\mu p}/r^2.$$

If it is assumed that $\dot{v} \gg v_s^\backprime$, then

$$\int_{\tau_1}^{\tau_2} \frac{v^n}{r^2}\, d\tau = \frac{v^{(n+1)}}{\sqrt{\mu p}(n+1)}\bigg|_{v_1}^{v_2}.$$

The limits, in terms of v, may be obtained from $r = q[1 + (ev^2/2) - \cdots]$ i.e.,

$$v_1 = \sqrt{\frac{2}{e}\{(r_1/q) - 1\}} \quad \text{and} \quad v_2 = \sqrt{\frac{2}{e}\{(r_2/q) - 1\}}.$$

Thus, considering only integration over the first scale height, we find that

$$\log_e\left[\frac{n}{n_0}\right] = 2\Psi\sqrt{\frac{\mu}{p}}\left\{\frac{(1+e)^2}{1-e}\int_0^{v_1} dv - \frac{e}{2}\int_0^{v_1}\left[\frac{1}{1-e} - \frac{a(1+e)}{H_1}\right] v^2\, dv\right\}$$

$$= 2\Psi\left[a(1+e)v_1 - \frac{ae}{(1+e)}\frac{H_1 - p}{H_1}\frac{v_1^3}{6}\right]. \quad (229)$$

Thus, the mean value of $n_s^\backprime$ is

$$\bar{n}_s^\backprime = \frac{(n - n_0)}{2\pi k_e} n_0$$

$$= \left[\exp\left\{2\Psi\left[a(1+e)v_1 - \frac{ae}{(1+e)}\frac{H_1 - p}{H_1}\frac{v_1^3}{6}\right]\right\} - 1\right] n_0^2/2\pi k_e. \quad (230)$$

9.2.5. General

Other integrals can be evaluated in a similar fashion to those of the last section. A useful set might be

$$a = a_0 + \int_0^\tau a^\backprime d\tau + \bar{a}_s^\backprime \tau$$

$$e = e_0 + \int_0^\tau e^\backprime\, d\tau + \bar{e}_s^\backprime \tau$$

$$i = i_0 + \int_0^\tau i^\backprime\, d\tau$$

$$\Omega = \Omega_0 + \int_0^\tau \Omega^\backprime\, d\tau$$

$$\pi = \pi_0 + \int_0^\tau \pi^\backprime\, d\tau$$

$$L = L_0 + \frac{n_0}{k_e}\tau + \int\int_0^\tau n^\backprime\, d\tau^2 + \int_0^\tau L^\backprime\, d\tau + \frac{\bar{n}_s^\backprime \tau^2}{2} \quad (231)$$

where the mean values $\bar{a}_s'$, $\bar{e}_s'$, and $\bar{n}_s'$ are the mean variations of these quantities caused by perigee drag; and the other integrals indicate the variation resulting from the Earth's gravitational harmonics. Other sets, e.g., the components of $\mathbf{U}_0$ and $\mathbf{V}_0$ or $\mathbf{a}$ and $\mathbf{h}$ etc. might prove to be a more profitable set for low e or low i orbits.

The foregoing formulae are accurate over limited ranges of e, e.g., the drag series expanded about $v = 0$ are accurate for $1 > e > 1/300$; while the gravitational harmonic series, expanded about $e = 0$, are good for $\frac{1}{2} > e > 0$. The drag integration can be carried out for values of $e < 1/300$ by utilizing the same series development as was employed in the case of gravitational harmonics (note that the drag perturbation acts almost continuously throughout the orbit for very small e).

As has been pointed out by Rowell and Smith,[98] Vinti,[99] and more recently by Sterne,[101] if one considers a *rotating* Earth there exist perturbative forces acting normal to the orbit plane. As a consequence of this they obtain a secular change in i (there also will exist a secular change in Ω, but this is presumably smaller than the term caused by the Earth's asphericity). Sterne finds that a "retardation in the determination of orbital period and eccentricity is produced in direct satellite orbits" if one considers a rotating rather than a fixed atmosphere because $|\mathbf{v}| < \dot{s}$—the reverse would be true for a retrograde orbit i.e., the orbital period and e would decrease more rapidly.

9.3. Three-Body Perturbations

The variation in the orbital elements occasioned by a third body, e.g., the Sun or Moon, can be computed in a manner similar to that followed in the preceding analysis. In this regard we will follow the work of Kozai[102] and utilize the perturbative potential, R. From Kozai's analysis

$$e' = -[\sqrt{1-e^2}/na^2e]\frac{\partial R}{\partial \omega}, \tag{232}$$

$$i' = [(na^2\sqrt{1-e^2}\sin i)]^{-1}\left[\frac{\partial R}{\partial \omega}\cos i - \frac{\partial R}{\partial \Omega}\right] \tag{233}$$

etc.

The partial derivatives indicated in these equations can be evaluated from Eqs. (166) and (167) if it is recognized that $u = v + \omega$.

As has been noted by O'Keefe, the luni-solar perturbations can be quite influential on highly eccentric satellites (see Kozai[103] for the effect of lunar perturbations on satellite 1959δ_2) and as discussed in Baker,[104] such perturbations, therefore, play a significant role in the analysis of the braking ellipse maneuver for return from interplanetary voyages. Furthermore, a significant "lift" in perigee distance occasioned by lunar perturbations could be utilized to increase the longevity of a near Earth satellite. Conversely, its lifetime could be decreased as in the case of 1959δ_2 and hence the relative position of the satellite's orbit and the Sun and/or Moon must be carefully considered.

10 NONGRAVITATIONAL AND RELATIVISTIC EFFECTS

The nongravitational effects discussed in this chapter are those arising from transitional drag, low thrust, electromagnetic fields, the absorption and re-emission of solar radiation, and radiation pressure. Relativistic effects are also included because of their influence on the motions of objects moving at high speed or in intense gravitational fields. All these effects usually play the role of perturbations of the second order, and they present a promising field for future research. No attempt is made to give a comprehensive discussion of any of these perturbations and the reader is invited to consult the listed references for a more detailed analysis.

10.1. Transitional Drag and Sputtering

Space vehicles, whether satellites or returning vehicles from interplanetary space, are affected by transitional drag while still on the periphery of the Earth's atmosphere. The transitional regime is defined as that aerodynamic regime of flow between the free-molecule flow and the slip flow regimes in which atmospheric molecules that have hit the surface of the vehicle and are emitted, scatter other atmospheric molecules in the neighborhood of the vehicle and, consequently, modify the flow of molecules around the space vehicle.

Free molecular flow is defined as the limiting flow where the molecules emitted from the surface of a space vehicle have no further effect, a condition that requires that the *mean free path* of molecules emitted from the surface of the space vehicle be much longer than a characteristic dimension of the vehicle, e.g., its diameter d. As soon as the mean free path of the emitted molecules becomes comparable with a characteristic dimension, the molecules begin to affect the flow and, in particular, tend to shield the vehicle from the oncoming stream of molecules. Such shielding will decrease the heat transferred to the vehicle, the drag coefficient, and modify the lift and pitching moment of the vehicle. Only the drag coefficient will be considered in the following discussion. For an analysis of lift and moment on a space vehicle the reader is referred to a paper by Charwat.[105]

Consider a space vehicle with cross-sectional or projected area, A, progressing through a resisting medium with speed $\mathbf{v}$. In time dt a volume $A\nu dt$ will be swept out by the object, (see Fig. 34). If there are N atoms per unit volume each of mass m, then the increment of momentum transmitted

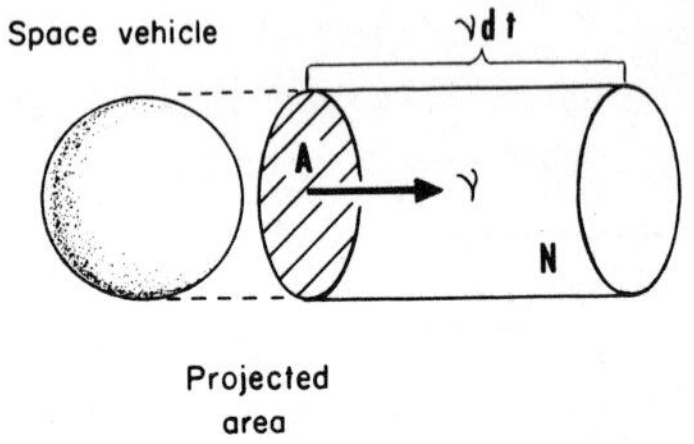

FIG. 34. Motion in free-molecule flow.

to the object in time dt by the oncoming stream will be $A\nu Nm\nu$. Assuming that the molecules upon reaching the surface of the object stick to it, then the total drag force, f_D, acting on the object will be simply $mNA\nu^2 = \rho A\nu^2$, where ρ is the local atmospheric density.

The classical definition of the drag coefficient C_D is as follows:

$$C_D \triangleq f_D/\tfrac{1}{2}\rho A\nu^2. \tag{234}$$

Hence, for this particular case, we find after substitution of $f_D = \rho A\nu^2$ into Eq. (234) that the drag coefficient is 2. Still in keeping with the assumptions of free-molecular flow one can also take into account the momentum transferred to the object by the emitted molecules. This momentum is quite small if the molecules leave the surface at a very low speed. Such would be the case if the molecules were *accommodated* to a speed associated with a thermal speed at the temperature of the object's surface. Hence the term *accommodation coefficient*, α. If this coefficient is zero there is no accommodation, if unity there is complete accommodation. If, however, the oncoming molecules are not perfectly accommodated, then the speed of the emitted molecules may be quite significant and the drag coefficient will have a value greater than 2 because of the momentum carried away by these emitted molecules. At this writing the data concerning the value of this accommodation coefficient is incomplete and to a certain degree ambiguous. Hence it is impossible to determine the precise value. In fact, as has been noted by Schaaf, disassociation of oncoming nitrogen molecules might remove so much of their energy that their speeds upon emission would become very small. Thus the "effective" value of α would be increased by this atomic process; this and other such processes greatly complicate the picture. The effect of the speed of the emitted molecules on drag will be explicitly derived for a flat plate; see Eq. (238).

As can be recognized in a quantitative way, the slower the emitted molecules emerge from the surface the greater will be their shielding effect on the oncoming molecular stream (i.e., a "cloud" of emitted molecules will form). Thus, the basic assumption of free-molecule flow is no longer valid (i.e., emitted molecules will scatter oncoming molecules) and the transitional flow effect must be considered. See Fig. 35, where the scattering at (a) deflects the oncoming molecule and prevents it from impacting the vehicle, the scattering at (b) has no net effect as the oncoming molecule is still scattered in such a way to impact the vehicle (at a different angle of incidence, however), and finally, the scattering at (c) deflects an oncoming molecule that would not have impacted the vehicle into an impact. The balance between these transitional flow effects will cause a net *decrease* in momentum transmitted to the vehicle by the atmospheric molecules. The magnitude of these effects will be dependent upon the ratio of a characteristic dimension of the vehicle d to the mean free path L_{eo}. The mean-free path, L_{eo}, is *not* the "ambient" mean-free path L_{oo} of the oncoming molecules in the atmosphere, but rather the shorter mean-free path of the slowly moving emitted molecules (e) relative to the field of oncoming molecules (o). That these paths are different can be gleaned from a consideration of the collision frequency—see Baker and Charwat.[106] This ratio has been denoted as B in reference 106, α in reference 107, and is sometimes called the inverse of a modified Knudsen number (such a usage of α should not be confused with its more common association with accommodation and right ascension). The effect of the transitional regime on satellites has been discussed by Whitney[108] and found to be particularly significant for satellites that come within 200 km of the Earth's surface. The transitional effects acting on vehicles on a return maneuver, i.e., during atmospheric braking is also found to be significant (cf. Baker[104]).

The combined effects of surface temperature of the space vehicle, T_s °K;

accommodation coefficient, α; molecular weight of the emitted molecules, m_e; number of nontransitional degrees of freedom excited in the surface-collision process, j; local atmospheric density ratio $\sigma = \rho/\rho_0$ (ρ_0 = the sea-

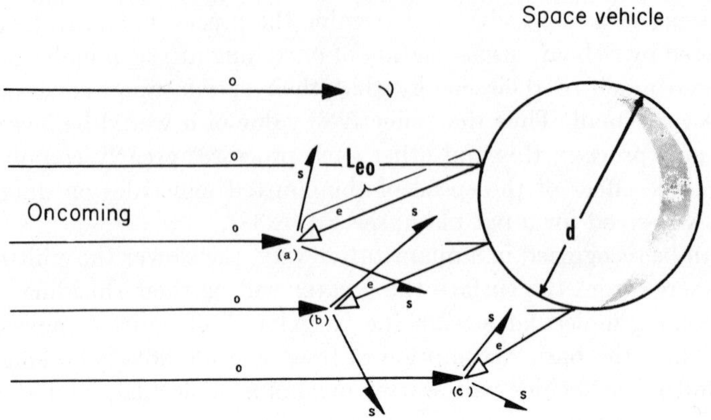

FIG. 35. Schematic of transitional flow scattering (motion relative to vehicle).

level density); characteristic length of the space vehicle, d in centimeters; and the speed of the vehicle $\mathbf{v}$ (in terms of surface circular-satellite speed) on the drag coefficient is given by

$$C_D = C_{D0}[a + b \exp(-c\sigma)], \text{ or } \gamma(\sigma) = C_D/C_{D0} = a + b \exp(-c\sigma) \quad (235)$$

where C_{D0} = the reference hypersonic continuum-flow drag-coefficient;

$$a \cong 1;$$

$$b \cong C_{DF}/C_{D0} - 1;$$

C_{DF} = the free-molecule-flow value of the drag coefficient;

$$c = C_{DF}d(4.7 \times 10^5 + 2.86 \times 10^6 F)/C_{D0}m_e bF;$$

and

$$F^2 \triangleq (1 - \alpha)/(4 + j) + 1.33 \times 10^{-4}\alpha T_s/m_e v^2. \quad \text{(see Baker[110])}$$

The exponential variation of C_D shown in Eq. (235) is also in agreement with experimental data found, for example, by N. A. Jensen in Fig. 36.

As an illustrative example of the principles involved in the transitional-drag analysis, let us compute the transitional drag of an infinitesimal disk moving with its face normal to its velocity. The analysis will consider only the effect of the first-order collisions and will assume an accommodation coefficient of unity.

The number of molecules reaching an infinitesimal area, dS', situated at a vector distance, $\mathbf{l}$, from a diffusely emitting surface, dS, is directly

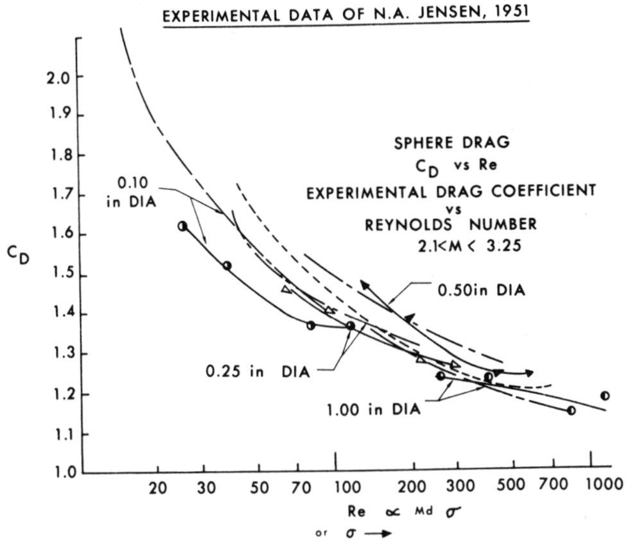

FIG. 36. Drag coefficient variation with density ratio.

proportional to the cosine of the angle that $\mathbf{l}$ forms with respect to the surface normal, $\mathbf{n}$ at dS (i.e., the angle Ω) and inversely proportional to the square of the distance l (see Fig. 37). Thus the incremental number of molecules that reach the infinitesimal area per unit time is

$$d\dot{n} = k_1 \dot{n}_s \frac{\cos \Omega}{l^2} \frac{dS}{S} dS',$$

where k_1 is a constant of proportionality, $\dot{n}_s$ is the total number of molecules per unit time reaching the surface S (i.e., the whole disk), and Ω is the angle between $\mathbf{l}$ and $\mathbf{n}$. Now k_1 can be evaluated by recognizing that the molecules are conserved; hence $k_1 = 1/\pi$, and

$$\frac{d\dot{n}}{dS'} = \frac{\dot{n}_s}{\pi} \frac{\cos \Omega}{l^2} \frac{dS}{S}. \tag{236}$$

The increment of momentum per unit time (i.e., the incremental force) transferred in the ν-direction by the emitted molecules with average speed $\bar{V}_e$ ($= 0.171 \sqrt{T_s/m_e}$ km/sec) passing through the incremental surface dS' of the sphere S' from the incremental area dS is

$$dF_e = m_u m_e \bar{V}_e \cos \Omega \left(\frac{d\dot{n}}{dS'} \, dS' \right), \tag{237}$$

where dF_e is the incremental ν-directed force (i.e., the drag force) m_u is the mass of a unit atomic weight in grams (1.66×10^{-24} gm), and m_e is the atomic weight of an emitted molecule. Integrating Eq. (237) over S' from 0 to $\pi/2$, we find that the drag force due to the emitted molecules is (with $dS' = 2\pi \sin \Omega l^2 d\Omega$)

$$F_e = \frac{2}{3} m_u m_e \bar{V}_e \dot{n}_s \int \frac{dS}{S} = \frac{2}{3} m_u m_e \bar{V}_e \dot{n}_s, \tag{238}$$

a result that was previously obtained by Epstein. At this point we have accounted fully for the drag under the assumption of free molecule flow, i.e., under the assumption that the emitted molecules do not affect the flow by scattering.

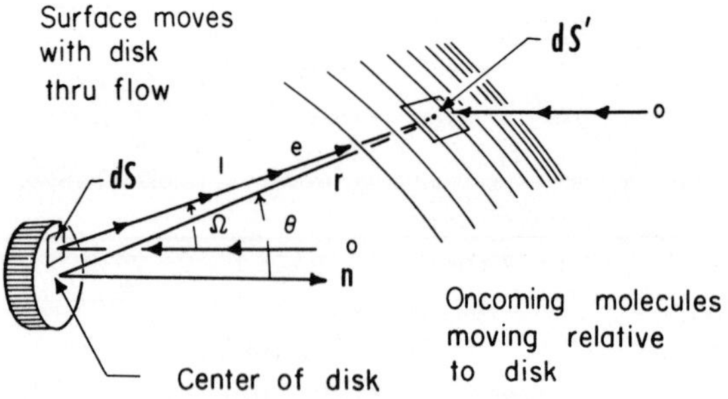

FIG. 37. Molecule emitted from disk (motion relative to disk).

Consider next that the surface S of the disk that is emitting molecules is replaced by an identical surface S'' that receives scattered molecules. Thus S and S'' are functionally, but not physically, different and serve only to compartmentalize the analysis. The number of molecules per unit time returning to the incremental area dS'' of the disk from the volume element $dS'dl$ is given by

$$\frac{d\dot{n}}{dS''} \, dS'' = k_2 \frac{d\dot{n}}{dS'} \, dS' \frac{dn}{dl} \, dl \left[\cos \Omega - \frac{\bar{V}_e}{\nu} (1 + \cos^2 \Omega) \right] \frac{\cos \Omega \, dS''}{l^2}, \tag{239}$$

where k_2 is a constant of proportionality; dn/dl is the fraction of molecules that reach and are scattered in the incremental distance dl; $[\cos \Omega - (\bar{V}_e/\nu)(1 + \cos^2 \Omega)]$ is the angular decrease in the number of molecules scattered from $dS'dl$, for $0 \leqslant \Omega \leqslant \pi/2$ and $\bar{V}_e < \nu$; and $(\cos \Omega dS'')/l^2$ is the solid angle subtended by dS'' with respect to $dS'dl$. Also k_2 can be evaluated exactly like k_1 and one finds that $k_2 = 2/\pi$.

The ν-component of momentum per unit time reaching the incremental area dS'' of the disk (S'') from $dS'dl$ (i.e., the force occasioned by the return of scattered molecules with atomic weight m_e) is given by

$$dF = \frac{d\dot{n}}{dS''} dS''(m_u m_e \nu \cos \Omega) \cos \Omega, \tag{240}$$

where one factor $\cos \Omega$ arises from the cosine decrease in the scattering speed (the $\bar{V}_e/\nu$ dependence of scattering speed is found to be of second order) and the other factor $\cos \Omega$ arises by taking into account only the ν-component of the force. Thus

$$dF_{scs} = \frac{2}{\pi^2} \frac{\dot{n}_s}{l^4} \frac{dS}{S} \frac{dn}{dl} dl m_u m_e \nu \cos^4 \Omega \left[\cos \Omega - \frac{\bar{V}_e}{\nu} (1 + \cos^2 \Omega) \right] dS' \, dS'',^* \tag{241}$$

where $dS' = 2\pi \sin \Omega \, l^2 \, d\Omega$.

In the limit of a small disk of diameter δ, l and Ω go over into r and θ (the polar coordinates of dS' as measured from the center of this disk; see Fig. (37)). Consequently, integration over S' yields

$$\begin{aligned} \left.\frac{dF}{dr}\right|_{scs} &= \dot{n}_s m_u m_e \nu \left(\frac{\delta}{r}\right)^2 \frac{dn}{dr} \int_0^{\pi/2} \left[\cos^5 \theta \sin \theta - \frac{\bar{V}_e}{\nu} (\cos^4 \theta \sin \theta \right. \\ &\qquad \left. - \cos^6 \theta \sin \theta) \right] d\theta \\ &= \dot{n}_s m_u m_e \nu \left(\frac{\delta}{r}\right)^2 \frac{dn}{dr} \left[\frac{1}{6} - \frac{\bar{V}_e}{\nu} \left(\frac{12}{35}\right) \right]. \end{aligned} \tag{242}$$

The drag force produced by the emitted molecules deflecting oncoming molecules out of the way (or rather the diminution of force) is simply

$$\left.\frac{dF}{dr}\right|_{scd} = -m_u m_e \nu \frac{dn}{dr} \int_C \frac{d\dot{n}}{dS'} dS',^* \tag{243}$$

* The subscript *scs* refers to molecules scattered back to the disk, and subscript *scd* refers to molecules deflected from the disk by the emitted molecules.

where the integral is computed over the end of a cylinder C that is swept out by the disk during its flight; molecules that are scattered out of this cylinder decrease the net drag force. Accordingly, we have

$$\left.\frac{dF}{dr}\right|_{scd} = -2m_u m_e \nu \dot{n}_s \frac{dn}{dr} \int_{\theta=0}^{\theta=\sin^{-1}(\delta/2r)} \cos\theta \sin\theta \, d\theta$$

or

$$= -\frac{m_u m_e \nu}{4} \dot{n}_s \left(\frac{\delta}{r}\right)^2 \frac{dn}{dr}. \tag{244}$$

If we assume that the density of the oncoming stream is not significantly modified by scattering, then the fraction of the molecules scattered between r and $r + dr$ is

$$\frac{dn}{dr} dr = \frac{e^{-(r-\delta/2)/L_{eo}}}{L_{eo}} dr, \tag{245}$$

where $r - \delta/2$ measures a rather arbitrary distance out from a point in space where the assumptions of an infinitesimal disk are valid (i.e., a distance $\delta/2$ out from the disk), and L_{eo} is the mean-free path of the emitted molecules with respect to the oncoming molecules.

Hence the integration for the force occasioned by the scattered molecules becomes

$$F_{sc} = F_{scs} + F_{scd} = m_u m_e \nu \dot{n}_s \left[\frac{1}{6} - \frac{\bar{V}_e}{\nu}\left(\frac{12}{35}\right) - \frac{1}{4}\right] \int_{\delta/2}^{\infty} \left(\frac{\delta}{r}\right)^2 \frac{dn}{dr} dr. \tag{246}$$

But

$$\frac{1}{L_{eo}} \int_{\delta/2}^{\infty} \left(\frac{\delta}{r}\right)^2 [e^{-(r-\delta/2)/L_{eo}}] \, dr = 2Be^{+B/2}E_2(B),$$

where $B \triangleq \delta/L_{eo}$, $R \triangleq r/(\delta/2)$, and $E_2(B)$ is a second-order exponential integral that may be found tabulated in Jahnke and Emde[111] (second order may be obtained through a recursion formula). We can expand $E_2(B)$ about $B = 0$ and obtain

$$E_2(B) = \int_1^{\infty} \frac{e^{-RB/2}}{R^2} dR = e^{-B/2} - \frac{B}{2}[\gamma_0 + \ln B - B + \cdots] \tag{247}$$

(where γ_0 = Euler's or Mascheroni's constant = 0.5772157). Thus

$$\int_{\delta/2}^{\infty} \left(\frac{\delta}{r}\right)^2 \frac{dn}{dr} dr \cong 2B \qquad \text{for} \qquad B \ll 1.$$

Therefore, finally,

$$F_{sc} = -m_u m_e \nu \dot{n}_s \left[(0.17)B + (0.68) \frac{\bar{V}_e}{\nu} B \right]; \tag{248}$$

so that the total drag force, F_D, occasioned by the oncoming, emitted, and scattered molecules is

$$F_D = F_o + F_e + F_{sc} = m_u m_e \nu \dot{n}_s \left[1 + \frac{2}{3} \frac{\bar{V}_e}{\nu} - 0.17B - 0.68 \frac{\bar{V}_e}{\nu} B \right]. \tag{249}$$

If it is noted that $\dot{n}_s = SN\nu$ ($S \equiv A$) and $\rho = m_u m_e N$, then the transitional drag coefficient in the limit of very low densities becomes

$$C_D = 2 \left[1 - 0.17B + (0.667 - 0.68B) \frac{\bar{V}_e}{\nu} \right]. \tag{250}$$

The coefficients of the more general formula (235), which is valid for higher densities than is Eq. (250), can be derived from the foregoing by analyses outlined in Baker.[106,109,110]

The drag occasioned by the space vehicle encountering meteoritic dust is almost identical to the neutral particle drag in the sticky surface model, the only unknown being the density of these small micrometeoritic particles in space. It has, however, been estimated that this density is between 1 and 5×10^{-20} gm/cm^3 or between 150 and 750 meteoritic atoms/cm^3.

The effect of *sputtering* or the almost instantaneous ejection of one or more surface atoms that results from the surface collision of an oncoming molecule, also causes a modification of the drag coefficient. This modification results because the sputtered atoms, due to their high speed, carry away a relatively large amount of momentum in the direction of the vehicle's motion and, hence, a "reverse-rocket" effect noted by Whipple causes an increase in drag. Sputtering differs from vaporization in that all of the molecules forming the surface need not be raised to the vibrational energy corresponding to the energy of sublimation in order for ejection to take place; furthermore, the molecules may be ejected from the surface with far greater energy than they would be if they were vaporized. This latter effect modifies the ablation and hence the luminosity of meteors and is discussed in reference 19. Equation (249) shows directly the influence of a large emission speed of molecules, $\bar{V}_e$, on the drag force acting on an infinitesimal plate.

If m_e is the atomic weight of an emitted (vaporized or sputtered) atom; m_o is the atomic weight of an oncoming atmospheric molecule; ν is, as usual, the speed of the vehicle relative to the atmosphere (in terms of surface circular-satellite speed); $\dot{n}_o$ is the number of oncoming molecules per second reaching the vehicle's surface; $\bar{\nu}_{sp}$ is the average speed of the sputtered atoms; and $\dot{n}_{sp}$ is the number of atoms sputtered per second; then the drag coefficient of a spherical body undergoing sputtering in free molecular flow is[19]

$$C_D = C_{D_0}\left\{1 + (0.444)\left(\frac{m_e}{m_o}\right)\left(\frac{\bar{\nu}_{sp}}{\nu}\right)\left(\frac{\dot{n}_{sp}}{\dot{n}_o}\right)\right\}$$

$$= C_{D_0}\left\{1 + \frac{(0.444)}{\nu}\left(\frac{m_e}{m_o}\right)\left(\frac{\bar{\epsilon}m_o}{m_e}\right)^{1/2}\beta V_{c0}^2(\nu^2 - \nu_t^2)^{3/2}\right\} \tag{251}$$

for $\nu > \nu_t$

where $\bar{\epsilon}$ = the average efficiency for energy transfer between oncoming and emitted sputtered atoms*; β is a measure of the slope of the sputtering yield*; V_{c0} is the surface circular-satellite speed in cgs units $= 7.905 \times 10^5$ cm/sec; and ν_t is the sputtering threshold speed.* If vaporization ablation occurs simultaneously, a more extensive formula is involved. Actually the effect of sputtering is quite small for vehicles returning from space missions on geocentric hyperbolic orbits and perhaps negligible for most geocentric satellites. Nevertheless, for meteorites and hyperspeed space vehicles the phenomenon is still influential.

Although of little dynamical consequence sputtering may have a very deleterious effect on certain photosensitive or other detector surface or upon optical surfaces. It has been estimated that there exist streams of protons in interplanetary space having a density between 10^3 and 10^5 particles per cm^3 and a speed of between 500 and 1500 km/sec that could produce significant sputtering.

10.2. Low Thrust Forces†

As is now well known, low-thrust propulsive devices, e.g., ion or plasma rocket motors, could be very efficiently utilized in a transfer from a geocentric satellite orbit to a planetocentric satellite orbit. Although the

* For definition of terms see Baker.[19]

† Superhigh thrust propulsion, e.g., the successive high impulses achieved by detonating nuclear charges aft of a space vehicle, also have unique astrodynamical features. For such devices exceedingly large thrust misalignments, caused by buffer shield tilt or off-axis detonations, would cause rather extensive and instantaneous perturbations that must be immediately corrected by the navigational-guidance system.

characteristics of these low-thrust propulsive units are entirely outside the scope of astrodynamics, their incorporation in the orbit computations is still germane.

Ordinarily the low-thrust devices would produce accelerations that could be treated as perturbations. In fact, as has been pointed out by Pitkin, a certain practical simplification arises because the thrust accelerations may be of constant magnitude or at worst a function of time—not position! The thrust force per unit mass may be resolved into three components; radial, circumferential, and normal (i.e., in the **U**, **V**, **W** directions), see Fig. 38. The tangential and vertical components may be rotated into directions of increasing right ascension, α, and declination, δ, as shown in Fig. 38. The trigonometry of the problem is discussed in detail in Appendix A in Baker.[78] Note that T_α, T_δ, T_v, and T_w are all in a plane tangent to the reference sphere as shown in the figure. The radial, T_r, and transverse, T_v, components of thrust are shown in Fig. 39. We have then

$$T_\alpha = T_v \cos\mu - T_w \sin\mu,$$

$$T_\delta = T_w \cos\mu + T_v \sin\mu,$$

and

$$T_r = T_r. \tag{252}$$

Expressions for sin μ and cos μ may be obtained from the spherical trigonometry of Fig. 38 and Fig. 40;

$$\cos\mu = r\sqrt{\frac{1-(Q_z^2+P_z^2)}{x^2+y^2}}$$

and

$$\sin\mu = \sqrt{\frac{(Q_z^2+P_z^2)r^2 - z^2}{x^2+y^2}}. \tag{253}$$

The x, y, and z components of perturbative thrust acceleration can then be obtained as

$$\dot{x}' = T_r \cos\delta\cos\alpha - T_\delta \sin\delta\cos\alpha - T_\alpha \sin\alpha,$$

$$\dot{y}' = T_r \cos\delta\sin\alpha - T_\delta \sin\delta\sin\alpha + T_\alpha \cos\alpha,$$

and

$$\dot{z}' = T_r \sin\delta + T_\delta \cos\delta, \tag{254}$$

where right ascension and declination in an equatorial system are obtained as usual from

$$\sin\alpha = y/\sqrt{x^2+y^2},$$

$$\cos\alpha = x/\sqrt{x^2+y^2},$$

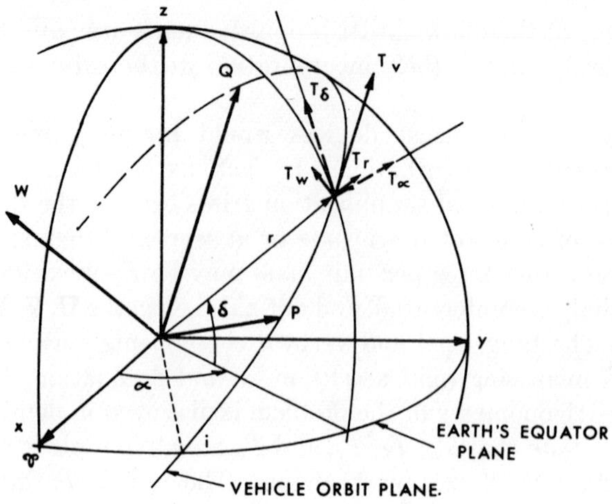

FIG. 38. Thrust components.

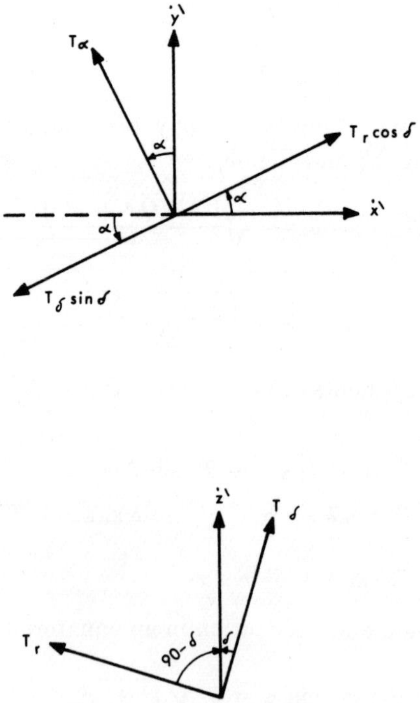

FIG. 39. Radial and transverse components.

and

$$\sin \delta = z/r$$
$$\cos \delta = \sqrt{x^2 + y^2}/r.$$

The perturbative derivatives are then functions of only T_w, T_v, T_r, x, y, z, P_z, Q_z, all of which are presumably known at any time as we numerically

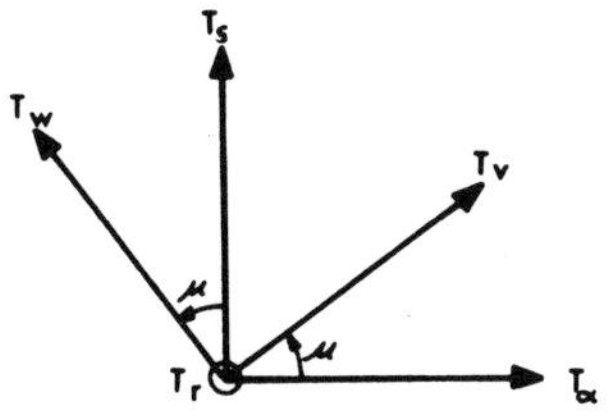

FIG. 40. Definition of the angle μ.

integrate the orbit. The thrust force per unit mass, which enters into Eqs. (252), may be expressed as

$$T = \dot{m}c/m$$

where $\dot{m}$ is the propellant flow rate, c the exhaust velocity, and m the instantaneous mass of the vehicle. The instantaneous mass is related to the initial mass m_0 by

$$m = m_0 - \int_{\tau_0}^{\tau} \dot{m}\, d\tau \qquad (\tau_0 \triangleq 0),$$

so that

$$T = T_0 \frac{\dot{m}c}{(m_0 - \dot{m}\tau)} \left(\frac{m_0}{\dot{m}c}\right) = T_0/(1 - \dot{m}\tau/m_0)$$

or

$$T = T_0 c/(c - T_0 \tau), \tag{255}$$

where T_0 is the initial thrust to mass ratio. The variation of thrust to mass ratio cannot, though small, be neglected in precise orbit computations.

A number of approximate integration methods suitable for feasibility studies have been proposed. In all cases only simple two-body orbits with the addition of a constant (or piecewise constant) thrust force have been investigated. Usually a normal force alone is considered for changing the orbit and a combination of circumferential and radial or tangential thrust force is employed to change orbit energy and eccentricity.

Stuhlinger[112] has proposed a method for use with very low tangential accelerations starting in a circular orbit. The first few hundred revolutions in an escape maneuver describe an orbit that is nearly circular with radius, a, so that the work done in each revolution on a vehicle of mass m is

$$\cong Tm2\pi a = \Delta \text{ Energy}. \tag{256}$$

From the *vis-viva* integral the total orbital energy is†

$$-\frac{\mu m}{2a}$$

so that

$$\Delta \text{ Energy} = \frac{\mu m}{2a^2}\,\Delta a$$

or

$$\Delta a \cong 4\pi T a^3/\mu. \tag{257}$$

The period for each cycle from Kepler's third law is

$$\Delta\tau = \frac{2\pi}{n} = \frac{2\pi a^{3/2}}{\sqrt{\mu}}. \tag{258}$$

The radius and time build-up are computed from these equations until a becomes greater than some specified value. Beyond this point special perturbations, i.e., numerical integration of the differential equations of motion, is carried out.

Tsien[113] and Levin[114] have developed approximate expressions for radius r in series form for purely circumferential thrust application. Tsien employs a power series expansion of the product of acceleration and time $(T/m)\tau$ while Levin employs a trigonometric series which, as he demonstrates, is more accurate.

The case of constant radial thrust has been considered by Tsien[113] and Copeland.[115] Exact closed solutions for r as a function of τ can be obtained, but this form unfortunately requires elliptic integrals. For very large accelerations, $T_r \gg 1$, these functions can also be expanded in series.

Levin[114] has shown that the node and inclination angles of nearly circular orbits vary under constant normal thrust as (cf. Eq. (186) p. 175)

$$\frac{d\Omega}{d\tau^*} \cong T_w a^2 \sin\tau^*/\sin i \tag{259}$$

† I.e., the *vis-viva* integral simply states that the kinetic energy $(m/2)\dot{s}^2$ plus the potential energy $-(m\mu/r)$ is a constant $-(m\mu/2a)$.

and from Eq. (185) with $T_w = r\dot{b}'$ and $r = p = a$

$$di/d\tau^* \cong T_w a^2 \cos \tau^* \tag{260}$$

where $\tau^* = U$, and for a circular orbit

$$\tau^* = U = M + \omega = \sqrt{\frac{\mu}{a^3}}\,\tau + \tau_0^*, \qquad \tau_0^* \triangleq k\sqrt{\frac{\mu}{a^3}}\,(t_0 - T) + \omega. \tag{261}$$

Irving and Blum[116] have computed a number of low-thrust interplanetary trajectories with constant tangential acceleration and find that it requires 39 cycles and 8.7 days to effect a maneuver for escape from the Earth from a 200-mile altitude satellite orbit with a $10^{-3}g$ acceleration. At $10^{-4}g$ the time was increased to 91.9 days and 398 cycles were required.

Perkins[117] has also considered the very important case of constant tangentially directed low-thrust acceleration. He finds that break away from an initially circular orbit with any acceleration less than 10^{-2} times local gravity can be characterized by a single generalized plot relating velocity and radial distance. The elapsed time for the maneuver is given in an adjunct plot. This graphical representation can be extremely useful for preliminary design studies.

In the preparation of this section we are greatly indebted to Edward Pitkin.

10.3. Electromagnetic Forces

Much interest has arisen of late in the investigation of electromagnetic forces (see e.g., the pioneering analysis described in Jastrow and Pearse[118] and Gringauz and Zelikman[119]). In this regard it should be recognized that there exists some gas in space at all altitudes, and this gas is essentially completely ionized, consisting mainly of free electrons and positively charged ions (usually the nuclei of hydrogen atoms) in equal concentrations. Even in interplanetary space it has been estimated that there are between 100 and 1000 charged particles per cubic centimeter. (See Section 5.1 for a discussion of the effect of these charged particles on radar determination of the solar parallax.) The energy of these small charged particles, termed *cosmoparticles* by F. C. Leonard, are measured in terms of *electron volts* (ev)—see the glossary of definitions.

Consider a unit surface existing in the plasma in which the electrons and positive ions are in thermal equilibrium. The rates at which the electrons and positive ions cross this surface will be proportional to their respective densities (assumed to be the same) and their respective speeds. As a direct consequence of this a body immersed in the plasma will be struck by more of the rapidly moving electrons than the slower positive ions and a net negative charge will be acquired by the object. When the negative potential of the objective is great enough to repel most of the electrons, a potential of a few volts will be reached. For example, this is the case of an ordinary probe suspended in a stationary plasma.

For a space vehicle moving at perhaps 8 km/sec, on the other hand, one encounters a trichotomy in which the ions move at about 1.2 km/sec (in keeping with a 2000°K kinetic temperature) and the electrons move at speeds of over 100 km/sec. Hence the positive ions are swept up,* i.e., the collision rate for positive ions is increased, whereas the collision rate for electrons will not be altered much above that of a stationary plasma; there fore, the negative potential is reduced somewhat (see Fig. 41). Thus the voltage on a satellite vehicle moving through a plasma is very small (cf. Chopra and Singer[121]). Nevertheless, the modification of the drag coefficient over the neutral drag coefficient is important in the consideration of perturbative forces acting on a satellite over many orbital periods. On the other hand, if the ion concentration is not neutral, then a larger force may be occasioned and the study of the drag of a satellite under these circumstances should prove to be interesting. Parenthetically, it should be noted that the photoelectric potential caused by high energy solar radiation striking the vehicle and expelling electrons is entirely negligible in view of the high conductivity of the plasma surrounding the vehicle.

A more quantitative study of satellite charging has recently been accomplished by Beard and Johnson[171] who find that the potential of a satellite moving through a plasma with speed ν is given by

$$\phi_0 = -\frac{kT}{q_e}\log_e\left(\frac{1}{2}\frac{\bar{\nu}_e}{\nu}\right)$$

where k is Boltzmann's constant ($= 1.380 \times 10^{-23}$ joule/°K), q_e is the charge of an electron ($= 1.602 \times 10^{-19}$ coulomb), T is the temperature of the plasma in °K, and $\bar{\nu}_e$ is the average thermal speed of the electrons in the plasma ($\bar{\nu}_e = 0.145\sqrt{T/m_e} = 0.145\sqrt{T/5.48 \times 10^{-4}}$ km/sec where m_e is the atomic weight of an electron; note that the average thermal speed of a molecule in a medium differs from the average thermal speed of a molecule leaving a surface, i.e., in the latter case $\bar{\nu}_e = 0.171\sqrt{T/m}$, cf. dis-

* In fact, C. L. Dolph has recently computed that there exists a cavity behind such a space vehicle, extending about fifty radii down stream, that has been swept free of many positive ions.

cussion of transitional drag). For $T = 2000°K$, $\bar{\nu}_e = 277$ km/sec, and $\nu = 8$ km/sec, we find that $\phi_0 = -0.49$ volts. This small negative potential attracts a few additional positive ions and, consequently, very slightly augments the momentum transferred to the satellite, i.e., it tends to increase the drag slightly.

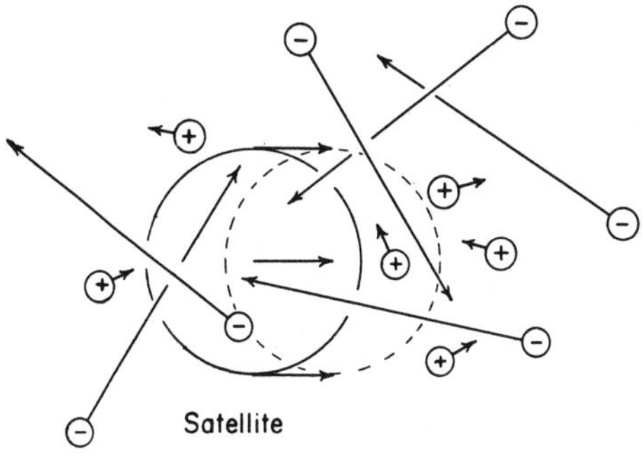

FIG. 41. Motion of satellite, electrons, and positive ions in a given length of time.

To gain some concept of the concentration of charged particles in space that might lead to electromagnetic forces on a satellite, it is useful to consider the present (1960) estimates for the flux and energy of those particles in the neighborhood of the Earth associated with the auroral zone, solar flares, solar winds, cosmic rays, and the inner and outer Van Allen radiation belts. The auroral zone, or the polar area where a large number of magnetic lines of force are directed vertically to the ground, includes protons and electrons whose fluxes amount to between 10^4 and 10^8 particles per cm^2 per sec and whose energies range between 10,000 and 100,000 ev. Solar flares, or small regions of the Sun that break out brightly, produce bursts having a flux between 10^3 and 10^4 protons per cm^2 per sec and 10 to 100 electrons per cm^2 per sec, both particles having energies ranging between 30 and 300 Mev. Solar winds, or low-energy protons and electrons that emanate from the Sun, have fluxes of 10^8 to 10^{10} particles per cm^2 per sec, the energy of the protons being 1000 to 100,000 (typically a few thousand) ev and of the electrons a few electron volts. Direct cosmic rays, mostly streams of protons with a few heavier nuclei, have flux rates something less than 2 per cm^2 per sec and energies in excess of 100 Mev. The inner Van Allen belt includes protons exhibiting fluxes of 1000 to 100,000 per cm^2 per sec with energies between 10,000 ev and 1 Mev (typically about 50,000 ev). The outer Van Allen belt includes protons exhibiting fluxes of less than one per cm^2 per sec with energies greater than 100

Mev and electrons exhibiting fluxes of between 10^4 and 10^8 particles per cm^2 per sec with energies between 20,000 ev and 1 Mev. The question of the effect of such particles and the associated magnetic fields on satellite dynamics is yet to be resolved.

One can also carry out a computation for the Lorentz force acting normal to the orbit plane caused by the fact that a charged satellite represents a current element moving through the Earth's magnetic field. In this case, as well, the effect of the magnetic force is extremely small. Also the Earth's magnetic field and the rotating metallic housing of the satellite induces in the latter eddy currents[122] and leads to the appearance of torques that retard the motion of a satellite about the center of mass; this retardation is small but might be taken into account in the investigation of the natural stability of satellite (cf. Roberson,[123] Baker,[124] and Robinson[125]).

There also exists a slight retardation of a space vehicle's center of mass due to its passage through a magnetic field. Such a motional-electromotive retardation force is simply a consequence of a conductor (the space vehicle) cutting through a magnetic field (e.g., the Earth's) and thereby building up a potential gradient (which amounts to at most 0.2 volts/meter if it passes normally through the Earth's magnetic field). This slight potential gradient has little effect on the incident positive ions but does deflect the less massive electrons. For space vehicles longer than 6 meters, one end becomes essentially grounded due to a high incidence flux of negative electrons, while the other end becomes positive (e.g., if the satellite is 10 meters long and passes normally through the Earth's field the other end has an induced voltage of $10 \times 0.2 = 2$ volts). The positive ions are still swept up by the front end of the satellite and thereby a current between this front end and the back end where the electrons strike is established. Due to this current a Lorentz force acts on the vehicle as it passes through the Earth's magnetic field and a slight retardation is experienced by the vehicle. As has been computed by Beard and Johnson[171] this retardation is equal to the aerodynamic drag for a 50 meter diameter satellite at an altitude of 1200 km.

10.4. Radiation Effects

The effect of solar radiation on particles moving through interplanetary space has been investigated for many years. In the case of very small meteorites or dust particles a theory was first developed by Poynting[126] and later refined in keeping with the principles of relativity by Robertson.[127]

The net effect of this *Poynting–Robertson* (P–R) force is to cause the eccentricity of small meteorites (or micrometeorites) to approach zero while their orbits spiral slowly into the neighborhood of the Sun.

Although the absorption and emission of light quanta produce no net force on a micrometeorite in a frame that is stationary with respect to the micrometeorite, when motion was referred to an inertial heliocentric frame a resisting force was found to act on the micrometeorite with a force proportional to its speed. Such a resisting force results in a slow but constant decrease in the semimajor axis and eccentricity of the micrometeorite's heliocentric orbit. In particular, the secular perturbations for an osculating ellipse of a micrometeorite have been calculated by Robertson and are simply

$$\grave{a}_s = -\alpha'(2 + 3e^2)/a(1 - e^2)^{3/2} \tag{262}$$

and

$$\grave{e}_s = -5\alpha' e/2a^2(1 - e^2)^{1/2}, \tag{263}$$

where $\alpha' \triangleq 3E_{\odot}k_s/32\pi c^2 s\rho_m$, $E_{\odot}$ = the total energy emitted by the Sun per second (3.79×10^{33} ergs/sec^3), d = the diameter of the micrometeorite in cm, ρ_m = the meteoritic density in gm/cm^3 ($k_s \cong 1/5.022 \times 10^6$ in cgs units), and c is the speed of light in cm/sec.

Wyatt and Whipple[128] found that the time in years for a micrometeorite to fall into the Sun is given by the relation

$$(t - t_0) \text{ years} = 10^7\, d\rho_m q_0^2 \left[\frac{2.26(1 + e_0)^2}{e_0^{8/5}} \int_0^{e_0} \frac{e^{3/5}de}{(1 - e^2)^{3/2}}\right] \tag{264}$$

where e_0 is the eccentricity and q_0 the perihelion distance at epoch, t_0.

The effect of sputtering, as discussed in previous subsection, will tend to augment the P–R effect. Unfortunately, before sputtering has much influence it causes the complete atomization of the micrometeorite. Such may be the ultimate end of all micrometeoritic interplanetary particles.

The P–R effect could never influence the motion of an interplanetary vehicle because the mass/area quotient is many millions of times larger than that of tiny meteorites. Nevertheless, the effects of radiation pressure are not negligible. As has been proposed by Garwin[129] in his preliminary articles, and more recently discussed by Tsu,[130] radiation pressure could be employed as a "low thrust" perturbative mechanism and a kind of "solar sailing" carried out from planet to planet. The radiation pressure acting on an interplanetary sailing vehicle gives rise to a logarithmic spiral $r = e^{A\phi}$, where $A \triangleq \cot \theta$, $\theta =$ the angle of elevation (angle between the $\dot{\mathbf{r}}$ and the local horizontal), and $\phi =$ the polar angle of the spiral. As has been suggested by Tsu, if an acceleration of the order of 0.2 cm/sec² is desired, then a mass/area quotient of 2.5×10^{-4} gm/cm² is required. Consequently, it is extremely important that if solar sailing is to be practical, the vehicle must have a very small mass/sail area quotient.

The effect of solar radiation pressure on satellites has recently been studied by Parkinson, Jones, and Shapiro[165] and Musen, Bryant, and Bailie.[166] Specifically, the investigators[165] carried out an integration of Eqs. (77) of Moulton[13] p. 404 (similar to Eqs. (254) of this chapter) and found a sizable perturbation of all the orbital elements of a satellite exhibiting a mass/area quotient of 0.04 gm/cm² or less. The radiation pressure affects such a satellite to a greater extent than transitional drag above about 800 km. In ref. 166 the researchers even report a significant solar radiation pressure modification of the motion of Vanguard I satellite. In fact, they find excellent agreement between theory and observation; both showing an 850 day periodicity and a perigee variation amplitude, Δq, of one or two kilometers for a mass/area quotient as large as 4.7 gm/cm². Quantitatively Parkinson, Jones, and Shapiro[165] find that for nearly equatorial circular orbits the amplitude of the perigee height variation is given by

$$\Delta q \propto \left\{ P_{\odot} \frac{A}{m} \left[\frac{3(2\pi - \alpha^*) + \sin \alpha^*}{4\pi n} \right] \cos \theta^* \right\} / |\dot{\beta} - \Omega_s' - \omega_s'|$$

where $P_{\odot} =$ the force on a sphere due to solar radiation pressure (4.5×10^{-5} dyne/cm² at one a.u.); $\alpha^* =$ the angle subtended at the geocenter by that portion of the satellite orbit within the Earth's umbra; $\theta^* =$ the angle between the Earth–Sun line of centers and the orbit plane; $A =$ the area of the spherical satellite; m its mass; and $\dot{\beta} =$ the angular rotational rate of the Earth–Sun line of centers. It is apparent that if $\dot{\beta} \cong \Omega_s + \omega_s$, Δq will become very large. Such a condition is termed a "resonance condition" and can occasion a monotonic increase or decrease in orbital eccentricity depending upon the timing of the satellite launch. We quote from reference 165 that for a nearly circular polar orbit with $a = 1.6$ Earth radii the satellite lifetime can vary between 1.3 and 3.1 years depending upon the time of launch. In conclusion it is noted that because of their exceedingly large mass/area quotient most celestial bodies such as planets are not appreciably perturbed by solar radiation pressure.

10.5. Relativistic Effects[131]

10.5.1. Special Relativity

The Special Theory of Relativity, announced by Einstein in 1905, was based on the two fundamental postulates: that the speed of light is invariant for a given observer irrespective of his motion relative to the source; and that all physical laws are the same when stated in terms of either of two inertial frames of reference. These two hypotheses explained why the Michelson-Morley experiment failed in its attempt to measure the motion of the Earth through the ether by sending out light signals in and perpendicular to the direction of the Earth's orbital motion and noting their travel times. Fitzgerald explained the failure of the experiment, without departing from the principles of Newtonian mechanics, as the result of a "contraction of measuring rods" along the line of motion. Einstein, however, declared that even if a stationary ether existed as the medium of the transmission of electromagnetic waves, the Earth's motion through it could not be determined *from the Earth* owing to the invariance of the speed of light.

Newtonian mechanics assumed as fundamental the hypothesis of a uniformly flowing absolute time and a universal space independent of the coordinate system used to define it. Absolute time implies that the statement that "two events occurred simultaneously" has a significance independent of the frame of reference. Einstein reasoned that it is impossible to devise an experiment by means of which simultaneity can be defined independently of a frame of reference; and that, in general, two events that are simultaneous with respect to one reference frame may not be simultaneous with respect to another. Hence the basis of absolute time, the concept of simultaneity of events, has no physical significance.

The classical or Galilean transformations from one uniformly moving inertial system to another must be replaced by new equations in which the only invariant is the speed of light. If the principle of relativity is to be observed, i.e., that space is homogeneous and all points in space and time shall be equivalent from the point of view of the transformation, there must be nothing in the equations that gives one coordinate system a preferred position. The Lorentz transformation equations meet the required conditions:

Given two inertial coordinate systems S_1 and S_2: S_1 moves along the x_1-axis (which for simplicity coincides with the x_2-axis) at a constant rate v. At time $t = 0$ the points of origin of S_1 and S_2 coincide. Points at rest relative to S_1 will therefore move at a speed v relative to S_2 in the x-direction. See Fig. 42. The transformation equations take the form:

$$x_1 = \alpha(x_2 - vt_2),$$
$$y_1 = y_2,$$
$$z_1 = z_2,$$

and

$$t_1 = \beta t_2 + \gamma x_2 \tag{265}$$

where α, β, and γ are constant coefficients.

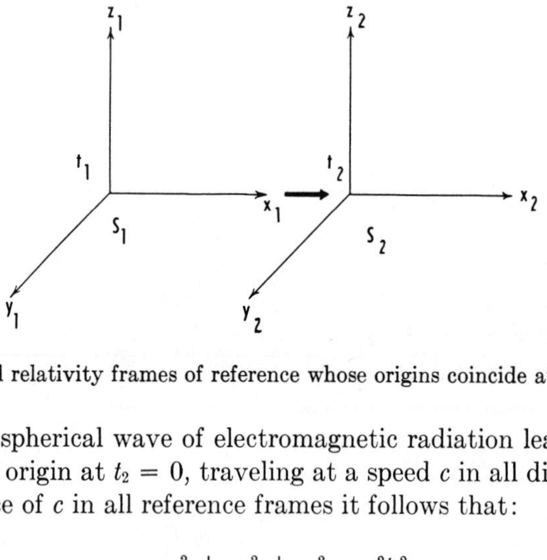

FIG. 42. Special relativity frames of reference whose origins coincide at $t = t_1 = t_2 = 0$.

Imagine a spherical wave of electromagnetic radiation leaving the common point of origin at $t_2 = 0$, traveling at a speed c in all directions. From the invariance of c in all reference frames it follows that:

$$x_1^2 + y_1^2 + z_1^2 = c^2t_1^2$$

and

$$x_2^2 + y_2^2 + z_2^2 = c^2t_2^2. \tag{266}$$

Substitution of Eqs. (265) in the first of Eqs. (266) and rearranging terms gives:

$$(c^2\beta^2 - v^2\alpha^2)t_2^2 = (\alpha^2 - c^2\gamma^2)x_2^2 + y_2^2 + z_2^2 - 2(v\alpha^2 + c^2\beta\gamma)xt_2. \tag{267}$$

Equating coefficients to those of the second of Eqs. (266), we find that

$$c^2\beta^2 - v^2\alpha^2 = c^2,$$

$$\alpha^2 - c^2\gamma^2 = 1,$$

and

$$v\alpha^2 + c^2\beta\gamma = 0. \tag{268}$$

These equations are then solved for α, β, and γ.

The well known formula $\beta^2 \triangleq 1/(1 - v^2/c^2)$ proves that the departure from the classical transformation equations, for which $\beta^2 =$ unity, is a second-order effect. A condition of the transformation is that it agrees with the classical transformation for small values of v.

Several important conclusions have followed from the Lorentz transformation equations. Among them are the following:

If two inertial coordinate systems are in uniform relative motion, to the observers in each system the clocks in the other system will appear to be running *slow*. A length which A measures as L_1 in his own system, will appear to B to have a shorter value, i.e.,

$$L_2 = \sqrt{1 - \frac{v^2}{c^2}}\, L_1. \tag{269}$$

Stated in general terms: Every clock appears to run at its fastest rate when it is at rest relative to the observer, i.e., time dilatation. If it is in motion relative to the observer with a uniform velocity v, its rate appears slowed down by a factor:

$$\sqrt{1 - v^2/c^2}. \tag{270}$$

Every rigid body appears longest when at rest relative to the observer, i.e., Fitzgerald-Lorentz contraction. When it is in motion, it seems to be contracted in the direction of the relative motion by the factor $\sqrt{1 - v^2/c^2}$; but its dimensions perpendicular to the line of motion are unchanged. Similarly, the mass, m, of a moving body is proportional to the rest mass, m_0, by the expression:

$$m = \frac{m_0}{\sqrt{1 - v^2/c^2}}, \tag{271}$$

i.e., for speeds approaching the speed of light, the mass approaches infinity.

Experimental proofs of the Special Theory of Relativity have not been slow in coming. The equivalence of mass and energy expressed in the well-established relation $E = mc^2$; the fine structure of spectral lines; the increase of mass of high-speed electrons, and the delay in the decay of mesons are a few of the demonstrations of the validity of the Lorentz transformation equations. For the astrodynamicists of the future, as space vehicles approach the speed of light, these special relativity effects may have a profound influence.

10.5.2. General Relativity

Einstein announced the General Theory, i.e., the relativistic theory of gravitation, in 1916. Lorentz transformations were no longer applicable since they referred to unaccelerated motion. Furthermore, Newtonian "action at a distance" was ruled out by the principle of relativity. There remained, then, the necessity for formulating a field theory for gravitation as Maxwell had done for electromagnetic theory.

The force of gravitation, unlike other forces, is proportional to the mass of the body acted *upon*, as well as the mass of the attracting body, but the acceleration of a body in a gravitational field is independent of its mass. Hence the accelerations of all bodies in a gravitational field are the same. Newton performed experiments that led him to conclude that the inertial mass, which measures the resistance of an object to motion, is equivalent to its gravitational mass, (see Section 1.5). From this relationship, Einstein inferred that the action of a gravitational field on a body was indistinguishable from the action of an inertial field. Hence all frames of reference are equally suitable for a formulation of the laws of nature.

The mathematical development of the General Theory of Relativity is too complicated to reproduce in this brief account; but the astronomical proofs are essential to the discussion. They are, briefly, as follows:

(i) The advance of the perihelion of Mercury: Long before the theory of relativity was formulated, astronomers knew that the line of apsides of the orbit of Mercury revolved at the rate of 574″ a century, 43″ more than could be explained on the basis of Newtonian celestial mechanics unless there was an unknown planet between Mercury and the Sun. The relativistic theory of gravitation predicted it exactly.

(ii) The deflection of a light ray: When a ray of light from a star passes close to a massive body, such as the Sun, the ray is slightly bent by the gravitational field. If photographs of a field of stars surrounding the Sun during a total eclipse are compared with the photographs of the same field when the Sun is not present, a small difference can be measured in the positions of identical stars on the two plates. As the result of a bending of the light rays toward the Sun, the stars appear to be displaced away from the

Sun. The maximum displacement for stars that appear very close to the Sun is 1''.75. Newtonian celestial mechanics predicts a displacement of only half this quantity.

(iii) The gravitational red shift in the spectral lines: According to the General Theory of Relativity, the frequency of light leaving a very massive star should be decreased, and the wavelength therefore lengthened, the effect caused by a change in time measurement in a strong gravitational field. The so-called "Einstein shift" was first looked for in the wavelength of lines in the solar spectrum, but as the effect is small in the case of the Sun, it was difficult to separate the relativity effect from that of pressure and other factors. The predicted displacement has been established, however, in the spectra of the very dense stars known as "white drwafs." In the companion of Sirius, for example, a predicted red shift 30 times that of the Sun was confirmed by observation.

Of the three astronomical tests of the General Theory of Relativity, the advance of perihelion is of particular interest to the astrodynamicist. The rotation of the line of apsides of an orbit expressed in radians per revolution, Υ^r, is:

$$\Upsilon^r = \frac{6\pi\mu}{a(1 - e^2)c^2}$$

where a is as usual the semimajor axis in astronomical units and e is the eccentricity. Expressed as radians per century:

$$\omega'_s = \frac{36525\,\Upsilon^r}{P} \text{ radians per century,} \tag{272}$$

where P is the period of revolution in mean solar days, and ω is the longitude of perifocus from the node. Since the period is proportional to $a^{3/2}$ by Kepler's third law, it follows that the advance of perihelion in radians per century, ω'_s, is inversely proportional to $a^{5/2}(1 - e^2)$.

Obviously, in order that the relativity effect be observable at all, the orbit must have a small semimajor axis and a large eccentricity. These conditions are fulfilled, as we have seen, in the case of Mercury, for which $a = 0.4$ and $e = 0.2$. The object which is most suitable after Mercury is the minor planet 1566 Icarus, for which $a = 1.08$ and $e = 0.8$. Gilvarry predicts an advance in the perihelion of the orbit of Icarus of 10'' per century.[132]

La Paz derives the equivalent expression for the relativity advance of perigee for a satellite, either natural or artificial, moving in an eccentric orbit close to the Earth.[133] He points out parenthetically that there is a strong probability that the observation of artificial satellites may lead to the discovery of small natural moons which have escaped detection hitherto. Following the reasoning by which Levi-Civita deduced his formula for the relativity advance of the perihelion of a planet moving about the Sun, La Paz finds for a satellite orbiting around the Earth:

$$\Upsilon'' = \frac{4.519 \times 10^{-5}}{1 - e^2}\left(\frac{a_☾}{a}\right),$$

where Υ'' is the advance of perigee of a satellite in seconds of arc per revolution, $a_☾ \cong 38.44 \times 10^9$ cm is the mean distance of the Moon from the Earth. If $\grave{\omega}_s$ is defined as the total advance of perigee in a century,

$$\grave{\omega}_s = \frac{100\,\Upsilon''}{P} \text{ sec of arc.} \tag{273}$$

This is the same formula as Gilvarry's Eq. (272) above, except that there the period was expressed in mean solar days, and in Eq. (273) it is in years.

La Paz calculated the perigee advance for four hypothetical satellites revolving around the Earth at diverse distances and in orbits of various eccentricities. The basic data and the results are given in Table XIV.

The valuable researches of Gilvarry and La Paz were carried out three or four years before the first artificial satellite was launched.

TABLE XIV. PERIGEAL ADVANCE IN ORBITS OF EARTH-SATELLITES*

Hypothetical object	Semimajor axis in Earth radii	Eccentricity	Advance of perigee in seconds of arc per 100 years
(1)	2.7	0.06	146″.0
(2)	2.7	0.40	194.6
(3)	1.1	0.02	1250.5
(4)	1.6	0.25	586.6

* La Paz.[133]

11 OBSERVATION THEORY

Observation theory has taken on a new aspect in light of the requirements of rapid and accurate observation of space vehicles. Since an understanding of time (perhaps the single most important coordinate of an observation) is requisite to any form of observational astronomy, the first section is devoted to this topic. The second deals with the space range system. In the third, optical observations are discussed with special emphasis placed on the Baker–Nunn tracking cameras, conventional astronomical plate measurement, space probe observation, and image intensification. The fourth section treats electronic tracking instruments, including a brief look at interferometric systems and Doppler systems. These latter sections are mere summaries and could be omitted by those who are already familiar with such instruments.

With regard to the optical versus electronic instrumentation question, undoubtedly there will always exist a demand for both types. Extremely precise electronic instruments have been plagued by anomalistic drift between observations and the problem of continual recalibration. The electronic engineer is gradually becoming aware of the great care that must be exercised in order to obtain accurate observational data. For instance, the seemingly trivial problem of keeping accurate station time, good to a millisecond, is now becoming more appreciated.[134] It should not be long, therefore, before electronic instruments will have accuracies that are competitive with optical. The other aspect of observation theory—namely, observation *from* a space vehicle of both terrestrial and celestial objects will not be dealt with here in great detail. The reader is directed to Chapter 12 and to the work of Mundo and Bock[135] and Larmore[136] for a more comprehensive treatment of celestial observations from a space vehicle.

11.1. Time

So important is the measurement of time to observational astronomy that more and more exact time-measuring devices are being developed to keep pace with more precise observing techniques. Coincident with these advances has come the discovery that a new theory regarding time is required. The old familiar time which we keep on our clocks and adjust occasionally by means of signals sent out from the naval observatories, is now known to be subject to irregular changes of rate perceptible only to an astronomer. Consequently, two distinct kinds of time must be recognized. One is the familiar fluctuating mean solar time (including standard time, universal time, etc.), which has as its fundamental unit the *day* or period of the Earth's diurnal rotation. The other, called ephemeris or Newtonian time is a uniformly flowing sequence based on the period of the Sun's apparent revolution around the Earth, i.e., the tropical year. The name comes from the fact that this uniform time, defined by the laws of dynamics, is the independent variable in the gravitational theories of the Sun, Moon, and planets. Hence the actual arguments of ephemerides computed from the formulas of celestial mechanics are necessarily given in *ephemeris time*, defined by the Newtonian laws of motion, and not in *universal time* defined by the variable rotation of the Earth.

Whereas a gravitational ephemeris expresses the position of an astronomical object as a function of abstract ephemeris time, the actual observations, on the other hand, are necessarily recorded in observed practical mean solar time. For a comparison between observed and predicted positions of a celestial object, therefore, we must reduce universal (i.e., Greenwich mean solar time) to ephemeris time or vice versa. The table on page viii of the *American Ephemeris and Nautical Almanac*[137] for 1960 contains annual values of ΔT from 1901.5, to be used in the conversion formula for past time:

$$\mathrm{ET} = \mathrm{UT} + \Delta T. \tag{274}$$

The observation of the meridian transits of stars carried on daily by the naval observatories is the only rapid, precise means of making the determinations of time essential for navigation, surveying, and civil life. It leads directly to *local sidereal time*, θ, (the local hour angle, LHA, of the vernal equinox—see Section 4.3.2) obtained from the right ascensions of stars on the meridian, and is obviously affected by variations in the Earth's rotation as well as by changes in the position of the meridian arising from "variation of latitude." Sidereal time is then converted to *mean solar time* (MST), which is defined as the hour angle (+12 hours) of a fictitious Sun that moves uniformly in the equator in the same annual period as that of the actual Sun moving at a variable speed in the ecliptic. Universal time, referred to the Meridian of Greenwich from which longitude is reckoned, was adopted by international agreement in 1925, when the beginning of the *astronomical day* was officially changed from noon to the preceding midnight, to conform to civil usage. Astronomical observations are customarily reported in universal time (see Fig. 43).

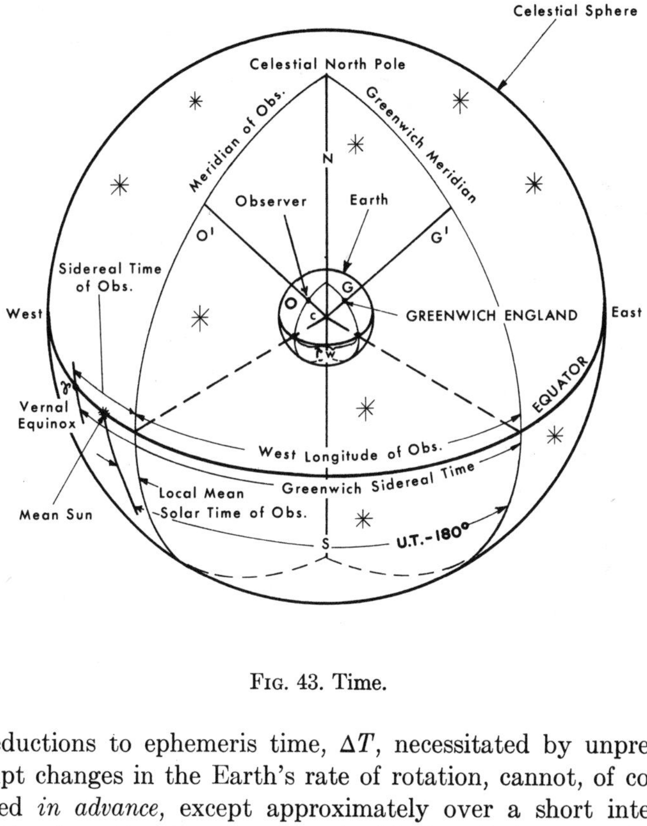

FIG. 43. Time.

The reductions to ephemeris time, ΔT, necessitated by unpredictable and abrupt changes in the Earth's rate of rotation, cannot, of course, be determined *in advance*, except approximately over a short interval by extrapolation from the above-mentioned table for ΔT. Accurate determinations must be made by observation of corresponding abrupt variations in the longitudes of the Sun, Moon, and planets which reflect the nonuniformity of the Earth's rotation. See Section 4.6.

The changes in the Earth's rotation fall into two distinct categories (cf. Van der Waerden[138]): a secular retardation or imperceptible lengthening of the day arising from tidal friction; and the unexplained irregular fluctuations, to which Newcomb called attention in his study of the Moon's actual motion as compared with Hansen's tables for the Moon. The numerical value of the secular terms was established by Fotheringham (1920) from records of ancient eclipses, which depend upon the relative positions of the Sun, Moon, and Earth. His results were revised by de Sitter. Brown's improved lunar theory and tables supported Newcomb's hypothesis that the Earth's rotation rate might be variable; and Spencer Jones (1939) established it beyond question when he proved that there were fluctuations in the mean longitudes of the Sun, Mercury, and Venus corresponding exactly to the fluctuations in time required to account for the changes in the Moon's mean longitude (cf. Spencer Jones[139]).

The formula for $\Delta T = 24.349 \Delta L_{\odot}$ derived by Spencer Jones[140] was adopted by the International Astronomical Union in 1950 and was used by Brouwer[141] in his calculation of the annual values of ΔT from 1820 to 1950, which are found in the *American Ephemeris.* With the substitution of the expression for $\Delta L_{\odot}$, the correction to the Sun's mean longitude, in terms of the interval T, counted in centuries from 1900, the formula becomes:

$$\Delta T = 24^{s}.349 + 72^{s}.3165T + 29^{s}.949T^2 + 1.821B; \qquad (275)$$

where the terms in T and T^2 represent the secular retardation and B is the observed mean longitude of the Moon, L, *minus* the corresponding value given by Brown's corrected Tables of the Moon. (The constant and linear terms are adjusted to the epoch 1900.)

Brouwer, after an exhaustive investigation, characterized the observed irregularities in the Earth's rate of rotation as the "cumulative effect of random changes with mean value zero, superposed on a secular decrease by tidal friction," which cannot be readily explained as the result of changes in the moment of inertia about the axis of rotation. He cites recent suggestions by geophysicists Munk and Revelle, supported by Runcorn, which ascribe the observed irregularities to "electromagnetic coupling of the mantle (or crust of the Earth) to a turbulent core."

Practically speaking, in order to define ET to one part in 10^{10} from observations of the Moon (i.e., in order to evaluate B) Clemence estimates that some 5 years of observation are needed. Consequently, atomic clocks, which can be immediately "read," are advantageous. Bullard has, in fact, defined a physical second, called the "essen," to be used in preference to the ephemeris second in refined experiments. Clemence, however, noted that atomic clocks cannot define an epoch and hence should serve only as a secondary standard to mark the passage of time between successive epoch determinations, just as pendulum clocks have done in the past.

As a practical application of the foregoing, let us consider in some detail the determination of both local sidereal time, θ, and ephemeris time, ET. In order to determine the local sidereal time of an observation one first notes the local standard time of the observation in the time zone of the observation station. As an example let us choose 3:05 a.m. PST, June 15, 1960. The local mean solar time at the Greenwich Observatory is, at this instant, $8^h + 3^h05^m = 11^h05^m$, i.e., there are eight time zone changes west of Greenwich to the PST zone. In Fig. 43 this time could be represented by the angle between the mean Sun and the Greenwich Meridian and is termed universal time (UT) (note that angles can be measured in hours, minutes, and seconds as well as in degrees, minutes, and seconds e.g., $24^h = 360°$). The local sidereal time at Greenwich at midnight on June 15, 1960 is tabulated in the *American Ephemeris and Nautical Almanac* (AE), e.g., on p. 13 of the volume for 1960, and is found to be $17^h33^m06^s.317$. The correction of the solar time after midnight to sidereal time at Greenwich (in this case the solar time after midnight is 11^h05^m) can be found in Table IX of the AE (e.g., pp. 469–471 of the 1960 volume) and amounts to $1^m49^s.243$. The Greenwich Sidereal Time, θ_g, corresponding to 3^h05^m PST is, therefore, (midnight is at the *beginning* of June 15 i.e., the *apparent sidereal time*)

$$\begin{array}{rr} \text{PST} + & 3^h05^m \\ \text{Time Zone Difference} + & 8^h \\ \theta_g \text{ at midnight} + & 17^h33^m06^s.317 \\ \text{Correction} + & 1^m49^s.243 \\ \hline \theta_g = & 28^h39^m55^s.560 \\ = & 4^h39^m55^s.560 \end{array}$$

and is shown in Fig. 43 as the angle between the vernal equinox and the Greenwich Meridian. If the observation was made at Mount Wilson, California, then the *West* longitude of this observatory (in hours, minutes, and seconds) must be *subtracted* from θ_g to yield θ (cf. Fig. 43). The longitudes of most of the principal observatories are listed in the AE (e.g., page 442 of the 1960 volume) and that of the Mount Wilson Observatory is found to be $+7^h52^m14^s.33$. Consequently, the local sidereal time of an observation made at the Mount Wilson Observatory at 3:05 a.m. PST on June 15, 1960 is (if *mean sidereal time*, subtract the nutation on June 15)

$$\begin{array}{ll} \theta_g & 28^{h}39^{m}55\overset{s}{.}56 \\ \lambda_w - & 7^{h}52^{m}14\overset{s}{.}33 \\ \hline \theta & 20^{h}47^{m}41\overset{s}{.}23. \end{array}$$

The ephemeris time is even simpler to obtain. If the time 3:05 a.m. PST June 15, 1960 is again utilized as an illustrative example, the tables for correction to ET (constructed from Eq. (275)) may be consulted, e.g., for 1960.5 page viii of the 1960 AE gives a correction of $\Delta T = 35^{s}$. This correction is then added to UT to obtain ET, i.e.,

$$\begin{array}{ll} \text{UT} & 11^{h}05^{m}00^{s} \\ \Delta T + & \qquad 35^{s} \\ \hline \text{ET} = & 11^{h}05^{m}35^{s}. \end{array}$$

More precisely, ΔT is computed directly from Eq. (275) where B is obtained by a Markowitz dual rate camera photograph of the Moon.[175]

11.2. The Space Range System

11.2.1. Requirements

The application of astrodynamics to the range problem has engendered much interest of late. In particular it has been pointed out by Herrick that the determination of an orbit of a space vehicle should not be made at each individual station in a range system, but rather that the most unadulterated observational data should be transmitted at once to a central computational facility.[142] A space range station will have electronic and possibly optical equipment and the advantages and disadvantages of various types of equipment will be discussed later in this section. Furthermore there will be some on-site adjustments of the observations prior to the transmittal of data to the central computational center. The on-site calculations may include:

(i) Coordinate transformations and correction for local instrumental and environmental systematic errors that can be carried out better on the site than at the central facility, e.g., instrument flexure and atmospheric refraction.

(ii) The determination of an ephemeris for acquisition in case there is a communications failure.

(iii) Data compression, in the case of a great many observations made at the same time of the same coordinate.

(iv) Some guidance and perhaps payload function, e.g., a command link to fire a retro-rocket.

(v) Telemetry reduction.

(vi) Discrimination between well-known space vehicles and new ones, i.e., identification (could, for example, be told where *not* to look by the central computation facility).

(vii) Searching pattern computation for acquisition.

The central computation facility might carry out the following functions, which are listed in chronological order: (i) Early initial acquisition. (ii) Elimination of spurious data and screening. (iii) Determination of an initial precision orbit, including differential corrections. (iv) Observation net control—related to discrimination and identification (e.g., instructs the stations where not to look). (v) Determination of a definitive orbit.

A brief description of each of these latter areas as they apply to the satellite tracking problem is discussed in the next section.

11.2.2. The Computational Center

11.2.2.1. Early Initial Acquisition (Preliminary Orbit)

The orbit determination problem will be most acute during the early period when the first observational data of the artificial satellite are received, and when urgent demands are made by the other stations for an acquisition ephemeris. The first data received, no matter how incomplete or inaccurate, must serve as a basis for the next observation; hence, an assumption or series of assumptions may be required. Table XV indicates the types of observations that might be obtained initially, and the assumptions to be made, and the orbit determination procedures possible for each type (the tabulation is not meant to be comprehensive and its extension and amplification will form a task for future astrodynamic research).

Hopefully, the first observational set will provide an adequate basis for acquisition by a second station. Immediately upon receipt of data from the second station, two more orbits may be computed; i.e., an orbit given by the second observational set alone (determined as was the orbit from the first observation) and an orbit derived from a combination of the two sets. It may well happen that all three orbits will be different and if they do differ, may yield different ephemerides. The confidence in each of these ephemerides may be initially estimated from the inaccuracies inherent in the two instruments. All three (or perhaps two) ephemerides would then be transmitted to the next station. Such a procedure is then followed from

TABLE XV. OBSERVATION REQUIREMENTS FOR PRELIMINARY ORBIT DETERMINATION

Observational data	Assumption	Method
3 3-dimensional fixes	None	Herrick–Gibbs or Gibbs (with or without differential correction to reduce residuals or discard data) See Section 6.2.2.
Overdetermined system with more than 3 fixes.	Random error distribution	Least-square differential correction of initial orbit
15 ρ 8 ρ 4 ρ	Low eccentricity Circular orbit Rectilinear parabola	Gibbsian as modified by Baker. See Sections 6.2.3, 6.2.4, and 6.2.5.
6-dimensional fix $(\rho, \alpha, \delta, \dot{\rho}, \dot{\alpha}, \dot{\delta})$ $\mathbf{r}, \dot{\mathbf{r}}$ $(\rho, A, h, \dot{\rho}, \dot{A}, \dot{h})$ (3ρ, $3\dot{\rho}$ for 3 times, triangulation)	None	Laplace, Lagrange (there are several variations of the Laplacian method). See Section 6.3.
2 3-dimensional fixes $\mathbf{r}_1, \mathbf{r}_2$ { ρ, α, δ 1 station $3\ \rho$ 3 stations $3\ \alpha$ 3 stations (triangulation) $3\ \delta$ 3 stations $2\alpha, 1\delta$ 2 stations etc.	None	Gauss and variants (method under development by Samuel Herrick). See Section 6.4.
$\alpha, \delta, \dot{\alpha}, \dot{\delta}, \ddot{\alpha}, \ddot{\delta}$, for one time	None	Laplacian. See Section 6.3.1.
3α, 3δ, for three times	None	(a) convert to $\alpha, \delta, \dot{\alpha}, \dot{\delta}, \ddot{\alpha}, \ddot{\delta}$, at middle date (Laplacian) (b) retain α's and δ's (1) Lagrange with Herrick–Gibbs velocity formula. (2) Gauss (ratio sector to triangle)[a] (3) Gibbs expansion method (by Herrick)
3ρ, $3\dot{\rho}$	None	Differential correction or pseudo-Laplacian[b]. (See Section 6.3.2)

[a] There are several variations of the Gaussian method, one of which is discussed in Section 6.4.

[b] Defective on orientation if only one station and if times are close together.

TABLE XV (*Continued*)

Observational data	Assumption	Method
6ρ	None	Differential correction or pseudo-Lagrangian[b] (or Gaussian—see reference 70)
$6\dot{\rho}$	None	Probably only differential correction; but see reference 70.
Other combinations of 6 observed quantities for three or more times.	None	Needs to be developed.
5 observed quantities for one or two times.	Parabolic or one condition orbits	Modified Olbers. (See Section 6.5), Laplacian or similar method.
4 observed quantities α, $\dot{\alpha}$, δ, $\dot{\delta}$, for one time[c] 2α, 2δ for two times 4ρ for four times 2ρ, $2\dot{\rho}$ for two times α, δ, ρ, $\dot{\rho}$ for one time	Circular or two condition orbits, e.g., *e*, *a*; 2ρ's; $2r$'s, etc. are assumed	Standard circular orbit methods. See, e.g., Section 6.2.3.
3 observed quantities α, δ, $\dot{\rho}$; or 3ρ's; or $3\dot{\rho}$'s; or h, A and heading, etc.	3 condition orbit variety to be investigated (e.g., assume circular orbit and size)	Needs to be developed.
2 observed quantities α, δ for one time A, h for one time 2ρ's for two times $2\dot{\rho}$'s for two times and other	4 condition orbit variety of assumptions to be investigated	Needs to be developed.

[c] There is an advantage with four observations in that there are no small determinants.

The authors were aided in the preparation of this table by S. Herrick and C. G. Hilton.

station to station. As this technique proceeds for the next two or three revolutions, other data from intermediate stations may also become available and will help to resolve the ambiguity.

11.2.2.2. Elimination of Spurious Data

After considerable data accumulate, those observations that involve transmission errors, birds, airplanes, natural ephemeral satellites, cometoids, and observational blunders must be eliminated. A few of the methods of eliminating these erroneous observations are: (i) drawing a smooth curve through the data points and eliminating points which deviate by large amounts; (ii) the more sophisticated method of least squares; or (iii) a method of elimination based on both dynamical and geometrical considerations. The fact that there may be a number of transmission errors that can be immediately eliminated on the basis of physical impossibility should not be overlooked (e.g., an obviously wrong time, or altitude well below the horizon).

One first selects 5 to 20 observations spaced over intervals from 1 to 10 minutes, depending upon observational data available. The "best" observations or normal places (observations reduced to a normal point) are taken for each time interval. The only criterion for "best" at this point is the type of instrument. The first choice might be Baker–Nunn observations if they exist during the desired time interval.

After this initial selection, two-body orbits are determined from combinations of three sets of data utilizing, for example, Laplace's method. From 15 observations there might result a total of $15 \cdot 14 \cdot 13 / 3 \cdot 2 \cdot 1 = 455$ orbits. One may be able to compute considerably fewer orbits because points common to each of three physically impossible orbits are to be rejected immediately and not used for any further calculations. The criteria for rejecting data offer great variety, for example:

(i) Do the observations lead to an orbit whose curvature does not meet dynamical constraints (such might be the case if the residuals in the Laplacian method did not decrease below the expected instrumental error)?

(ii) For a satellite orbit, is the perigee well underground or is the energy such that the semimajor axis is negative (hyperbolic orbit)?

(iii) Do the observations lead to an orbit with an inclination less than the (known) ballistic injection latitude? In this case, care must be taken to avoid confusion if, e.g., a corrective thrust had been employed to achieve a transfer to an orbit of a different inclination (termed "dog-legging").

(iv) Do the orbital elements determined from this observational set fall outside a three or four sigma statistical limit (based on average elements determined from all the physically possible sets)?

Any observation appearing in three rejected orbits is to be discarded and no more orbits are to be calculated through this rejected point. Care must therefore be exercised in programming so that only one observation is common to two consecutive orbits. If the orbit determination method chosen is restricted to small arcs, then care must also be taken to combine only observations that are less than one or two radians apart on the orbit cf. Section 6.6.3.

11.2.2.3. Initial Precision Orbit

Given some 100 to 1000 new data points, it becomes important to generate a preliminary precision orbit. The data are screened in a manner similar to the initial procedure. First of all, the more accurate observations or normal places obtained by combining observations are chosen within each selected time interval, in order to provide a continuous time sequence of data if possible. It should be recognized, however, that a good set of accurate observations should not be rejected only for the sake of achieving observations over equally spaced time intervals. Second, based on the improved initial orbit, the observations or normal places are represented by means of, for example, special perturbations. Three- or four-sigma deviates are then eliminated and the remaining data employed to improve the orbit by standard differential-correction procedures as outlined in Section 6.6.2.

After a set of elements has been determined that fits the observations of an initial arc of the trajectory to the desired accuracy, these elements can be adopted as satisfying the instantaneous orbit at some time during the initial arc. Of course, the object will depart rapidly from this two-body orbit. It is necessary, therefore, to include the principal perturbations in the extrapolation of the initial precision orbit. In fact, it may be advisable to determine the effect of the perturbations over the initial arc also, and to repeat the differential correction and improve the instantaneous osculating satellite orbit (the corrected parameters may include non-2-body terms, e.g., ω_s').

These perturbations will probably include only the effects of the aerodynamic forces and of the second zonal harmonic of the Earth's gravitational field. Each effect can be expressed in the form of perturbative accelerations that can be integrated numerically (special perturbations, see Chapter 8) or in terms of variations of the orbital elements, i.e., an expansion of the elements in a harmonic or power series with time as argument (general perturbations, see Chapter 9). The choice is not merely between these methods: one could alternatively select a combination of numerical integration and series expansion which would result in the most rapid production of ephemerides. Note the distinction between orbit determination (utilized in the preliminary orbit) and orbit computation (utilized in the initial precision orbit) first discussed in Section 6.1.2.

An interesting statistical problem must also be considered with respect to the initial precision orbit. Consider the oversimplified example of defining the semimajor axis of a satellite by means of a continual reckoning of the orbital period, i.e., by keeping a record of the successive transits of a satellite. If it is assumed that the main source of error occurs in making the observation and that no perturbations accumulate between observations, then the question arises as to how to handle the data. Should only the first and last observation times be subtracted and this over-all time interval divided by the number of intervening circuits to yield the period, or should each individual time of transit be subtracted from the next and an average of all of these periods taken? Clearly, the former approach discards much useful information while the latter approach utilizes each transit time reading twice and the data, therefore, is not statistically independent. Without independent data the cross-product term in the derivation of the propagation of error formulas would not vanish and the error would be increased. As can be rather easily demonstrated on the basis of elementary statistical theory, there does exist a clear-cut answer to this problem. It turns out that only the first and the last third of the observed transit times should be utilized. Specifically, if there are n satellite transits, then the first time of transit should be subtracted from the $(2n/3)$ time of transit and the second time of transit subtracted from the $(2n/3 + 1)$ time of transit, etc. These $n/3$ time intervals should be averaged and divided by $2n/3$ to yield the most probable period. Paradoxically, to utilize additional data only gives rise to a decrease in precision. Although this example may not be very realistic, it does suggest that a statistical study should be mounted before all of the data from a satellite orbit is greedily digested by the orbit improvement or differential correction procedure.

11.2.2.4. Observation Net Control

Control of the observation net involves the issuance of both up-to-date ephemerides (generated by representing an orbit from either general or special perturbations) to alert detection stations of all expected objects, and directives to tracking stations (perhaps different from detection stations) as to what objects to follow and how carefully (i.e., whether to simply note the object's presence, make one tracking point for verification, or obtain a complete precision track).

In this latter regard, having successfully determined the preliminary precision-orbit by differential correction, perhaps via special perturbations, it is then necessary to estimate when the next observations are to be required and by what stations. In order to make this estimate, a series of variant orbits may be computed. Each of these variants represents the effect of a two- or three-sigma deviation in one of the six or eight elements.*

* It is tentatively assumed that these variant orbits will be represented by means of general perturbations; i.e., series expansion. Such a procedure is indicated because of

(The standard deviation of the elements may be obtained from the differential correction of the preliminary orbit or from other statistical procedures.) Certain stations may, without added labor, provide actual observed residuals; these could also be monitored periodically.

The technique proceeds as follows for satellite vehicles:

(i) Predicted observations obtained from a precision instrument (e.g., Baker–Nunn camera or precision radar) are represented on the reference orbit and variant orbits after, say, ten revolutions.

(ii) If these hypothetical observed-minus-computed residuals are not deemed to be excessive, then another representation is carried out after perhaps ten more revolutions.

(iii) When these residuals are found to be significant, an acquisition ephemeris is computed for the appropriate precision instrument, as well as for other such instruments before and after it on the orbit to serve as a "back-up." The routine ephemeris provided to all the stations may be adequate.

(iv) Such ephemerides and reminder communications are then transmitted to the selected stations.

(v) Upon receipt from the stations, the residuals are evaluated as to size. If the space vehicle is lost, then other stations such as moonwatch, etc. are alerted and provided with acquisition ephemerides.

(vi) Assuming the residuals are reasonably small, a differential correction of the orbit is carried out on the basis of these new data alone. It is probable that a better estimate of the orbital elements would now be possible because of the longer time interval.

(vii) The cycle is then repeated. For low altitude satellites, as the time of final atmospheric descent approaches, the extrapolation from observation to observation will tend to decrease. When it is clear that after ten or so revolutions the satellite will descend, a change over to special perturbations may be carried out and ephemerides then generated on this new basis. See, for example, the method indicated in Section 8.3.3.

11.3. Optical Observations

Optical devices have the advantages of high-resolution, small power requirements, compact physical size, and reliability; and the disadvantages of their inability to measure range and to observe other than illuminated

---

the inefficiency of special perturbations in representing an orbit for perhaps hundreds or thousands of revolutions.

objects (with a reflective coating) against a dark sky background. Furthermore, optical devices can resolve multiple targets a feat that is difficult or impossible to accomplish with electronic devices.

The typical missile range has included such optical devices* as the

(i) Recording optical tracking instrument (ROTI), characterized by a small field of view (long-focal length) and an automatic reading of the h and A setting circles; it has the disadvantage of mechanical mount inaccuracies;

(ii) Ciné theodolite, characterized by a small field of view and small light-gathering power (6-in. objective), giving a 35-mm motion picture of the object, and an automatic reading of h and A; and

(iii) Ballistic camera, characterized by a very wide field of view, low light-gathering power, being fixed in concrete, and the ability to find the satellite position from the coordinates of stars on the photographs.

New requirements have arisen for optical tracking equipment because of the demands of satellite and space-vehicle orbit determination and the devices enumerated above are usually considered inadequate.

11.3.1. Baker–Nunn Camera

In order to track a satellite most effectively, an optical system must meet certain requirements. Because of the uncertainty in the satellite's position before acquisition and its rapid apparent motion, a large field of view is the first essential. Secondly, in order to measure positions accurately, the optical system must have a rather long focal length. Thirdly, in order to photograph faint objects such as satellites and space probes, a high photographic speed is necessary. All these requirements indicate that a Schmidt type telescope might be the most useful.†

The optics of a special purpose satellite camera were designed by James Baker and its mechanical features worked out by Joseph Nunn; hence the instrument was named the Baker–Nunn camera. The Baker–Nunn camera is a modification of the basic Schmidt design that has a field of view

* Characteristics obtained from E. Durand in discussion.

† A Schmidt-type telescope is one that employs a spherical mirror whose spherical aberration is corrected by a thin aspherical plate that refracts the rays sufficiently before they are reflected by the objective.

Another optical system, designed by Bouwers in Belgium and Maksutov in Russia termed the *Maksutov*, utilizes concentric spherical optics and has greater resolution for wide view fields than the Schmidt, e.g., for a 60° field of view it resolves to 0.17 milliradians, the Schmidt to only 11.7 milliradians both at f/1. cf. reference 143. Another useful optical system is the *Baker Catadioptic*. See the glossary of terms, pp. 286 and 298.

of 5° $\times$ 30° and a focal length of 20 in., which allows a measurement accurate to 2″. For high speed a focal ratio of f/1 has been used in the camera. Probably the most important part of the Baker–Nunn camera is the correcting system, which allows the camera to have a wide field of view and yet cuts the aberrations down to a point where the satellite's position can be measured accurately. Dr. Baker found that a single correcting plate, as in the Schmidt, was inadequate. He devised a successful system employing three elements, two of the surfaces being spherical and four aspherical. It was also found necessary to utilize two special types of glass.

Since the satellite's position is to be measured relative to the stellar background, it is important that the star images as well as the satellite's image be on the exposed film, as is the case for all astronomical photographic observations. By measuring an object's position relative to certain stars whose positions are already well-known and are tabulated in catalogues, it is possible to reduce refraction and aberration to small differential effects, since they affect both the star image and the satellite image by nearly the same amount. See the discussion of plate constants in section 11.3.2.

To make it possible to distinguish the satellite on the Baker–Nunn film, one might have the camera track the satellite and allow the stars to trail; however, if this procedure is employed exclusively, only stars brighter than magnitude 5.8 will be recorded. Usually there will be only two or three such stars within the 5° $\times$ 30° field,* and even they may be so far from the satellite image that the errors introduced by film stretching, for example, will be greater than can be tolerated. To overcome this problem two exposures are taken on the same film: in the first, the camera follows the satellite and allows the stars to trail; in the second, the camera tracks at the stellar rate and lets the satellite trail. While the film is being exposed the trailing images are chopped into four segments by a rotating barrel-shutter. After the image has been chopped into these four segments, the film is covered by a clam-shell shutter while the camera accelerates to the next rate. The camera can be set for exposure times of $0\overset{s}{.}2$, $0\overset{s}{.}4$, $0\overset{s}{.}8$, $1\overset{s}{.}6$, and $3\overset{s}{.}2$. When the barrel-shutter cuts off the image for the second time, while the camera is tracking the satellite, the time is ordinarily recorded on the film by illuminating a time display unit with a stroboscope. The time is kept by a crystal clock manufactured by Ernst Normal Laboratories, and displayed on three

* Depending on the distance from the Milky Way (galactic latitude), there are fewer bright stars per square degree than dim, e.g., for fourth magnitude stars between 0.016 and 0.005; for sixth magnitude between 0.129 and 0.037; for eighth between 1 and 0.275 and for tenth between 7.8 and 1.8 stars per square degree (the greater number nearer the Milky Way).

dials (cf. Henize[144]). Two circular dials are readable, one to $0^s.1$, the other to $0^s.01$. A circular sweep oscilloscope can be read to $0^s.0001$. The WWV time signal is ordinarily compared with the time output of the clock and the error is reduced to $0^s.001$. From 10 to 100 exposures can be made during a single satellite passage. Cinemascope film is used and each exposure has dimensions of 2 × 12 in.

11.3.2. Conventional Astronomical Plate Measurement

The advantages of photography over visual methods of observing minor planets and space vehicles can hardly be overstated. Objects too faint to be seen visually in the telescope can be found on photographic plates because the latter accumulate light, and the eye does not. When the telescope is guided on a star during an hour's exposure, for example, the minor planets and space probes show up as trails. Hence, not only the right ascensions and declinations, but also the amount and direction of the hourly motion can be found directly from the plate by differential measurement of distances from comparison stars.

Another advantage of photographic observations is that the plates can be searched and the positions of planets measured in a leisurely fashion. When one is in doubt about an observation or a comparison, the plate can be remeasured, and checked, an impossibility in visual observations. Finally, the archives in which the plates are stored may yield valuable information. When Pluto was discovered in 1930 and the orbit computed, the planet was found on Mount Wilson plates of 1919 and on old plates of several other observatories by means of ephemerides computed for prediscovery oppositions.

Long-focus achromatic refractors with focal lengths of approximately 8 m or more and focal ratios up to f/20 are generally employed in conventional photography to obtain higher magnification. Photographic negatives rather than positives are measured because the black star images have greater contrast than do white images and because the copying process introduces blurring. The measurement of these plates can be made on various types of plate-measuring engines such as the Mann two-screw comparator. As was mentioned, small changes in refraction and aberration between the stars and the image to be measured enter only differentially and may be considered as linear functions of the position of the star on the plate. Scale and orientation errors, nonperpendicularity of axes (in the measuring engine), annual aberration of light, the effect of plate tilt (generally negligible for long-focus instruments), etc., also enter differentially.

All such systematic errors can, therefore, be accounted for by the determination of plate constants. Thus a true position of an ideal image on an ideal plate, ξ and η, is taken to be a linear combination of its measured (approximate) position on the plate, x, y, i.e., for the measurement of the ith star

$$\begin{aligned} \xi_i &= ax_i + by_i + c, \\ \eta_i &= dx_i + ey_i + f. \end{aligned} \tag{276}$$

e.g., if $i = 1, 2, 3, \ldots n$ for n stars and $i = O$ for the object, then Eqs. (276) represent $2(n + 1)$ equations in the eight unknowns a, b, c, d, e, f, ξ_o, η_o (the ξ_i and η_i actual or ideal coordinates of the stars are found in star catalogues using Eq. (277), and all of the x_i and y_i are the known measured coordinates of the stars and object taken from the photographic plate). The a, b, c, d, e, and f coefficients are called the *plate constants,* and by employing a number of stars (three or more) these constants can be evaluated and will take into account all the errors enumerated above.

Several procedures for determining the positions of objects have been proposed, e.g., the Comrie or three-star dependence method, the three-star plate constant method, the four-star method, and the least-squares method. (cf. Smart.[145]) The purpose of each of these methods is to determine the true ξ_o and η_o "standard" plate coordinates of the object after the effects of aberration, refraction, etc., have been eliminated. These standard coordinates are then utilized to provide spherical, equatorial, topocentric coordinates, α and δ, of the object for some specified vernal equinox and equator. Either closed or series relations can be employed. The series relation is

$$(\alpha_o - \alpha_c) = \xi_o \sec \delta_c + \frac{F}{1000} \eta_o(\xi_o \sec \delta_c) + \cdots$$

and

$$(\delta_o - \delta_c) = \eta_o - \frac{G}{100} (\xi_o \sec \delta_c)^2 + \cdots \tag{277}$$

where

$$\begin{aligned} F &\triangleq 0.004{,}848{,}1 \tan \delta_c, \\ G &\triangleq 0.027{,}271 \sin 2\delta_c. \end{aligned}$$

The c subscript refers to the plate center (from which ξ and η are measured); ξ and α are measured in seconds of time, and η and δ are measured in seconds of arc. Thus given ξ_o and η_o of the object, from the solution of the plate constant Eqs. (276), the topocentric coordinates of the object,

α_o and δ_o, relative to some *arbitrarily* chosen plate center α_c and δ_c, can be obtained through Eqs. (277).

An alternate procedure, which has found application in the reduction of highly accurate mapping or cartographic photographs, is that of the *Reseau grid.* Such a device is a precisely inscribed flat glass plate placed at the front of a camera's focal plane. Every few millimeters a grid of crosses is accurately etched on the plate (e.g., every 2.0 ± 0.001 mm) and, since these crosses appear on the final photograph along with the star (or ground) images, it is possible to make direct determination of plate constants that have arisen from film stretching, shrinking, etc.

Because the measurement of star images is extremely tedious and speed is essential, the requirement has arisen for automatic plate-measuring devices. To make the process of star measurement fully automatic, it is necessary to accomplish the following tasks:

(i) Among the stars whose images are shown on the plate, the images of the catalogued comparison stars must be identified (e.g., by means of comparison with photographic star charts such as the *Carte du Ciel*).

(ii) The carriage of the measuring engine must be moved to a position that accurately represents the coordinates of the particular star or object image being measured.

(iii) The precise measured coordinates of the image must be recorded.

As an example, let us consider the automatic measuring engine at the Watson Laboratories. A photoelectric scanning device was substituted for the visual microscope ordinarily employed to observe star images. A set of approximate coordinates of the comparison stars is fed in on IBM punch cards. Such coordinate cards are now being prepared by Whitney at the Smithsonian Astrophysical Observatory. After the approximate coordinates are read by the machine, the card passes to another station where the automatic measurement of this particular star is completed. The machine pauses in its sequence to allow the operator to inspect visually the star image. If the image is of a good quality, an error signal from the optical scanning head causes the horizontal drive motor and vertical correction motor to position the carriages so that the optical axis of the scanner will pass through the "center of gravity" of the star image. Following this, a new card is read in and a new star measured. In a set of 450 star image measurements with this machine, the average difference from two readings of the same star amounts to only 0.004 mm. The coordinates of the star are read off automatically from the vertical and horizontal screwheads.

A semiautomatic measuring engine at Mount Wilson Observatory uses a Coleman digitalizer consisting of two sets of six plastic disks. One set of disks is rigidly mounted in a line in the digitalizer case, while the other set is mounted opposite them in a movable rack operated by an electric solenoid. Each disk on the rack can be rotated by means of a gearing system attached to the screw axis. When a position reading is desired, the solenoid is actuated, the disks are brought into contact and the angular orientation of the screw axis read out in digital form.

Even in these automatic measuring engines the lead screws (which move either the photographic plate or the microscope and cross hairs) are subject to variations due to temperature, wear, and backlash. It has been suggested that such difficulties could be alleviated through use of interferometric devices, or by the measurement of electrical inductance that changes for different settings of the cross hairs. These procedures could allow for accurate positioning to ± 0.002 mm or better.

11.3.3. Space Probe Observation

If a space probe is to be tracked from the Earth by optical means for an appreciable portion of an interplanetary voyage, it must be quite large so as to reflect a considerable quantity of sunlight. For example, a sphere of 20-in. diameter similar to the Vanguard satellites, specularly reflecting in full sunlight, would be of only the sixth magnitude in the zenith at a distance of 250 miles from the observer. (A sixth-magnitude object is about the faintest that can be detected by the naked eye on a clear, dark night.) It is to be remembered that the magnitude, denoted by superscript m, increases numerically with decreasing brightness. When this particular vehicle is at a distance equal to the average distance of Mars from the Earth at opposition (48,700,000 miles) it will be at $32\overset{\mathrm{m}}{.}3$, far beyond the limiting magnitude of the Baker–Nunn Satellite Tracking Camera (limiting magnitude $= 17\overset{\mathrm{m}}{.}2$ when tracking a star on the celestial equator), and even beyond the reach of the 200-in. Hale telescope (limiting magnitude $= 23\overset{\mathrm{m}}{.}2$). In this regard, even a sphere of 500 ft radius and 100% reflecting power would be $19\overset{\mathrm{m}}{.}0$ at a distance of 50,000,000 miles.*

In the case of minor planets the following simple relationship gives the magnitude of a minor planet at a distance of ρ a.u.'s from the observer and r a.u.'s from the Sun:

$$m = g + 5 \log \rho + 5 \log r + 0.03\beta^{\circ}. \tag{277a}$$

In this formula g is a constant that is different for different minor planets and is obtained empirically from a series of observations of the minor

* The foregoing remarks are based upon the research of Paul Koskela.

planet's magnitude (given ρ and r) e.g., for minor planet 772, $g = 8.9$; and $\beta°$ is the "phase angle" of the minor planet expressed in degrees, i.e., the angle between $\boldsymbol{\rho}$ and $\mathbf{r}$ measured at the minor planet, thus

$$\cos \beta = (r^2 + \rho^2 - R^2)/2\rho r.$$

The 5 log ρ and 5 log r terms in the magnitude equation are a direct result of the fact that magnitude is proportional to $-5/2$ the logarithm of brightness, and the brightness in turn varies as $1/r^2$ (decrease in light intensity illuminating the minor planet from the Sun) and $1/\rho^2$ (decrease in light intensity between the object and the observer).

In the case of a specularly reflecting spherical satellite having diameter, d, the magnitude equation becomes

$$m = m_\odot + 5 \log (2\rho/d) - 2.5 \log (\gamma) + A \qquad (277b)$$

where γ = the reflecting power of the satellite, ($\gamma = 1$ is equivalent to 100%), $m_\odot = -26.7$ (apparent visual magnitude of the Sun), and $A = 1.505 + 0.21 \csc (h)$ (correction for atmospheric absorption). For a diffusely reflecting sphere

$$m = m_\odot + 5 \log (2\rho/d) - 2.5 \log (\gamma) + A$$
$$-2.5 \log \{2/3\pi [\sin \beta + (\pi - \beta) \cos \beta]\}, \qquad (277c)$$

where the last term accounts for the phase of the satellite as illuminated by the solar source (the source assumed to be at a great distance). The rather low magnitude of satellites near the Earth may now be roughly computed—note the strong dependence on the ratio of the distance from observer to satellite and the diameter of the satellite.

The use of large inflated spheres would, therefore, be a rather obvious choice for permitting high accuracy tracking to great distances, as has been suggested many times in the recent literature. These spheres (of silver- or aluminum-coated polyethylene or Mylar for specular reflection, or with white paint or powder coatings for diffuse reflection) would be placed into orbit in a folded condition and then inflated by a small tank of pressurized gas. Even with such a device the Earth-bound optical tracking of interplanetary probes does not look promising and the best observational data will, no doubt, be obtained from on board the space vehicle.

This inverse problem of observing *from* satellites is not so much affected by dim images as it is by the deleterious changes in focal length, internal misalignment of optical axis, lens distortion, etc. caused by the high

g-loads during boost off (a recalibration of the camera after photography is, therefore, indicated). If such an observation is of a ground target, then in addition account must be taken of the camera's orientation with respect to the local vertical and of the relative ground motion.

The first of these problems associated with a ground target may be alleviated through use of what might be termed a "Zedir" technique in which an astronomical photograph of a star field (in the direction of the zenith or at some angle to the zenith) is exposed simultaneously with a ground or cartographic photograph (in the direction of the nadir). Analyses of these two photographs, taken with an instrument of well-known geometry, allows for the computation of the camera's precise orientation in space. See Andersen, *et al.*[146] The second problem of relative ground motion can be compensated for by either moving the camera laterally or in an arc.

Optical observations from the space vehicle would either be automated (e.g., a star tracker for stellar observations or an automatic reconnaissance or cartographic camera for terrestrial observations) or manual in the case of a manned vehicle. In the latter case the observations would be reduced in a fashion similar to that employed in the case of ground based observations (cf. Section 11.3.2). Some problems peculiar to space vehicle observation of celestial bodies do, however, exist. As noted in references 135 and 136 planet crescent shape must be carefully accounted for, relative star magnitudes and background light will differ from that seen on Earth, while various types of deleterious radiation will increase sensor noise, e.g., fog photographic plates.

11.3.4. Image Intensification and Infrared

Recent developments in the field of photoelectronics may make it possible to increase the range of optical telescopes as much as 45 times by image intensification. Image intensification instruments are divided into two basic types: the signal generating or television type and the conventional cascade image inverter. In the television type an image is changed into a modulated current that is sent through an amplifier and transformed into a regular television image. The converter tube operates similarly except that the image is reproduced in recordable form within the tube itself. Most of the research in the employment of television as an intensification technique has been undertaken at Wright Air Development Command and at Wittenberg College. The Air Force development is the result of extensive research on the part of their scientists to produce a means of magnifying light intensity in order to enable pilots flying at high altitudes at night to observe the ground as if it were daytime. Pioneering work in the field of converters has been undertaken by Professor André Lallemand at the Observatoire de Paris. Research devoted to the development of the cascade image converter principle has been carried out mainly by Tuve, Ford, Hall, and Bain.[147]

Performance of a photoelectric instrument is measured in terms of quantum efficiency. In the ordinary photographic process one grain of silver salt can be developed for every 1000 light photons striking it; in contrast, one electron is emitted from a photoelectric surface after only ten photons strike it. Certainly advances in this field will aid the detection and tracking of space vehicles.

Perhaps the observation of space vehicles in the infrared 1–2 micron region will serve to complement these image intensification techniques—particularly in the area of extending optical tracking beyond the twilight limitation. Eastman Kodak estimates from extrapolations of data acquired through use of a 50-element lead sulfide scanner operating on Sputnik II at 900 miles, that a 5 ft diameter satellite having a surface temperature of 50°C could be detected by a 36 in. telescope at 10,000 miles with a signal to noise ratio of better than five! Such an instrument promises to yield data good to 30 minutes of arc very near the horizon and good to 1 minute of arc 5 degrees from the horizon. The use of the zinc-doped Germanium (ZIP) cells would improve sensitivity and allow the detection of satellites with 0°C skin temperatures.

11.4. Electronic Observations

Although the angular accuracy of electronic measuring systems is currently less than that of optical systems as mentioned in the foregoing, it is to be expected that electrical methods will be sufficiently improved so as to compete in accuracy with optical methods during the next decade. The pulsed radar system, radio interferometer, and Doppler systems are the most commonly employed means of obtaining observational data electronically from space vehicles. The principle of the pulsed radar system is well-known and will not be specifically considered here in detail (cf. Bowen[148]). Briefly it involves both distance determination of ρ by the measurement of the transit time of a high-frequency electromagnetic pulse from a transmitter to a vehicle (or vehicle-borne transponder) back to a nearby receiver and an angular measurement obtained by utilizing the directionality of the transmitting and receiving antennas (often supplemented by a lobe or beam switching technique; see page 525 in Bowen[148]). The following sections will be concerned with the details of the interferometer and Doppler techniques. Acknowledgment is made of the assistance given to us in the preparation of these subsections by E. Pitkin, E. Frazier, and E. C. Sternke.

11.4.1. Interferometer Systems

The principles of interferometer or phase comparison tracking systems have been discussed in detail in a number of articles (by Mengel,[149] Mengel and Herget,[150] and Fishman[151]). They will be reviewed here in concept. The receiving system compares the path length from a radiofrequency energy source to a pair of antennas separated by a known distance called the base line. The principle is illustrated in Fig. 44. The signal arrives at antenna B_1 at one end of the base line at the same time that it arrives at point P some distance removed from antenna B_2 on a line between the

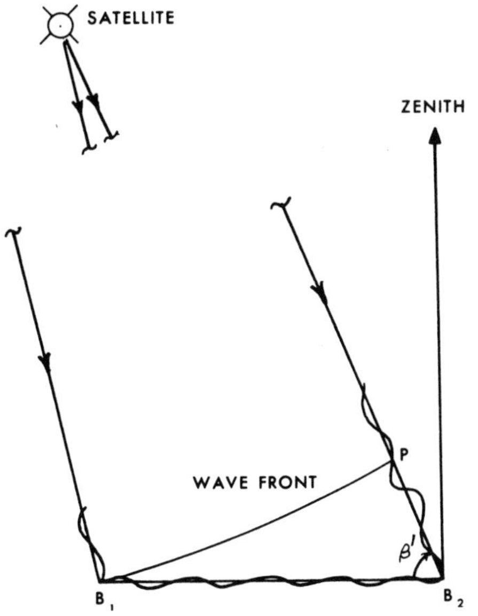

Fig. 44. Interferometer.

source and B_2. Points B_1 and P are both located on the surface of a sphere whose center is at the radio source. When the signal arrives at B_2, its phase is different from that of the signal arriving at B_1 at the same instant, because of the greater distance traveled. This phase difference is a direct measure of the path length PB_2. Assuming the radius of curvature of the arc PB_1 to be nearly infinite, one finds that

$$PB_2 = B_1B_2 \cos \beta'. \tag{278}$$

Thus, measurement of the phase difference gives the information necessary for determining the angular position β' from the antenna B_2 to the radiating energy source, and hence the altitude, h. The addition of another set of antennas perpendicular to the first set is necessary in order to get angular position in a plane perpendicular to that of the first measurement. The topocentric position angles, α' and β' are measured by the interferometer and are mathematically equivalent to the common altitude-azimuth coordinates, h and A. Since the orientation of the base plane, i.e., the Earth's surface, is relatively well-known, these two measurements are sufficient to determine a precise angular position of the satellite in space with respect to altitude-azimuth coordinates. Knowledge of the antenna's geocentric position allows transformation to equatorial geocentric coordinates (cf. Section 4.4) while observational data from the antenna can be utilized for orbit determination by, e.g., Laplace's method, cf. Section 6.3.1.

The basic satellite tracking system being used with IGY Vanguard and Explorer satellites is the Minitrack system developed by the Naval Research Laboratory.[150,152,153,154] The antenna system consists of eight dipole arrays arranged in a criss-cross pattern (cf. Mengel and Herget[150]). Three pairs of antennas are connected in the north–south direction and two pairs in the east–west direction. The outermost pair are 500 ft apart and the north–south innermost pair are only 12 ft apart. The individual arrays are oriented with their long dimension of 60 ft in the east–west direction so that the resulting antenna pattern is a fanshaped beam about 100° wide in the north–south direction. This gives the maximum coverage in the north–south direction that is desirable to intercept satellites with orbits in the general east–west direction that result from launches at Cape Canaveral.

The sensitivity and accuracy of the prime Minitrack system are its distinguishing features. Once installed and calibrated the antenna system is never moved. Angular revolution of the electronic and antenna system is estimated to be good to about 20″ to 40″ or 0.1 to 0.2 milliradian for optimum atmospheric conditions. A 400″ resolution is expected for the worse conditions of ionospheric radiowave refraction at 108 megacycles carrier wave frequency. The electronic system resolution, not including the antenna and lead-in wiring has been shown to be equivalent to ±8″, and the system has remained stable for a period of five weeks. It is expected that approximately 10% of the received data will be obtained under optimum conditions where the 20″ over-all resolution accuracy will apply. Thus, even though relatively accurate, electronic angular measurements essentially limited by the vagaries of ionospheric refraction, do not yet approach optical accuracies of 0.2″ to 0.02″. Furthermore, particularly for space vehicles moving at great geocentric distances whose angular positions vary slowly with time, electronic angular measures are not nearly as useful in orbit determination and improvement as electronic range measures.

Since the original Minitrack system was designed, a number of improvements in interferometric tracking have been developed. A typical example is the Microlock system. A good tracking system should perform its function with minimum transmitter power on the part of the vehicle being tracked because it is axiomatic that increased transmitter power will be reflected in increased vehicle weight. New methods of increasing receiver sensitivity have recently been developed to reduce the transmitter power requirements. These are called phase-lock or frequency lock; side band folding; and correlation detection (cf. Richter, *et al.*,[155] Crooks,[156] and Sternke[157]). In the Microlock system, as in the Minitrack system, the ground station generates a reference signal for comparison with the incoming signal from the antenna; but the manner in which this signal is controlled is quite different. Three main antennas are used on each base line. (Ambiguity resolving antennas can also be used if necessary.) The two outer antennas give the interferometer signal while the center antenna gives a signal of the same frequency with a phase angle halfway between the signals from the two outer antennas. This signal is used as a phase and frequency reference for the frequency generator of the ground transmitter. As the satellite transmits to the ground receiver a change in the received signal frequency occurs due to the rate of change of the satellite's distance (called the "Doppler effect"; see below). The Microlock system uses this instantaneous frequency for the reference signal rather than a constant frequency from a stable oscillator as is used in the Minitrack system. The Doppler frequency shift is then automatically eliminated from the information given to the interferometer receiver and only the desired relative time-of-arrival signals remain.

11.4.2. Doppler Radar

The Doppler effect in physical wave motion (i.e., sound) and electromagnetic radiation has been well-known and used for many years. By analogy with sound the Austrian physicist, Christian Doppler (1842) suggested that the color of an approaching light-source would appear bluer, and that of a receding light-source redder, than when they were standing still with respect to the observer. Fizeau (1848) showed, however, that there would be no resulting change of color, because if the whole spectrum were shifted toward the violet, for example, by an increase in the frequency of light from an approaching source, some infrared radiation would move into the visible and the color of the whole spectrum would remain as before. The spectral lines, on the other hand, would appear to be shifted by an amount proportional to their normal wavelengths and the relative velocity of the source in the light of sight. Sir William Huggins (1868) was the first to realize the enormous possibilities of the Doppler–Fizeau shift for determining the radial velocities of astronomical lightsources; but it was not until the development of photographic processes (1888) that exact measurements of the spectral shift could be made with reference to the standard lines of a comparison laboratory spectrum and observations of stellar velocities on a large scale became practicable. Tremendous advances in the realm of stellar motions and multiple star systems have resulted from the discovery.

The *Doppler–Fizeau shift* as applied to radar is also a direct effect of the relative velocities of a transmitting source and a receiver. The effect is an alteration of the wavelength and frequency of the transmitted energy while it is traveling through the medium. There are two discrete components of this phenomenon. If the transmitter has a velocity with respect to inertial space, the actual waves are compressed in the direction of motion, and spread out in the opposite direction; if the receiver has a velocity with respect to inertial space, e.g., if it is traveling opposite to the direction of motion of the radiation, it will receive the waves at a higher frequency than their actual one, and the effective wavelength will be shortened. This argument is applied conversely to a receiver traveling in the same direction as the waves. (See also *Doppler shift* in the glossary p. 289.)

The standard equation describing the Doppler effect is:

$$f = f_0 \frac{c + v_r}{c - v_s} \tag{279}$$

where f_0 = the transmitted frequency; c = the velocity of the radiation in the medium; v_r = the speed of the receiver towards, or away from the source; and v_s = the speed of the source towards, or away from the observer. Observing a convention of signs is very important. Here the positive direction is taken as that in which the distance from the observer to the source is increasing, and a negative sign means that the relative distance is diminishing.

It would appear at first glance that the matter of the velocities is rather complicated, leading to confusing and bulky calculations. In practice, however, a simplification can be made, which leads to much easier calculation. Although there are two discrete effects involved, it makes no difference to the observer which of these effects is the actual cause of the final shift in frequency. Only the relative radial velocity between the source and the observer is of importance. On the basis of this, the origin of the coordinate system used can be placed at the observer, as is usually done. Then the v_r term of equation would drop out, and the v_s term would represent the radial velocity of the source with respect to the observer.

Then adopting our conventional notation, the simplified form of Eq. (279) is:

$$f = \frac{f_0 c}{c - \dot{\rho}} \qquad \text{or} \qquad \dot{\rho} = c(1 - f_0/f). \tag{280}$$

Clearly, an accurate determination of the range rate, $\dot{\rho}$, requires a well-determined value of the frequency, f_0, of the source. In practice a comparison is made between a stationary source of frequency f_0 and the moving source of the same frequency f to obtain $\dot{\rho}$.

11.4.3. High-accuracy Doppler (HIDOP)

To date it has not been possible to achieve an accurately-known and stable source of frequency, f_0, on board the vehicle, so a "transponder" technique has been employed. This technique involves a receiver coupled to a transmitter (*transponder*) on board the vehicle. Such a device immediately retransmits signals that it receives from a ground transmitter and a nearby ground receiver detects these retransmitted signals.

Specifically, the HIDOP system utilizes multiple frequencies and thereby obtains range, ρ, as well as range rate $\dot{\rho}$. The range measurement is made by comparison of a pair of frequencies (from the transmitter–responder system) that are nearly equal. When added together a very low frequency signal is generated (much like the "beat" frequency in acoustics). This low-frequency signal has, of course, a long wavelength, (up to several hundred miles). Hence, it is possible to measure the phase and count the number of wavelengths traversed as the space vehicle recedes from the ground station. Knowing the frequency accurately, it is possible to determine the length of the wave, and, consequently, to determine the range to the vehicle accurately. Like other Doppler systems the accuracies are ultimately limited by our knowledge of the speed of light, c (see page 88) and typically ρ can be determined to a few parts in a million. See Sternke.[157]

11.4.4. General

There exist several special schemes for the reduction of Doppler and other electronic data, most of which are based upon a determination of the orbit at the observing station.[70] Some schemes do not involve the accumulation of data from several stations or a final determination based upon a variety of data. These latter schemes have been found to be extremely wasteful of computational time as well as causing an introduction of certain errors in the data before they are transmitted to a central computing facility. As has been pointed out by Herrick,[142] "If a large number of observations are obtained in a short period of time, it will generally be advantageous to condense them locally and smooth out the accidental errors. Systematic errors that are local in character, especially instrumental errors that are best known and kept track of by the observer, should be treated locally; others, such as refraction, precession, and nutation, might be corrected by either the observer or orbit analyst; still others, such as a zero-frequency in radio-Doppler observations, may best be revealed by a least-squares treatment of all of the observations in the final analysis of the orbit."

A number of problems either unknown or of minor importance in optical tracking arise with the use of radio techniques. The most serious is the refraction or bending of radio waves due to induced motion of charged particles in the ionosphere. The amount of ionospheric refraction depends on the ion-density gradient, as waves are always bent away from regions of high ion-density. This refraction may be expressed in terms of a local refractive index, n, which varies throughout the ionosphere.

$$n = \sqrt{1 - \frac{81N}{f^2}}, \tag{281}$$

where: n = refractive index, N = ion density in particles/cc, and f = frequency in kilocycles. Inspection of this relation shows that ionospheric refraction can be minimized by utilizing the highest possible frequency for the carrier wave. This frequency is limited at present by the capability of electronic circuit components and 108 Mc is the current frequency being used on United States satellites. (Recently, however, the frequency has been extended to about 1000 Mc.) The Russian satellites have transmitters operating at 40 to 20 Mc. The degree of ionospheric refraction is respectively 7 and 28 times greater at these frequencies than at 108 megacycles. Use of these frequencies, however, has given us valuable information on ionospheric refraction characteristics through comparison of optical and radio tracking data on the Sputniks I and II.

In this regard Guier and Weiffenbach[158] have developed a theoretical expression that is designed to account for the variable index of refraction in the case of the Doppler shift, i.e.,

$$f - f_0 = n_0 \frac{r_c f_0}{c} \left[\cos h \frac{d\chi(t)}{dt} + \frac{1}{r} \frac{dr}{dt} \sqrt{r^2 \mu^2 - \cos^2 h} \right]$$

where n_0 = the equivalent refractive index at the Earth's surface;
r_c = the geocentric distance of the observatory (see Eq. (24));
$\chi(t)$ = the angle measured at the center of the Earth between $\mathbf{r}$ to the space vehicle and $\mathbf{r}_c$ to the observatory; and
$\mu^2 \triangleq n/n_0$ (note that the index of refraction, n, is a function of height and hence of r).

Certain constants such as n_0 and a polynomial representing μ could be determined, along with the orbital parameters, in a differential correction procedure.

12 APPLICATION TO INTERPLANETARY ORBITS

In the field of interplanetary orbits, one finds a particularly clear-cut distinction between feasibility and definitive orbit work. The astronomical constants and perturbation techniques discussed in Chapters 5, 8, and 9 are particularly relevant to the analysis of definitive interplanetary orbits and, except for the problem of coordinate transformations, can be applied without further discussion. Two-body relationships, on the other hand, are more varied in nature and owe their usefulness to their ability to yield simple solutions to problems of feasibility in which semiquantitative analysis suffices.* In addition to the definitive and feasibility approaches, the question of interplanetary navigational philosophy is also of paramount importance to the astrodynamicist, and this topic will be dealt with in the last section of this chapter.

12.1. Definitive Orbit Studies

12.1.1. Transfer Points

Initially, the definitive orbit will be computed (probably with special perturbations) in a geocentric coordinate system. As the vehicle recedes from the Earth, a point will be reached where it becomes computationally efficient to transfer to a heliocentric coordinate system. Finally, at landing or at the terminal maneuver, a planetocentric coordinate system becomes

* Many analysts have, in fact, carried out interplanetary orbit computations by employing such approximations, e.g., Herrick in 1946 and, more recently, Breakwell, *et al.*[159] and Karrenberg and Arthur.[160]

more appropriate. Such transfers should be carried out when, e.g., the vehicle passes from a predominantly geocentric to a predominantly heliocentric "field." The regions in space where one would expect the vehicle to be in a predominantly geocentric, heliocentric, or planetocentric field, can be delineated by calculating the ratio of the perturbative accelerations to the two-body acceleration, i.e., by comparing the geocentric

$$(|\dot{x}_g^{\backprime}| + |\dot{y}_g^{\backprime}| + |\dot{z}_g^{\backprime}|)/(1/r^2{}_g) \tag{282}$$

with the heliocentric

$$(|\dot{x}_h^{\backprime}| + |\dot{y}_h^{\backprime}| + |\dot{z}_h^{\backprime}|)/(1/r_h^2), \tag{283}$$

where, in this instance, the subscripts g and h refer to perturbations *reckoned in* a geocentric or a heliocentric system respectively, e.g., in a geocentric system $\dot{x}_g^{\backprime}$, $\dot{y}_g^{\backprime}$, and $\dot{z}_g^{\backprime}$ would include solar, lunar, and perhaps, drag perturbations (r_g differs from r_h in that r_g is measured in Earth radii from the center of the Earth, and r_h is measured in astronomical units from the center of the Sun).

At the point where the former ratio (Eq. (282)) exceeds the latter ratio (Eq. (283)) (at about 128 Earth radii), the heliocentric field will predominate. It should be noted that this point is *not* where the force due to the Sun acting on the vehicle exceeds the force due to the Earth acting on the vehicle (at about 40 Earth radii). Adoption of such an erroneous criterion would, e.g., disinherit the Earth of the Moon! A similar analysis holds for heliocentric and planetocentric fields. In this latter case a comparison of

$$(|\dot{x}_h^{\backprime}| + |\dot{y}_h^{\backprime}| + |\dot{z}_h^{\backprime}|)/(1/r_h^2)$$

to

$$(|\dot{x}_p^{\backprime}| + |\dot{y}_p^{\backprime}| + |\dot{z}_p^{\backprime}|)/(1/r_p^2)$$

is carried out (the subscript p refers to the planet). The locus of these points where the solar perturbations dominate forms a roughly spherical surface enclosing each planet that is nearly independent of the specific interplanetary trajectory. The radius of this surface is referred to as the "tidal radius," and any planetary satellite exterior to this surface will eventually stray away from its parent planet and take up its own independent heliocentric orbit. For the purpose of interplanetary orbit computations, however, such a surface is utilized primarily to define the point where coordinate systems should be changed in order to afford the most efficient computation.

12.1.2. Perturbative Analyses

Special (or general) perturbation procedures can now be employed in the appropriate coordinate system. In this regard the perturbative forces due to the planets can be reckoned as in Chapter 7 (the coordinates of the planets can be obtained from the references listed in Section 4.6) and a definitive interplanetary orbit determined.

It is, of course, important to change units at the point where the transformation occurs, otherwise a loss in accuracy as well as an increase in formula complexity is incurred. As an example $\dot{s}_{\infty}$, for a vehicle leaving the Earth on a geocentric orbit, must be changed from Earth circular-satellite speed at one equatorial radius over to Sun circular-satellite speed at 1 a.u. See Section 2.5.

The actual evaluation of Eqs. (282) and (283) and the generation of the n-body perturbative forces require tables of the rectangular components (x, y, z) of the following position vectors (see Section 4.6):

$\mathbf{r}_{\oplus\odot}$ = the coordinates of the Sun relative to the Earth in Earth radii and astronomical units,

$\bar{\mathbf{r}}_{\oplus\odot}$ = the coordinates of the Sun relative to the Earth–Moon center of mass in astronomical units,

$\mathbf{r}_{\odot p}$ = the coordinates of the target planet relative to the Sun in astronomical units,

$\mathbf{r}_{\odot 2\!\!\downharpoonright}$ = the coordinates of Jupiter relative to the Sun in Earth radii and in astronomical units, and

$\mathbf{r}_{\oplus☾}$ = the coordinates of the Moon relative to the Earth in Earth radii.

The initial geocentric integration of the orbit (see Chapter 8) will yield the components of $\mathbf{r}_{\oplus\Delta}$. From Eq. (164) the geocentric perturbative terms are

$$\dot{x}_g' = m_{\odot}\left(\frac{x_{\Delta\odot}}{r_{\Delta\odot}^3} - \frac{x_{\oplus\odot}}{r_{\oplus\odot}^3}\right) + m_{☾}\left(\frac{x_{\Delta☾}}{r_{\Delta☾}^3} - \frac{x_{\oplus☾}}{r_{\oplus☾}^3}\right)$$

$$+ m_{♃}\left(\frac{x_{\Delta♃}}{r_{\Delta♃}^3} - \frac{x_{\oplus♃}}{r_{\oplus♃}^3}\right) \qquad x \to y, z$$

where

$$x_{\Delta\odot} = x_{\oplus\odot} - x_{\oplus\Delta},$$

$$x_{\Delta☾} = x_{\oplus☾} - x_{\oplus\Delta},$$

$$x_{\Delta♃} = x_{\oplus♃} + x_{\Delta\oplus} = x_{\odot♃} + x_{\oplus\odot} - x_{\oplus\Delta},$$

$$x_{\oplus♃} = x_{\odot♃} + x_{\oplus\odot};$$

and the masses are in terms of Earth masses, lengths in terms of Earth radii, and time in "k_e^{-1} min." Of course, $k = k_e$ and $\mu = 1$. Similarly, the heliocentric perturbative components are

$$\dot{x}_h' = (m_\oplus + m_☾)\left(-\frac{x_{\oplus\Delta}}{r_{\oplus\Delta}^3} + \frac{\bar{x}_{\oplus\odot}}{r_{\oplus\odot}^3}\right) + m_p\left(\frac{x_{\Delta p}}{r_{\Delta p}^3} + \frac{x_{\odot p}}{r_{\odot p}^3}\right) + m_♃\left(\frac{x_{\Delta ♃}}{r_{\Delta ♃}^3} - \frac{x_{\odot ♃}}{r_{\odot ♃}^3}\right) \qquad x \to y, z$$

where, prior to the transfer to the heliocentric system $x_{\odot\Delta}$ is obtained from

$$x_{\odot\Delta} = x_{\oplus\Delta} - \bar{x}_{\oplus\odot}$$

while

$$x_{\Delta p} = x_{\odot p} + \bar{x}_{\oplus\odot} - x_{\oplus\Delta},$$

$$x_{\Delta ♃} = x_{\odot ♃} - x_{\odot\Delta};$$

and the masses are in terms of solar masses, lengths in terms of astronomical units, and time in k_s^{-1} days. In this case $k = k_s$, but μ may be taken as equal to $m_\odot + m_♀ + m_☿$. When the transfer to the heliocentric system is accomplished, $\mathbf{r}_{\odot\Delta}$ is obtained directly from the integration.

12.2. Two-Body Studies

The following sections are devoted to the application of simple, albeit approximate, two-body relationships to the study of the feasibility of interplanetary missions. The topics included are analyses of launch direction, errors, and sensitivities, and effective gravitational cross sections. Illustrative examples of two-body interplanetary orbits have already been considered in Sections 2.5 and 3.4 and the reader might review these sections prior to his consideration of the following material.

12.2.1. Direction of Launch

The question is often raised as to the proper launch direction for an interplanetary orbit. Let us consider the two-body trajectory from Earth to Venus (μ is assumed equal to unity, i.e., the "restricted" two-body problem). Suppose that a rocket is launched directly towards the Sun. In this case the tangential speed (measured in terms of circular-satellite speed at 1 a.u.), $r\dot{v}$, which in the case of the transfer from an assumed circular

Earth's orbit amounts simply to unity, is not modified at all. Hence if $r\dot{v} = 1$ and $r = 1$ at launch from the Earth (i.e., at 1 a.u.), $r^4\dot{v}^2 = 1 = p = r$. Therefore, the space vehicle, when leaving the Earth, must be at the point where the radius equals the parameter, p, of its orbit, i.e., on the y_ω-axis.

From the *vis-viva* integral,

$$\dot{s}^2 = 2/r - 1/a = 2 - 1/a$$

and from Eq. (8)

$$\dot{s}^2 = \dot{r}^2 + r\dot{v}^2 = \dot{r}^2 + 1;$$

hence

$$2 - 1/a = \dot{r}^2 + 1, \qquad \text{or} \qquad 1 = a(1 - \dot{r}^2).$$

Since

$$p = 1 = a(1 - e^2),$$

then

$$e = \dot{r}. \tag{284}$$

Thus, a purely radial launch velocity results directly in a change in eccentricity. The perihelion of the transfer orbit is

$$q = a(1 - e) = a(1 - \dot{r}) = \frac{(1 - \dot{r})}{(1 - \dot{r}^2)} = \frac{1}{1 + \dot{r}}. \tag{285}$$

For the sake of argument, let it be assumed that the thrust directed towards the Sun, $\dot{r}$, is equal to $1/12$ in an astronomical system of units (i.e., in units of circular-orbit speed about the Sun at 1 a.u. = 18.6 mi/sec). From Eq. (285) we can readily find that $q = 12/13 = 0.923$, so that by launching towards the Sun, the vehicle can never get closer to the Sun than 0.923 a.u. at perihelion. Consequently, it could not possibly reach Venus, which describes a nearly circular orbit of radius 0.723 a.u.

Let it next be assumed that we fire along a tangent to the Earth's orbit. In this case, if we move opposite to the direction of the Earth's motion, the heliocentric vehicle orbit will have its aphelion near the Earth at launch and its perihelion near Venus at landing (such an orbit will be tangent both to the Earth's orbit at launch and to the orbit of Venus at landing). If $\Delta\dot{s}$ is defined as the increment of speed relative to the Earth's orbital velocity in heliocentric units, then

$$\dot{s} = 1 - \Delta\dot{s} \quad \text{and} \quad \frac{1}{a} = 2 - (1 - \Delta\dot{s})^2 = 1 + 2\Delta\dot{s} - (\Delta\dot{s})^2,$$

while

$$r\dot{v} = \dot{s} = 1 - \Delta\dot{s}$$

also, because $r = 1$ at injection again (see the bottom of p. 113 with $\mu = 1$)

$$p = r^4\dot{v}^2 = \dot{s}^2 = (1 - \Delta\dot{s})^2$$

and, finally,

$$e^2 = 4[(\Delta\dot{s})^2 - (\Delta\dot{s})^3] + (\Delta\dot{s})^4. \tag{286}$$

For $\Delta\dot{s} = 1/12$ one obtains $q = 0.724$ a.u. Clearly, therefore, it is preferable to fire tangentially to the Earth's orbit rather than normal to it. A more general analysis of this problem can be found in Chapter 8 in Herrick,[1] where it is demonstrated that the least speed and hence energy required for a transfer between two circular orbits is achieved when one employs such doubly-tangent orbits. The first recognition of this principle was due to Hohmann in 1925 and such orbits are, therefore, termed *Hohmann orbits*.[161] Other considerations often preclude the employment of such simple orbits for orbital transfer. The field of orbital transfer is a vast one, however, and the widely published work of D. F. Lawden should be consulted by the interested reader. In particular, if one is willing to initiate a rather large thrust while on the heliocentric transfer orbit, Lawden and others have found by two-body studies that the use of a multiple-orbit transfer is superior to the simple single Hohmann orbital transfer. (See exercise.)

12.2.2. Errors and Orbit Sensitivity

In heliocentric ecliptic or equatorial coordinate systems, the distance from the Sun to a space vehicle is defined by $r^2 = x^2 + y^2 + z^2$. Consequently, an error in r, Δr, is a function of the errors in x, y, z, i.e.,

$$\Delta r = (x\Delta x + y\Delta y + z\Delta z)/r. \tag{287}$$

Let us assume for simplified two-body interplanetary orbits that the errors in velocity and position can be considered separately and added linearly when they are combined. Thus, we may assume that the velocity is correct and that an error enters only in the distance. Then from differentiation of the *vis-viva* integral with μ set equal to unity, we obtain

$$\Delta a = (2a^2/r^2)\Delta r. \tag{288}$$

While

$$\Delta p = 2r(r\dot{v})^2\Delta r + 2r^2(r\dot{v})\Delta(r\dot{v}).$$

If it is assumed that the tangential component of velocity, $r\dot{v}$, is correct, then

$$\Delta p = (2r^3\dot{v}^2)\Delta r.$$

Also

$$\Delta p = (1 - e^2)\Delta a - (2ae)\Delta e,$$

so that the error in eccentricity occasioned by an error in position, Δr, is simply

$$\Delta e = [(1 - e^2)(a - r)/er^2]\Delta r. \tag{289}$$

Specifically, the error in position as reflected in the perihelion distance becomes

$$\begin{aligned} \Delta q &= (1 - e)\Delta a - a\Delta e \\ &= [2a^2(1 - e)/r^2 - a(1 - e^2)(a - r)/er^2]\Delta r \\ &= \{[2a^2e - a(1 + e)(a - r)](1 - e)/er^2\}\Delta r. \end{aligned}$$

or

$$\Delta q/q = \{[r(1 + e) - q]/er\}\Delta r/r, \tag{290}$$

and in the case of the aphelion distance, q_2, the relation is

$$\Delta q_2/q_2 = \{[q_2 - r(1 - e)]/er\}\Delta r/r. \tag{291}$$

In the case of nearly zero eccentricity, the eccentric anomaly must be introduced in order to resolve the indeterminacy of $(a - r)/e$. Thus, the equations for the perihelion and aphelion reduce to

$$\Delta q/q = \{a[2 - (1 + e) \cos E]/r\}\Delta r/r \tag{292}$$

and

$$\Delta q_2/q_2 = \{a[2 + (1 - e) \cos E]/r\}\Delta r/r. \tag{293}$$

Unfortunately, these relations are still indeterminate when e is zero because perihelion is then undefined. Nevertheless, as suggested by Walters, one might assume E to have a value resulting from a random position error and therefore obtain for $e = 0$:

$$\overline{(\Delta q/q)^2} = \overline{(2 - \cos E)^2}\ \overline{(\Delta r/r)^2} = 4.5\ \overline{(\Delta r/r)^2} \qquad q \rightarrow q_2. \tag{294}$$

If the position is assumed to be perfectly known and all the error arises from the velocity, then the equations are precisely those for variation-of-parameters, and relations for Δa and Δe (i.e., $a^{`}$ and $e^{`}$) may be employed. Consequently, (again assuming $\mu = 1$) from Section 8.3.1 we find that

$$\Delta a = (2a^2\dot{s})\Delta\dot{s} = 2a^2(\dot{x}\Delta\dot{x} + \dot{y}\Delta\dot{y} + \dot{z}\Delta\dot{z}) \tag{295}$$

and

$$e\Delta e = (r^2\dot{r}/a)\Delta\dot{r} + ([p/r - r/a]r\dot{s})\Delta\dot{s} \tag{296}$$

(see Chapter 17 in Herrick[1]), where r is the distance from the Sun *at the time when the errors* $\Delta\dot{r}$ *and* $\Delta\dot{s}$ *are introduced* and

$$r\Delta\dot{r} = x\Delta\dot{x} + y\Delta\dot{y} + z\Delta\dot{z}.$$

For the aphelion and perihelion uncertainties it can be shown that

$$\Delta q = ([r^2 - a^2 + 2a^2e - a^2e^2]\dot{s}^2/e)\Delta\dot{s}/\dot{s} - ([r\dot{r}]^2/e)\Delta\dot{r}/\dot{r} \tag{297}$$

and

$$\Delta q_2 = ([a^2 - r^2 + 2a^2e + a^2e^2]\dot{s}^2/e)(\Delta\dot{s}/\dot{s}) + ([r\dot{r}]^2/e)\Delta\dot{r}/r. \tag{298}$$

Again the indeterminacy for e can be resolved by introducing $r\dot{r} = \sqrt{a}$ $(e \sin E)$ and computing a mean-square error. Consequently for perihelion

$$\overline{\left(\frac{\Delta q}{q}\right)^2} = \frac{1}{2}\overline{\left(\frac{\Delta\dot{r}}{\dot{s}}\right)^2} + 6\overline{\left(\frac{\Delta\dot{s}}{\dot{s}}\right)^2} \qquad q \rightarrow q_2. \tag{299}$$

As has been noted already, if the errors are small, it is possible to combine the position and velocity errors in a linear fashion. The foregoing error equations can, of course, also be applied to geocentric orbits and in particular are quite useful for the preliminary estimation of injection errors for satellite and lunar trajectories.

In the case of interplanetary trajectories it is important to recognize that the error in speed results both from observational uncertainties and from the uncertainties occasioned by lack of exact knowledge of the laboratory unit in terms of the astronomical unit (see Chapter 5).

Let us consider the case of a launch from Earth on a trip to Venus. One of the first questions to be decided is exactly when and where to determine our initial conditions. If we associate $\dot{s}_\infty$ with the speed that our Venusian probe will have at a considerable distance from the Earth relative to the Earth (i.e., its asymptotic or "hyperbolic excess" speed),

$$\left(\dot{s}_\infty{}^2 = \frac{2}{\infty} - \frac{1}{a} = -\frac{1}{a}\right),$$

and $\dot{s}_p$ the parabolic or escape speed at any given radial distance from the Earth,

$$\left(\dot{s}_p{}^2 = \frac{2}{r} - \frac{1}{\infty} = \frac{2}{r}\right),$$

then the *vis-viva* equation reduces to the form

$$\dot{s}^2 = \dot{s}_p{}^2 + \dot{s}_\infty{}^2. \tag{300}$$

Consequently an error in launch speed, $\dot{s}$, propagates itself into an error in the speed of recession from the Earth at a great distance, $\dot{s}_\infty$, by

$$\Delta\dot{s}_\infty = \frac{\dot{s}}{\dot{s}_\infty}\,\Delta\dot{s}.$$

Percentage-wise, we have

$$\left(\frac{\Delta\dot{s}_\infty}{\dot{s}_\infty}\right) = \left(\frac{\dot{s}}{\dot{s}_\infty}\right)^2\left(\frac{\Delta\dot{s}}{\dot{s}}\right). \tag{301}$$

For a Hohmann or doubly-tangent Earth–Venus trajectory, this relationship becomes specifically

$$\frac{\Delta\dot{s}_\infty}{\dot{s}_\infty} \cong 16\,\frac{\Delta\dot{s}}{\dot{s}},$$

so that $\frac{1}{16}$ of 1% error in launch is reflected by a 1% uncertainty in the speed of the vehicle as it recedes to great distances from the Earth. Since the geocentric speed of the vehicle must be added to the heliocentric speed of the Earth (which is over ten times larger), the heliocentric speed of the vehicle is known to perhaps $\frac{1}{10}$ of 1%. It is clear, however, that in order to circumvent the amplification of launch error, it is advisable to measure the interplanetary probe's speed after it has moved ten or so Earth radii from the Earth (cf. Baker[162]), e.g., Doppler radii measurements of interplanetary and lunar vehicles are more effectively made after the vehicle has receded a significant distance from the Earth!

Given the hypothetical $\frac{1}{10}$ of 1% error in the initial heliocentric speed of the vehicle and assuming its initial position to be perfectly well-known, we obtain a cumulative error on a Hohmann orbit at Venus amounting to

$$\frac{\Delta q + \Delta q_2}{a} = 4a\dot{s}^2\left(\frac{\Delta \dot{s}}{\dot{s}}\right) = (4)(0.86)(0.916)^2\frac{1}{10} = 0.288\%$$

and for a Hohmann orbit to Mars an error of 0.628% (note that the addition of Eqs. (297) and (298) and division by a will result in the foregoing equation).

12.2.3. Effective Gravitational Cross Section

The question of error sensitivity on interplanetary, or for that matter, lunar trajectories cannot be resolved by the computation of the terminal offset distance alone. It is necessary as well to consider the attraction of the planet on the vehicle as it approaches the target. This effect tends to increase the probability of making a landing. As was mentioned in the introduction to this section, it is often useful to divide interplanetary trajectories into three phases and apply two-body considerations to each of these phases individually. In the case of the interplanetary landing phase, for example, it is useful to assign to the planet at landing a size that is greater than its physical size, a size that represents the extent of its predominant gravitational attraction. This concept is employed by atomic and nuclear physicists and is termed the *effective cross section.* Its radius is called the *collision parameter*, b, and it is evident that any space vehicle coming towards the planet with an offset distance less than the collision parameter will strike the planet. If we employ a two-body approximation during the landing phase, the radius of this cross section is easily derived from the principle of the conservation of angular momentum and from the *vis-viva* integral (cf. Baker[104]). Equating the angular momentum $b\dot{s}_\infty$ at a point a great distance from the planet to that at a grazing encounter with its surface, we find that

$$b\dot{s}_\infty = q\dot{s}_0, \tag{302}$$

(see Fig. 45) where s_∞ is now the asymptotic speed of the vehicle as it approaches the planet, $r_0 = q$ is the planet's radius (or the orbital perifocus for grazing encounter with a planetary surface), and s_0 is the speed the vehicle would have at a grazing encounter with the surface of the planet.

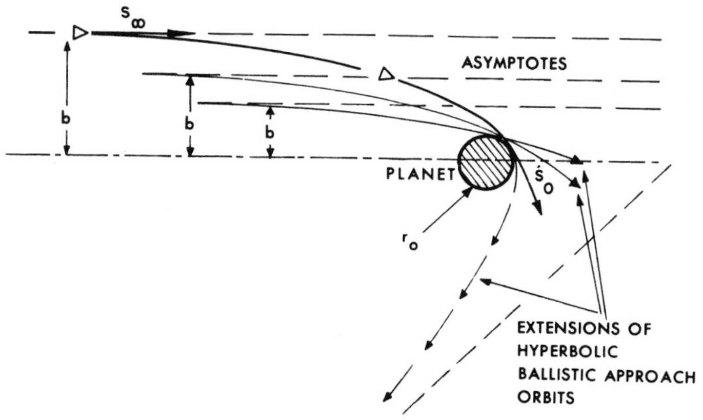

FIG. 45. Collision parameter.

From the *vis-viva* integral (Eq. (13)) applied to the planetocentric orbit

$$\dot{s}_0^2 = \frac{2\mu}{r_0} + \dot{s}_\infty{}^2 \text{ since } \dot{s}_\infty{}^2 = -\mu/a \quad \text{(i.e., } \dot{s}_\infty \text{ is the speed as } r \rightarrow \infty)$$

so that solving for b, we obtain

$$b = r_0\sqrt{\frac{2\mu}{\dot{s}_\infty{}^2 r_0} + 1}. \tag{303}$$

With regard to Eq. (303) it should be noted that as $\dot{s}_\infty \rightarrow \infty$ (i.e., infinite speed of approach), $b \rightarrow r_0$, the physical radius of the planet; and as $\dot{s}_\infty \rightarrow 0$ (i.e., no relative velocity at ∞) all objects will eventually be attracted to the "lone" planet and $b \rightarrow \infty$.

The effective gravitational cross section (sometimes called a "sphere of action" or a "capture arc") represents a rather large target. If one wishes to take advantage of atmospheric retardation, however, a much smaller target must be considered: only a narrow band of the Earth's atmosphere situated at a radial distance r_0 from the planet's center (i.e., in this case r_0 is not exactly equal to the planet's radius). If the allowable width of this band is dr_0, then differentiation of the foregoing equation will yield

$$db = \frac{1}{b}\left[\frac{1}{\dot{s}_\infty{}^2} + r_0\right] dr_0. \tag{304}$$

For the trip to Venus $db = 2.5\ dr_0$ so that the effective target will be a thin annulus of radius b and width db as depicted in Fig. 46. Hence, the gravitational field of Venus will not be of much advantage. A more detailed discussion of the braking ellipse maneuver and of other possible alternate lift re-entry orbits will be found in Baker.[104]

In this regard, it is now recognized that, aside from polar orbits, the Van Allen radiation belt hazard will preclude the utilization of the multiple braking ellipse maneuver for the return of manned vehicles. Still, however, the accuracy requirements for either the single-pass ballistic (drag capsule)

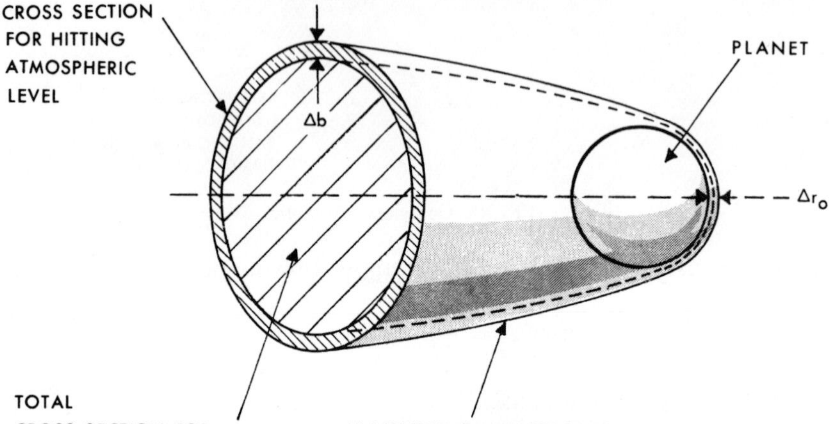

FIG. 46. Effective gravitational cross sections.

or lift (glider) entry orbits are most stringent. Often these single-pass orbits are specified by their *elevation angle*, θ, (an angle between the velocity vector of the vehicle and the local horizontal) reckoned at a particular altitude above the Earth, e.g., 100 miles. (Note that for a nonrotating atmosphere $\theta = 90 - \zeta$, where ζ is the "entry angle" defined in Section 8.4.) For grazing entry the equation for this elevation angle, from pp. 14, 113, 116

$$\tan \theta = \dot{r}/r_1\dot{v} = er_1 \sin v/p, \tag{305}$$

(see Chapter 4F of Herrick[1]), can be approximated near perigee by

$$\theta \cong er_1 v/p, \tag{306}$$

where r_1 is the reference radius from the Earth (e.g., Earth's radius plus 100 miles). Thus, the change in θ due to a change in b (holding r_1 and $\dot{s}_\infty$ constant) is

$$\frac{\partial \theta}{\partial b} = \frac{r_1}{p}\left\{-\frac{ev}{p}\frac{\partial p}{\partial b} + v\frac{\partial e}{\partial b} + e\frac{\partial v}{\partial b}\right\};$$

but, since for a constant $\dot{s}_\infty$, a is a constant also, we find that $\dfrac{\partial e}{\partial b} = -\dfrac{\partial p}{\partial b}/2ae$ and for small v

$$e\frac{\partial v}{\partial b} = \frac{1}{v}\left(\frac{\partial e}{\partial b} - \frac{1}{r_1}\frac{\partial p}{\partial b}\right) = -\frac{1}{v}\left(\frac{1}{2ae} + \frac{1}{r_1}\right)\frac{\partial p}{\partial b}.$$

Combining these expressions, we find that

$$\frac{\partial \theta}{\partial b} = -\frac{r_1}{p}\left\{\frac{ev}{p} + \frac{v}{2ae} + \frac{1}{v}\left(\frac{1}{2ae} + \frac{1}{r_1}\right)\right\}\frac{\partial p}{\partial b} \cong -\frac{r_1}{pv}\left(\frac{1}{2ae} + \frac{1}{r_1}\right)\frac{\partial p}{\partial b}.$$

Since $p =$ the angular momentum per unit mass squared (see Section 6.1.1), then

$$p = b^2\dot{s}_\infty{}^2 \qquad \text{and} \qquad \frac{\partial p}{\partial b} = 2b\dot{s}_\infty{}^2.$$

Consequently, an accuracy given for elevation angle, $d\theta$, can be translated into a value of db, by

$$db = -\{pv/r_1 b\dot{s}_\infty{}^2(1/ae + 2/r_1)\}\, d\theta = -\left\{bv/\left(\frac{r_1}{ae} + 2\right)\right\} d\theta, \quad (307)$$

(the exact relationship is $db = \{-b \sin v \sec^2 \theta/[2r_1 e \sin^2 v/p + r_1/ae + 2\cos v]\}\, d\theta$) where b decreases for increasing θ at the same $\dot{s}_\infty$. Ordinarily pure drag entry vehicles require an accuracy in $d\theta$ of a fraction of a degree, while lift vehicles (with a ratio between lift and drag forces amounting to about two) can have $d\theta$ variations amounting to a few degrees. This advantage of the lifting vehicle (including its maneuverability) must, however, be weighed against an almost two to one mass penalty—a glider being twice as ponderous as a drag capsule for the same payload.

12.3. Navigational Philosophy

As was noted in Baker,[163] the navigational problem in space is often quite different from the Earthbound navigational problem. In this concluding section we will address ourselves to the question of a vehicle-born navigational system. Specifically, let us consider the function and utility of an onboard navigational computer. The uses of this onboard navigational computer would be:

(i) To process observational data acquired in flight (it is usually assumed that such data can be more easily, or more accurately obtained from the vehicle than from the ground).

(ii) To serve as a "back-up" for a ground computer (here it is assumed that both data transmitted from the ground and data generated on board the vehicle would be available).

It is clear that if the best data should prove to be obtainable from the ground, then any navigational maneuvers of the vehicle should be executed through a command link between the ground and the vehicle, and the use of an on-board navigational computer would be unwarranted.

It is concluded then that the principal application of on-board navigational computers will be to lunar and interplanetary probes. In particular, in the midcourse guidance of such probes, the employment of a navigational computer may be mandatory. Advantage can be taken of the fact that the midcourse interplanetary and the midcourse lunar orbits are very nearly two-body orbits and, in keeping with the philosophy adopted by Baker,[163] the navigational principle involved would be that of a differential correction to the orbit. The purpose of the on-board navigational computer then would be to process observational data obtained from the vehicle as well as that transmitted from the ground, and to compute the velocity error or corrective velocity that the vehicle must gain in order to accomplish its lunar or interplanetary mission. Before embarking upon this subject of differential correction a word should be included on the non-coplanar nature of the vehicle and the planetary orbit (the vehicle proceeding initially along the ecliptic plane).

12.3.1. Inclination Change

In the case of the interplanetary trajectory an optimum time to change from the ecliptic plane to an orbit plane that will reach the planet at time of landing (since the planet will not in general be situated at a node of its orbit in the ecliptic plane) is when the true anomaly at the vehicle differs by 90°* from the true anomaly it will have at the time of intercept with the planet. This principle can be gleaned from a consideration of the spherical

* It is emphasized that the position of the node of the planet's orbit plane has *nothing* whatsoever to do with the problem. Only the planet's ecliptic latitude, β_p, at the time of landing is relevant and the planet's itinerary is irrelevant. The planet could be on any orbit and as long as the angle between the planet's position at the time of landing and the vehicle (at the point of inclination change) Δv was 90° (as measured on the heliocentric celestial sphere), the change of inclination, Δi, would be minimized.[163] The true optimization for minimum fuel expenditure might, however, be at a point slightly different from this due to guidance and the slowly varying speed of the vehicle on its orbit.

geometry involved i.e., $\sin \beta_p = \sin \Delta i \sin \Delta v$ (see Fig. 32). $\mu \rightarrow \Delta v$, $\beta_p \leq \Delta v \leq \pi/2 - \beta_p$. If, on the other hand, the vehicle cannot maneuver in midcourse, then a single orbit plane passing through the Sun and leading from the Earth at time of take-off to the planet at time of landing must be employed (as shown by Bock and Mundo[135] such a single orbit plane trajectory is not very efficient, e.g., if such a plane is inclined only 10° to the ecliptic a 100% increase in launch weight is required for conventional chemical propellants). In any event, after the last thrust period, whether it be at take-off or in a maneuver to reach the planet's orbit plane, observational data must be taken in order to determine any accumulated error and the orbit corrected.

12.3.2. Differential Correction

The differential correction proceeds as follows for both the lunar and interplanetary trajectories: before the flight, precomputations are made of observations *as they would appear from the vehicle* if it traveled along the ideal orbit. As noted by Bock[164] such observations will probably be differential measures of angles between planets and *nearby* stars (long a standard procedure in observational astronomy) and will be supplemented by inertial stabilization of the instruments. Any other data, such as electronic could, however, also be employed, e.g., active Doppler radar, pulsed radar, phase comparison, or even measurement of the Doppler shift of the 21-cm neutral interstellar hydrogen line. Since the vehicle will not in general travel along this ideal orbit because of inaccuracies in initial launch or midcourse maneuvers and errors in the astrodynamical constants, actual observations during the trip will differ from the precomputed observations. From the comparison between the two, residuals are found, and a differential correction is made to obtain an improved orbit. From these "observed minus computed" differences, e.g., $\Delta\rho_i$, (where ρ_i is meant to stand for some typical observational datum) improved elements can be obtained by a least squares solution (see Chapter 6). The question as to which elements to correct must be decided. Either the six components of ideal position and velocity: x_I, y_I, z_I, $\dot{x}_I$, $\dot{y}_I$, and $\dot{z}_I$ or $\mathbf{U}$, $\mathbf{V}$, a, and e_I, either set of elements being reckoned for the time at which a corrective thrust is to be made (determined before hand), epoch, could be utilized as elements. The following equations (308) based upon the former set of elements must be inverted by least squares (if $n > 6$) to yield improvements, $\Delta\dot{x}_I$, $\Delta\dot{y}_I$, $\Delta\dot{z}_I$, Δx_I, Δy_I, and Δz_I to the six ideal velocity and position component orbital elements. Specifically velocity and position that the vehicle *will have* at the time of correction (epoch), $\dot{\mathbf{r}}_0$ and $\mathbf{r}_0$, are $\dot{\mathbf{r}}_0 = \dot{\mathbf{r}}_I + \Delta\dot{\mathbf{r}}_I$ and $\mathbf{r}_0 = \mathbf{r}_I + \Delta\mathbf{r}_I$.

$$\Delta\rho_1 = (\partial\rho_1/\partial x_I)_{t_1}\Delta x_I + (\partial\rho_1/\partial y_I)_{t_1}\Delta y_I + (\partial\rho_1/\partial z_I)_{t_1}\Delta z_I + (\partial\rho_1/\partial \dot{x}_I)_{t_1}\Delta \dot{x}_I + (\partial\rho_1/\partial \dot{y}_I)_{t_1}\Delta \dot{y}_I + (\partial\rho_1/\partial \dot{z}_I)_{t_1}\Delta \dot{z}_I$$

$$\Delta\rho_2 = (\partial\rho_2/\partial x_I)_{t_2}\Delta x_I + (\partial\rho_2/\partial y_I)_{t_2}\Delta y_I + \cdots$$

$$\vdots$$

$$\Delta\rho_i = (\partial\rho_i/\partial x_I)_{t_i}\Delta x_I + (\partial\rho_i/\partial y_I)_{t_i}\Delta y_I + \cdots$$

$$\Delta\rho_n = (\partial\rho_n/\partial x_I)_{t_n}\Delta x_I + (\partial\rho_n/\partial y_I)_{t_n}\Delta y_I + \cdots. \qquad (308)$$

where $\rho_i = \rho_i(x_I, y_I, z_I, \dot{x}_I, \dot{y}_I, \dot{z}_I, t_i)$ and the partials are computed at the time of the observation t_i (the sensitivity to clock drift has not been found to be particularly severe). All partials involved in these equations would be evaluated beforehand and stored. In this regard it should be emphasized that the observations, e.g., ρ_i, made all along the path at different t_i's, are functions of certain *time constant* orbital parameters and t_i—sufficient to say that a, e, T, i, Ω, ω; or $\mathbf{a}$, $\mathbf{b}$, n_0, M_0; or x, y, z, $\dot{x}$, $\dot{y}$, $\dot{z}$, on the ideal orbit reckoned at *any specified time* are all possible alternative sets (that position and velocity are reckoned at some special time makes them nonetheless orbital constants that define the orbit). From these solutions of Eqs. (308) corrections to the elements can be computed; for example, improved values of position and velocity, at a predetermined time for correction (epoch), could be calculated.

Since there exists a unique orbit connecting any two points in space for a given transit time (found by Gauss' method, see Chapter 6), it is possible to compute an orbit that will terminate at the desired target, such as Mars, from every possible space position at a given epoch (the landing time will usually not be the same for all such orbits).

In principle, one could compute a large number of such heliocentric orbits for all the possible path deviations that could be expected in view of the probable uncertainties, and store them on board the vehicle. Subsequently, given the correct position at the moment of correction (epoch), $x_0 = x_I + \Delta x_I$, $y_0 = y_I + \Delta y_I$, $z_0 = z_I + \Delta z_I$, tables could be entered with argument of position to yield the velocity necessary to complete the mission, i.e., with components $\dot{x}_c$, $\dot{y}_c$, $\dot{z}_c$. The improved velocity components of the vehicle could then be subtracted from the velocity components necessary to complete the mission and the required correction to the velocity or *velocity to be gained*, $\dot{\mathbf{r}}_g$, thereby obtained, i.e.,

$$\dot{\mathbf{r}}_g = \dot{\mathbf{r}}_c - \dot{\mathbf{r}}_0 = \dot{\mathbf{r}}_c - (\dot{\mathbf{r}}_I + \Delta\dot{\mathbf{r}}_I).$$

In practice such a tabulation would become an exorbitant burden upon the on-board computer storage. A series expression for the velocity required

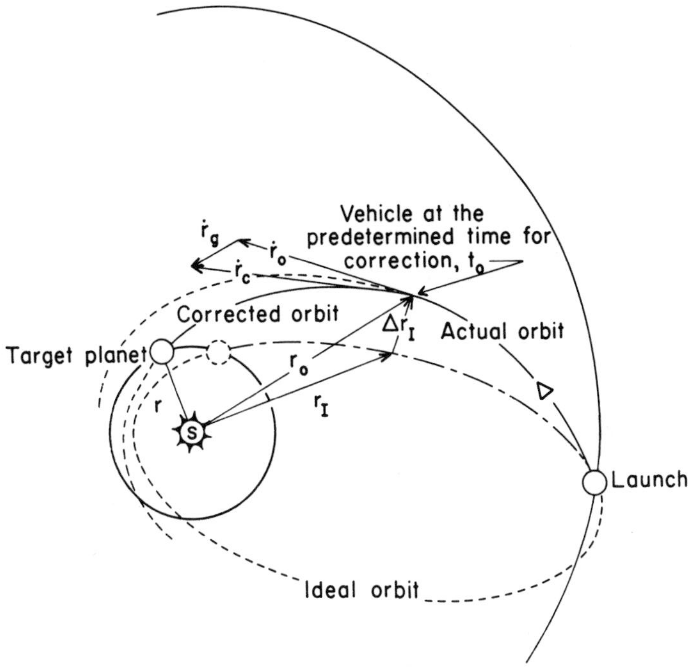

FIG. 47. Interplanetary navigation.

to complete the mission, $\dot{\mathbf{r}}_c$, or more efficiently for a residual velocity $\Delta\dot{\mathbf{r}}_c$ above that of the reference orbit where $\dot{\mathbf{r}}_c = \dot{\mathbf{r}}_I + \Delta\dot{\mathbf{r}}_c$ (i.e., the so-called guidance error coefficients) could be utilized as follows: ($\Delta\dot{\mathbf{r}}_c$ in component form)

$$\Delta\dot{x}_c = \left(\frac{\partial\Delta\dot{x}_c}{\partial x}\right)\Delta x_I + \left(\frac{\partial\Delta\dot{x}_c}{\partial y}\right)\Delta y_I + \left(\frac{\partial\Delta\dot{x}_c}{\partial z}\right)\Delta z_I + \left(\frac{\partial^2\Delta\dot{x}_c}{\partial x\partial y}\right)\Delta x_I\Delta y_I + \cdots \quad x \to y, z. \qquad (309)$$

If a predetermined change, e.g., in orbital inclination, not just a correction of unpredictable errors is involved, then $\dot{\mathbf{r}}_I$ should be replaced by some precomputed value for the maneuver. Consequently, the velocity to be gained would be simply the difference between this $\Delta\dot{\mathbf{r}}_c$ and the $\Delta\dot{\mathbf{r}}_I$ found for the improved orbit. A more general philosophy that could be applied to low-thrust trajectories is given in Baker.[163] It should be noted that the determination of "lines of position," or position fixes are *not* necessary and serve only to complicate the analysis i.e., a series of position fixes is unnecessary. Given $\dot{\mathbf{r}}_g$, a corrective thrust monitored by inertial guidance could then place the vehicle on the desired orbit. See Fig. 47.

12.3.3. Guidance Equations

If the gravitational force field changes appreciably during the application of the corrective thrust, then a thrust control system might be employed based upon the initial velocity to be gained, $\dot{\mathbf{r}}_g$. Several guidance equations might be utilized for thrust control. A particularly simple and effective guidance equation relating $\dot{\mathbf{r}}_g$, $\ddot{\mathbf{r}}_g$, and the applied thrust per unit mass (obtained from accelerometers) was devised in 1956 by J. H. Laning, Jr. and R. H. Battin of M.I.T. Unfortunately their analysis is classified and cannot be discussed. Specifically, in the case of lunar and interplanetary terminal guidance, not only is the gravitational field rapidly changing but also $\dot{\mathbf{r}}_g$ would require continuous revision—in this case thrust control via a guidance equation is definitely required.

Although it is not within the scope of this book to deal with guidance equations in any greater detail, it is important to define more clearly the general problem area of guidance and control as it is related to navigation. We draw a distinction between *guidance and control*, which is the active counteraction or overcoming of the effects of deviations (from nominal conditions) in order for a space vehicle to accomplish a given mission, and *navigation*, which is the gathering and reduction of observational data in order to *define* the proper counteraction (e.g., orbital alteration or redirection) to be accomplished by the guidance and control system. A rather oversimplified maritime analogy would be to classify a sextant as a navigational device and a tiller as a guidance and control device. Under this definition navigation plays an indispensible role in the total navigation-guidance-control system of a space vehicle. In particular, it should again be emphasized that navigation does *not* necessarily imply fixing the position of a space vehicle in space—navigation is purely an operational concept. With respect to guidance and control it has been pointed out by Roberson in his excellent monograph on astronavigation, that there is an inherent unity between guidance and control "They are just different loops in the overall control system, . . ." On the other hand Roberson recommends a division between "path control" and "attitude control." The proper directioning and variation of corrective thrust would be an example of the former, and the use of flywheels or gas jets to retain a stabilized platform would be an example of the latter.

APPENDIX

This appendix should only be consulted after the reader has considered the first section in Chapter 6.

The *vis-viva* integral evolves directly from an algebraic manipulation of the basic equations of relative motion, i.e., let us multiply each component of this equation by $2\dot{x}$, $2\dot{y}$, and $2\dot{z}$, respectively, and add

$$\begin{array}{rl|l} \ddot{x} = & -\mu x/r^3 & 2\dot{x} \\ \ddot{y} = & -\mu y/r^3 & 2\dot{y} \\ \ddot{z} = & -\mu z/r^3 & 2\dot{z}. \end{array}$$

Upon adding we find that

$$2(\ddot{x}\dot{x} + \ddot{y}\dot{y} + \ddot{z}\dot{z}) = \frac{-2\mu}{r^3}(x\dot{x} + y\dot{y} + z\dot{z}) = \frac{-2\mu r\dot{r}}{r^3} = \frac{-2\mu\dot{r}}{r^2}.$$

The integral of this expression can be found by inspection to be

$$\dot{x}^2 + \dot{y}^2 + \dot{z}^2 = \dot{s}^2 = 2\mu/r + \text{const.}$$

The constant of integration can be evaluated by imposing the boundary condition at the perifocus, i.e., at $r = q$, $\dot{s} = r\dot{v}$ ($\dot{r}$ being equal to zero) so that with $p = r^4\dot{v}^2/\mu$ (see p. 113)

$$\dot{s}^2 = \frac{r^4\dot{v}^2}{r^2} = \frac{\mu p}{r^2}.$$

Consequently, the constant is equal to

$$\frac{\mu p}{r^2} - \frac{2\mu}{q} = \frac{\mu}{q^2}(p - 2q) = \frac{\mu}{q^2}[q(1+e) - 2q] = \frac{\mu(e-1)}{a(1-e)} = -\frac{\mu}{a}.$$

In fine,

$$\dot{s}^2 = \mu\left(\frac{2}{r} - \frac{1}{a}\right) \qquad Q.E.D.$$

The derivation of Kepler's equation also makes use of the very important identification of the geometrical quantity μp (μ times the parameter or semi-latus rectum, see the bottom of p.113) with the square of the angular momentum per unit mass $r^4\dot{v}^2$ or $|\mathbf{r} \times \dot{\mathbf{r}}|^2$. In fact we simply set

$$\sqrt{\mu p} = \sqrt{\mu a(1 - e)^2} = |\mathbf{r} \times \dot{\mathbf{r}}| = x_\omega \dot{y}_\omega - y_\omega \dot{x}_\omega.$$

From Chapter 4 it is clear that

$$x_\omega = a(\cos E - e) \text{ and } y_\omega = a\sqrt{1 - e^2}\sin E$$

so that the first derivatives are given by

$$\dot{x}_\omega = -a\dot{E}\sin E \text{ and } \dot{y}_\omega = a\dot{E}\sqrt{1 - e^2}\cos E.$$

Consequently,

$$\sqrt{\mu a(1 - e^2)} = a^2\dot{E}\sqrt{(1 - e^2)}\,(\cos^2 E - e\cos E + \sin^2 E)$$

or

$$\sqrt{\mu a} = a^2\dot{E}(1 - e\cos E).$$

By definition, $\dot{E} = dE/d\tau = dE/kdt$, therefore,

$$\frac{k\sqrt{\mu}\,dt}{a^{3/2}} = (1 - e\cos E)\,dE.$$

The quantity $k\sqrt{\mu}/a^{3/2}$ is termed the "mean motion" and symbolized by n. Including this notation and integrating the preceding equation from the perifocus ($t = T$ and $E = 0$) to some arbitrary point, we find that

$$n\int_T^t dt = \int_0^E (1 - e\cos E)\,dE$$

or

$$n(t - T) = E - e\sin E \triangleq M. \qquad Q.E.D.$$

In the case of parabolic orbits $a = \infty$, $e = 1$, and Kepler's equation is indeterminate. Clearly a new relationship between position and time must be sought. The equation of a conic, specialized to the parabola, is given by

$$r = \frac{p}{(1 - e \cos v)} = \frac{2q}{(1 - \cos v)}$$

(since $p = q(1 + e) = 2q$ for the parabola) or by the half angle formulas

$$r = q\left[1 + \tan^2\left(\frac{v}{2}\right)\right] = q\left[\sec^2\left(\frac{v}{2}\right)\right].$$

Again employing the dynamical interpretation of p, we find that for the parabola

$$\sqrt{\mu p} = \sqrt{2\mu q} = r^2\dot{v} = q^2\left[1 + \tan^2\left(\frac{v}{2}\right)\right]\left[\sec^2\left(\frac{v}{2}\right)\right]\frac{dv}{d\tau}.$$

Upon simplification

$$\frac{\sqrt{\mu}\, d\tau}{\sqrt{2}\, q^{3/2}} = \frac{k\sqrt{\mu}\, dt}{\sqrt{2}\, q^{3/2}} = \left[1 + \tan^2\left(\frac{v}{2}\right)\right]\left[\sec^2\left(\frac{v}{2}\right)\right] d\left(\frac{v}{2}\right)$$

so that integration between the limits T and t (or 0 and $v/2$) yields

$$\frac{k\sqrt{\mu}\,(t - T)}{\sqrt{2}\, q^{3/2}} = \tan\frac{v}{2} + \frac{1}{3}\tan^3\left(\frac{v}{2}\right)$$

which is Barker's equation in its canonical form. The reader is invited to verify that for the parabola

$$D = \frac{r\dot{r}}{\sqrt{\mu}} = \sqrt{2q}\tan\left(\frac{v}{2}\right)$$

so that Barker's equation can be reduced to the more useful form given in Chapter 6, namely,

$$k\sqrt{\mu}\,(t - T) = qD + \frac{D^3}{6}.$$

GLOSSARY OF TERMS MORE FREQUENTLY USED

A

Ablation: the gradual removal or erosion of an exposed surface of an object resulting from its high-speed passage through a resistive medium.

Accommodation coefficient: $\triangleq (E_o - E_e)/(E_o - E_s)$ where E_o and E_e are the energies of the oncoming and emitted molecules respectively, and E_s is the energy which would be carried away by a Maxwellian gas in thermal equilibrium at the surface of the vehicle.

Altitude: a topocentric coordinate in the horizon system; the angular distance of an object above the horizon, measured on a vertical circle. Also synonymous with the height of an object above some surface.

Analytical integration: the specification of an explicit closed algebraic or series relation to represent the integral of a given function.

Anomaly: or angle; see true anomaly, mean anomaly, and eccentric anomaly.

Antinode: the two points on the orbit where a line perpendicular to the line of nodes, which passes through the focus and lies in the orbit plane, intersects the orbit.

Apareon: the apsis on a Mars-centered or areocentric elliptic orbit where the satellite is farthest from the planet.

Aphelion: the point on a heliocentric ellipse farthest from the Sun.

Apofocus: the apsis on an elliptic orbit farthest from the principal focus or center of force.

Apogee: the point on a geocentric elliptical orbit farthest from the Earth's center.

Apsis (pl. *apsides*)*:* the point on a conic where $dr/dt = 0$, i.e., the radius vector is a maximum or minimum.

Areocentric: centered about Mars.

Argument of latitude: the angle in the orbit from the ascending node to the object; the sum of the argument of perifocus and the true anomaly.

Argument of perifocus: the angular distance measured in the orbit plane from the line of nodes to line of apsides.

Asteroid: a starlike object; used erroneously for minor planet, q.v.

Astrodynamics: the engineering or practical application of celestial mechanics and other allied fields such as high-altitude aerodynamics; geophysics; attitude dynamics; and electromagnetic, optimization, observation, navigation, and propulsion theory to the contemporary problems of space vehicles. Astrodynamics is sometimes meant also to include the study of natural objects such as comets, meteorites, and planets.

Astronomical unit: the mean distance or semimajor axis of the orbit of a fictitious unperturbed planet having the mass (0.000,002,819 $m_\odot$) and sidereal period (365.256,383,5 mean solar days) that Gauss adopted for the Earth in his original determination of the gravitational constant k_s (= 0.017,202,098,95). Approximately equal to 93,000,000 statute miles or 149,500,000 km.

Atomic clock: a clock that derives its basic frequency standard from the natural vibrations of certain atoms. Ammonia and cesium clocks, for example, provide a means of stabilizing the frequency of a quartz oscillator by comparison with the resonance absorption frequency of the ammonia or cesium atom. The Maser clock (q.v.) does not depend on the mechanism of absorption, but utilizes the frequency standard of the atom directly.

Azimuth: a topocentric coordinate measured in the plane of the horizon from the north (or south) point on the horizon clockwise to the object.

B

Baker Catadioptic: an optical system involving a correcting plate, spherical mirror (including a hole on the optical axis), reflector inserted in the correcting plate, a lens, and finally the film behind the hole in the spherical mirror (*a la* Cassegrain). The system exhibits a flat field and good spherical and coma correction.

Bank angle: an angle reckoned in a plane normal to the vehicle's velocity relative to the resistive medium, $\mathbf{v}$; measured between the lift force vector and a vector that is mutually perpendicular to $\mathbf{r}$ (or $\mathbf{U}$) and $\mathbf{v}$.

Barker's Equation: an equation that relates position, through D or $\tilde{X}$, to time for an object traveling on a parabolic orbit i.e.,

$$k\sqrt{\mu}(t - T) = qD + D^3/6.$$

Barycenter: center of mass of a system of masses.

Base altitudes: reference altitudes or levels of the atmosphere between which the atmospheric temperature gradient is assumed to be a constant.

Boltzmann's constant: the ratio of the mean total energy of a molecule to its absolute temperature. Its value is 1.380×10^{-23} joule/°K.

Booster: consists of one or a combination of propulsion stages that have the capability of placing a given payload on orbit.

Braking ellipses: a series of ellipses whose semimajor axes decrease due to aerodynamic drag. Such a maneuver is useful in the retardation of a space vehicle when it attempts a landing on a planet that has an atmosphere.

Burnout: is the point on a trajectory where the thrust is terminated—it usually coincides with the injection point.

C

Celestial equator (Earth's): a great circle on the celestial sphere in the plane of the Earth's equator.

Celestial sphere: a hypothetical sphere of infinite dimensions centered at the observer (or center of the Earth or Sun, etc.) on the inner surface of which the celestial bodies are projected and appear to move.

Centrifugal force: a fictitious position dependent force that apparently arises when the motion of an object is reckoned with respect to a rotating coordinate system. The relationship yielding this "force" is $-m\boldsymbol{\omega} \times (\boldsymbol{\omega} \times \mathbf{r})$, where m is the mass of the object and $\boldsymbol{\omega}$ is the angular velocity vector of the rotating coordinate system.

Collision parameter: the offset distance between the extension of a velocity vector of an object at a great distance from a center of attraction or repulsion and this center.

Coma: the gaseous envelope that surrounds the nucleus of the comet.

Component equations: see definition of vector equations.

Conjunction: a point on the orbit of a planet (or the Moon) where its right ascension equals that of the Sun. If the alignment is Sun–planet–Earth, the planet is said to be in "inferior conjunction" with the Sun; if it is planet–Sun–Earth, the planet is in "superior conjunction." Similarly, when the Moon is between the Earth and the Sun, i.e., "new," it is said to be at conjunction.

Continuum flow: a flow regime in aerodynamics in which the medium resisting the motion of an object can be treated as a continuous compressible fluid rather than a collection of discrete molecules, i.e., the mean free path of the emitted molecules is much shorter than a characteristic linear dimension of an object. The fluid immediately adjacent to the surface of an object is at rest with respect to the object in continuum flow.

Coriolis force: a fictitious velocity dependent force that apparently arises when the motion of an object is reckoned with respect to a rotating coordinate system. The relationship yielding this "force" is $-2m\boldsymbol{\omega} \times \dot{\mathbf{r}}_r$, where m is the mass of the object, $\boldsymbol{\omega}$ is the angular velocity vector of the rotating coordinate system, and $\dot{\mathbf{r}}_r$ is the velocity of the object reckoned with respect to the rotating system.

Cosmic dust: fine dust particles (micrometeorites) that are concentrated in the solar system in the plane of the ecliptic (e.g., giving rise to the phenomenon of "zodiacal light") and also dispersed in a more rareified manner in interstellar space, being more concentrated in the galactic spiral arms; also a component of comets.

Cosmic rays (direct): high-energy charged particles (e.g., with energies in excess of 100 Mev), protons, and alpha particles plus a few heavy nuclei, that are stripped of electrons and have apparently been ejected by stars and were caught up in and accelerated by vast magnetic fields in interstellar space.

Cosmoparticle: a discrete material entity of submeteoritic mass, either in or from space. They may be "free" or individual molecules or atoms, or molecular or atomic constituents of any kind, e.g., ions, atomic nuclei, protons, neutrons, electrons, positrons etc.

Cross product: or vector product (denoted by $\mathbf{A} \times \mathbf{B}$) of two typical vector quantities $\mathbf{A}$ and $\mathbf{B}$ can be defined either as a vector mutually perpendicular to both $\mathbf{A}$ and $\mathbf{B}$ with magnitude $|\mathbf{A}|\,|\mathbf{B}| \sin(\angle \mathbf{A},\mathbf{B})$ or equivalently as

$$(A_yB_z - A_zB_y)\mathbf{I} + (A_zB_x - A_xB_z)\mathbf{J} + (A_xB_y - A_yB_x)\mathbf{K}$$

where the subscripts denote the components of the vectors on the three orthogonal axes denoted by the unit vectors $\mathbf{I}$, $\mathbf{J}$, $\mathbf{K}$.

D

Declination: the arc of an hour circle (great circles passing through the poles) intercepted between the celestial equator and the object.

Definitive orbit: an orbit that is defined in a highly precise manner with due regard taken for accurate constants and observational data, and precision computational techniques including perturbations.

Differential correction: a method for finding from the observed minus computed $(O - C)$ residuals (q.v.) small corrections which, when applied to the elements or constants, will reduce the deviations from the observed motion to a minimum.

Direct motion: the term applied to eastward or counterclockwise motion of a planet or other object as seen from the North Pole (i.e., in the direction of increasing right ascension). Thus, it is motion on an orbit in which $i < 90°$.

Diurnal: daily.

Doppler shift: a shift in observed frequency when the source of the frequency is receding from or approaching relative to the observer. Can be thought of in terms of a person running into or out of the ocean. If he runs into the ocean the frequency of the waves breaking on the swimmer will be increased, if out of the ocean it will be decreased.

Dot product: or scalar product (denoted by $\mathbf{A} \cdot \mathbf{B}$) of two typical vector quantities $\mathbf{A}$ and $\mathbf{B}$ can be defined as $|\mathbf{A}|\,|\mathbf{B}| \cos(\angle \mathbf{A}, \mathbf{B})$ or equivalently as $A_xB_x + A_yB_y + A_zB_z$ where the subscripts denote the components of the vectors on three orthogonal axes.

Drag: the force occasioned by the passage of an object through a resistive medium acting in a direction opposite to that of the object's motion relative to the medium.

Drag coefficient: is defined as the total drag force acting on an object divided by one half the local atmospheric density, the projected frontal area of the object, and the square of the magnitude of the velocity of the object relative to the resistive medium.

Drift, anomalistic: the variation or drift of a frequency source (e.g., a crystal oscillator) such that the frequency changes due to a variety of causes (e.g., temperature variation, component aging, etc.), none of which can be predicted in advance or completely controlled.

E

Eccentric anomaly: an angle at the center of an ellipse between the line of apsides and the radius of the auxiliary circle through a point that has the same x-coordinate as a given point on the ellipses. (See Fig. 14).

Eccentricity: the ratio of the radius vector through a point on a conic to the distance from the point to the directrix.

Ecliptic: a great circle on the celestial sphere cut by the plane of the Earth's orbit; the apparent annual path of the Sun.

Ecliptic coordinate system: rectangular axes with the ecliptic as the fundamental plane and with spherical coordinates: celestial longitude and latitude.

Electron volt: the amount of energy acquired by a single electron that starts from rest and moves in an unhampered way through a potential difference of one volt. One electron volt equals 3.82×10^{-20} cal or 1.60×10^{-12} erg. The mean translation kinetic energy of a molecule at room temperature is $\frac{1}{40}$ ev.

Elements of orbit: constants defining the orbit: e.g., (1) orientation elements: Ω longitude of ascending node; i inclination of orbit plane; ω longitude of perifocus (2) dimensional elements: e eccentricity; a semimajor axis; M_0 mean anomaly; t_0 epoch.

Elevation, angle of: the angle between the inertial velocity vector $\dot{\mathbf{r}}$ and the local horizontal, i.e., the plane normal to $\mathbf{r}$ passing through the vehicle.

Eliminant: a determinant that is formed when $n - 1$ linear unknowns are eliminated from a set of n equations. The elimination of x and y, for example, from:

$$\begin{aligned} a_1x + b_1y &= c_1 \\ a_2x + b_2y &= c_2 \\ a_3x + b_3y &= c_3 \end{aligned}$$

yields the eliminant:

$$\begin{vmatrix} a_1 & b_1 & c_1 \\ a_2 & b_2 & c_2 \\ a_3 & b_3 & c_3 \end{vmatrix} = 0.$$

Elongation, angle of: the angle between the direction to an object and to the center of the coordinate system reckoned at the observer.

Entry angle: the angle between the velocity vector of a space vehicle relative to a resistive medium, $\mathbf{v}$, and the local vertical, e.g., the local geocentric vertical in which case it would be the angle between $\mathbf{v}$ and $\mathbf{r}$.

Ephemeris (pl. *ephemerides*)*:* a table of calculated coordinates of an object with equidistant dates as arguments.

Ephemeris time (ET): uniform or Newtonian time. See also universal time.

Epoch: arbitrary instant of time for which the elements of an orbit are valid (e.g., initial, injection, or correction time).

Equator system: rectangular axes referred to the equator as the fundamental plane and having spherical coordinates right ascension and declination.

Equatorial bulge: the excess of the Earth's equatorial diameter over the polar diameter (i.e., about 27 miles).

Equatorial satellite: a satellite whose orbit plane coincides with the Earth's equatorial plane.

Equilateral triangle solutions: a particular case of the three-body problem in which an object situated at one vertex of an equilateral triangle formed with the Sun and a planet has a stable orbit. It was predicted by Lagrange (1772) and amply confirmed in the case of Jupiter. See Trojan asteroids.

Equinoxes: intersections of the equator and ecliptic; the vernal equinox (♈) being the point where the Sun crosses the equator going from south to north in the spring.

Euler's equation: a relation in a parabolic orbit involving two radii vectors, their chord, and the time interval between them; discovered by Euler (1744).

Evection: a large perturbative term in the Moon's longitude discovered by Hipparchus, amounting to 1°15′ at maximum.

F

f and g series: a series employed in calculating the coordinates at some arbitrary time in terms of the coordinates at the epoch and their first derivatives.

Feasibility orbit: an orbit that can be rapidly and inexpensively computed on the basis of simplifying assumptions (e.g., two-body motion, circular orbit, rectilinear orbit, three-body motion approximated by two two-body orbits, etc.) and yields an indication of the general feasibility of a system based upon the orbit without having to carry out a full-blown definitive orbit computation.

Fitzgerald–Lorentz contraction: a hypothesis that all measuring rods contract in the direction of the Earth's motion through the "ether," invented to explain why the Michelson–Morley experiment failed to demonstrate the existence of the ether by measuring the difference in the speed of light rays moving parallel and perpendicular to the direction of the Earth's motion. See *Lorentz transformation.*

Fix: a set of raw observational data such as angles or range rates that are processed or mathematically reduced to form a single point in space—usually involves some theory as to the motion of the object or spherical trigonometry.

Free-molecule flow: (or free-molecular flow) is a flow regime in aerodynamics in which molecules emitted from an object, as it passes through a resistive medium, do not affect the flow of oncoming molecules by scattering interactions, i.e., the mean-free path of the emitted molecules is much longer than a characteristic linear dimension of an object.

Fundamental star places: the apparent right ascensions and declinations of 1535 standard comparison stars obtained by leading observatories and published annually under the auspices of the International Astronomical Union.

G

Galilean transformation: the classical transformation of coordinates in which the form of a law (e.g., the law of inertia) remains unchanged; i.e., the law is invariant or covariant with respect to the transformation.

Gaussian gravitational constant k_s the factor of proportionality in Kepler's third law: $k_s = 2\pi a^{3/2}/P\sqrt{m_1 + m_2}$; the numerical value depending on the units employed. See *Astronomical Unit.*

Geocentric: referred to the center of the Earth as origin.

Geocentric parallax: see parallax.

Geocentric sub-vehicle point: the point where the radius vector from the geocenter to a space vehicle intersects the spheroid.

Geodetic sub-vehicle point: the point where a normal to the spheroid that passes through a space vehicle intersects the spheroid.

Geoid: the mean sea-level figure of the Earth.

Geoidal surface: the mean sea-level surface of the Earth.

Geometric meter: the standard meter.

Geopotential altitude: an altitude that is useful in atmospheric density calculations and is defined by Eq. (69).

Geopotential meter: a unit of length employed in reckoning geopotential altitude.

Gravitational potential: at a point, the work needed to remove an object from that point to infinity. For n discrete masses in the n-body problem

$$\Phi = \frac{1}{2} k^2 \sum_{i=1}^{n} \sum_{j=1}^{n} \frac{m_i m_j}{r_{ij}} \qquad (i \neq j).$$

Greenwich Meridian: the zero meridian from which geographical longitude is measured, passing through the Greenwich Observatory, England.

Guidance and control: a system that actively counteracts or overcomes the effects of deviations (from nominal conditions) in order to accomplish the given mission with the desired degree of exactness. Navigational inputs allow the guidance and control system to sense these deviations.

H

Harmonics of the Earth's gravitational field: a series representing the gravitational potential of the Earth whose terms form a harmonic progression, i.e., include powers of the reciprocal of r. In potential theory language the second harmonic is the "dipole" term, the fourth the "quadrupole" term, etc.

Heliocentric: referred to the center of the Sun as origin.

Hiran: a precise method for geodetic surveys in which an airplane flies back and forth (at constant altitude) along a line that perpendicularly bisects the line from one station to another. The airplane continuously transmits and receives radio pulses from these stations and a timing of these pulses allows an accurate estimate to be made of the distance between stations.

Hohmann orbit: an elliptic heliocentric trajectory for interplanetary flight, having tangency to the Earth at one apsis and to another planetary orbit (e.g., that of Venus or Mars) at the opposite apsis. More generally stands for any such doubly tangent transfer ellipse.

Horizon coordinate system: a system of topocentric coordinates either spherical (azimuth and altitude) or rectangular, having as reference plane the celestial horizon, which is perpendicular to the direction of gravity through the place.

Horizon scanner: an optical device that senses the radiation discontinuity between a planet or lunar surface and the stellar background of space. It can be utilized to establish a "vertical" reference based upon a "visual" horizon (which differs from both the astronomical and geodetic horizon).

Hour circle: one of the great circles that pass through the celestial poles and therefore, are at right angles to the equator.

Hour angle (LHA): angle at the celestial pole between the observer's meridian and the hour circle passing through the object; a coordinate in the equator system.

Hydromagnetic wave: a compressional wave in a plasma that is generated by the passage of a pulse (or pulses) of intensified magnetic field strength through the plasma.

Hydrostatic equilibrium: a body that is in motion, e.g., rotating, and retains or returns to the figure occasioned by this rotation, (e.g., an oblate ellipsoidal form) in spite of small disturbances.

I

Inclination i: angle between orbit plane and reference plane (e.g., the equator is the reference plane for geocentric and the ecliptic for heliocentric orbits).

Inertial axes: axes that are not in accelerated or rotational motion.

Injection: the place and time when nongravitational forces (typically thrust, lift, or drag) become relatively negligible in their action upon a space vehicle (could, for example, occur again in space as soon as the thrust of orbit correction rockets is terminated, i.e., several injections are possible).

Interferometer: an instrument in which radiation from a source travels via two different paths and when brought together again produces interference fringes whose number indicates the difference in path lengths traveled. Such a device is useful for measuring linear and angular distances.

Intermediate orbit: an orbit tangent to the actual (or disturbed) orbit, having the same coordinates but not velocity at point of tangency.

Inversion: in this context is meant to be synonymous with the numerical solution of a set of algebraic equations.

Ionosphere: the ionized portion of the atmosphere above about 60 km. The degree of ionization is strongly under solar control and varies with the hour of the day, season of year and solar cycle. The four main regions are termed the D, E, F_1, and F_2 layers.

Isostatic equilibrium: a situation in which the pressure under the Earth's surface is the same regardless of whether it is measured under a mountain, valley, or ocean, i.e., less dense strata underlie mountains while higher density strata underlie oceans.

J

Jacobi integral: an integral of the equations of motion in a rotating coordinate system which relates the square of the velocity and the coordinates of an infinitesimal body referred to the rotating coordinate system; see Moulton[13] pp. 280 to 294.

Julian date: the number of mean solar days that have elapsed since January 1, 4713 B.C., e.g., the Julian date of January 1, 1960 is 2,436,934, and of February 1, 1965 is 2,438,792 etc.

K

Kepler's planetary laws: (i) Every planet moves in an ellipse about the Sun with the Sun at one focus. (ii) Every planet moves in such a way that its radius vector sweeps over equal areas in equal intervals of time. (iii) The squares of the periods of revolution of two planets are to each other as the cubes of their mean distances from the Sun.

k_e^{-1} *min:* the characteristic time for geocentric orbits, i.e., the time required by hypothetical satellites to move 1 radian in a circular orbit of radius a_e (equatorial Earth's radius); equal to 13.447,052 min.

k_s^{-1} *day:* the characteristic time for heliocentric orbits, i.e., the time required for a planet at 1 a.u. to move 1 radian (or 1 a.u.) along its orbit; equal to 58.132,440,87 days.

Knudsen number: the ratio of the ambient mean-free path of a molecule in the atmosphere, L_{oo}, to a characteristic linear dimension of an object (e.g., diameter, boundary layer thickness, etc.) and was named in honor of Martin Knudsen who pioneered in theoretical and experimental research on gases at low densities.

L

Lagrangian solutions: particular solutions of the three-body problem in which an infinitesimal object moves under the attraction of two finite bodies (e.g., the Sun and Jupiter), which revolve in circles around their center of mass, and the distances from the infinitesimal object to the finite bodies remain constant. See also equilateral triangle solutions and synodic satellites i.e., the so-called straight line solutions.

Lambert's Equation: an equation of the 8th degree expressing the curvature of the apparent path of a body moving around the Sun, as seen from the Earth: discovered by Lambert (1771).

Latitude (astronomical): the angle (ϕ_a) between the direction of gravity through the point and the equatorial plane.

Latitude (celestial): the angular distance of an object north (+) or south (−) of the ecliptic plane; a coordinate (β) in the ecliptic system.

Latitude (geocentric): the angle (ϕ') at the center of the Earth between the radius through a given point and the equatorial plane.

Latitude (geodetic): the angle (ϕ) between a normal to the reference spheroid at the point and the equatorial plane.

Least squares inversion: a solution of a set of overdetermined linear equations such that the sum of the squares of the residuals is a minimum, e.g. from Eq. (148) if $\dot{\rho}_i$ is some typical observed datum we will want to solve the set of equations

$$\Delta\dot{\rho}_i - \sum_{j=1}^{n} \left(\frac{\partial \dot{\rho}_i}{\partial p_j}\right) \Delta p_j = 0$$

$i = 1, 2, \ldots N$. If $N > n$ then, in general, no matter what values are selected for the Δp_j's all of the equations will not equal zero, i.e.,

$$\Delta\dot{\rho}_i - \sum_{j=1}^{n} \left(\frac{\partial \dot{\rho}_i}{\partial p_j}\right) \Delta p_{j\text{selected}} = \delta_i$$

where δ_i is the ith residual. In the least squares inversion the Δp_j's are selected under the condition that $\sum_{i=1}^{n} \delta_i^2$ is a minimum.

Legendre polynomials: the coefficients $P_n(c)$ in the expansion $(1 - 2ch + h^2)^{-1/2} = \sum_{n=0}^{\infty} P_x(c)h^n$ where $P_0(c) = 1$, $P_1(c) = c$, $P_2(c) = \frac{1}{2}(3c^2 - 1)$, $P_3(c) = \frac{1}{2}(5c^3 - 3c)$, or, in general, $(n + 1)P_{n+1}(c) - (2n + 1)cP_n(c) + nP_{n-1}(c) = 0$.

Libration: (1) Apparent tilting and side-to-side movements of the Moon that render 18% of its surface alternately visible and invisible. (2) Long-period orbital motions of, e.g., the Trojan asteroids around the equilateral triangle points of the three-body Lagrangian solutions. (3) Periodic perturbative oscillations in orbital elements.

Lift: the force arising from the passage through a resistive medium of a vehicle presenting an asymmetrical form or orientation, which acts in a direction normal to the object's motion relative to the medium.

Limb: the edge of the visible disk of the Sun, Moon, planet, etc.

Line of apsides: a line connecting the near to the far apsis, i.e., defines the major or transverse axis.

Line of nodes: the intersection of a reference plane and the orbit plane.

Line-of-sight: the apparent or observed direction of an object.

Longitude (celestial): the angular distance measured along the ecliptic from the vernal equinox eastward to the foot of a great circle passing through the object.

Longitude (terrestrial): the angular distance from the foot of the Greenwich meridian, measured along the equator, east or west, to the foot of the meridian through the place.

Longitude of ascending node: the angular distance from the vernal equinox measured eastward in the fundamental plane (ecliptic or equator) to the point of intersection of the orbit plane where the object crosses from south to north.

Longitude of perifocus: sum of the angle in the fundamental plane between the vernal equinox and the line of nodes and the angle in the orbit plane between the line of nodes and the line of apsides, measured in the direction of motion.

Lorentz force: that force exerted on a moving charge by a magnetic field. Explicitly

$$\mathbf{f}_L = q(\mathbf{v} \times \mathbf{B}),$$

where $\mathbf{f}_L$ is the Lorentz force, q is the charge on the moving object, $\mathbf{v}$ is its velocity, and $\mathbf{B}$ is the magnetic induction vector.

Lorentz transformations: coordinate transformation equations of the Special Theory of Relativity in which the absolute space and time of Galileo and Newton are replaced by the invariance of the speed of light.

Lunar equation: a factor required for reducing observations to the barycenter of the Earth–Moon system. It is useful for finding the Earth/Moon mass ratio when $\pi_\odot/\pi_☾$ is known.

Lunicentric: referred to the Moon's center as origin; selenocentric.

M

Mach number: the ratio of the speed of a vehicle to the local speed of sound. Accounts for the compressibility of the resistive medium.

Macrometeorites: meteorites that are sufficiently massive to become fallen meteorites and whose origin appears to be related to that of minor planets.

Magnetic storms: extensive disturbances in the Earth's magnetic field usually occasioned by solar activity. The duration of these storms may be from a few hours to a few days and are often accompanied by Sun spots, solar flares, brilliant auroras, and by electric currents above and below the Earth's surface that tend to disrupt terrestrial electronic communications.

Magnitude (stellar): is a measure of the brightness of a star conceived of subjectively by Hipparchus who in 140 B.C. classified the brightest 20 stars as the *first* magnitude and those just visible to the naked eye as the *sixth*. An objective mathematical statement of magnitude that closely approximates Hipparchus (Pogson scale) is

$$n - m = 2.5 \log_{10} (l_m/l_n)$$

where l_m and l_n are the observed brightness of the stars of magnitude m

and n respectively. Note that a difference of five magnitudes represents a factor of 100 in brightness.

Maksutov: sometimes called the Meniscus-Schmidt. It is an optical system composed of a curved correcting plate that is simply a constant thickness meniscus, a spherical mirror with a hole at the optical center, a reflector on the correcting plate, and the film behind the spherical mirror (*a la* cassegrain). The system exhibits a large aperture, and is free of spherical, coma, and chromatic aberration.

Map matching: the simultaneous electronic or mechanical-optical scanning of an observed map image (obtained on board a space vehicle) and a reference map image, while the reference map image is being oriented and scaled until a close comparison between the two is achieved. At this point an inspection of the scale and orientation of the reference map will indicate the position of the space vehicle.

Maser: an abbreviated expression for "Microwave Amplification by Stimulated Emission of Radiation." See *atomic clock.*

Mean anomaly: the angle through which an object would move at the uniform average angular speed n, measured from perifocus.

Mean center of Moon: the point on the lunar surface intersected by the lunar radius that is directed toward the Earth's center when the Moon is at the mean ascending node and when the node coincides with the mean perigee or the mean apogee. Actually, the mean center of the Moon is expected to give way to a permanent feature of the Moon, such as the craterlet Mösting A, as the control point for selenographic coordinates, i.e., the lunar prime meridian will be defined as a certain given distance from Mösting A.

Mean distance: the semimajor axis. Since the term does not represent the time-average distance from the focus of a body traveling on an ellipse (which amounts to $a(1 + e^2/2)$) it can be considered only as an historical term.

Mean equinox of date: a fictitious equinox whose position is that of the vernal equinox at a particular date with the effect of nutation removed.

Mean free path: when molecules are assumed to be smooth rigid spheres and no external field of force acts on them, each molecule travels freely on a straight line between impacts with other molecules. The distance traversed between two successive impacts is called the free path and the average value of this distance the mean-free path.

Mean molecular speed: the mean or arithmetic average "thermal" speed of molecules, i.e., within a gas it amounts to $\sqrt{8kT/\pi m m_u} = 0.145\sqrt{T/m}$ km/sec, where m_u = the mass of a unit atomic weight 1.66×10^{-27} kg,

m = the atomic weight of the molecule, k = Boltzmann's constant, and T = the temperature in °K. While for molecules escaping from a surface at temperature T (assuming the molecular temperature is in equilibrium with the surface temperature) it amounts to

$$\frac{3}{4}\sqrt{\frac{2\pi kT}{mm_u}} = 0.171\sqrt{\frac{T}{m}}\ \text{km/sec}$$

which is a larger speed because the escape of molecules from the surface is a selective process in which faster molecules are more likely to escape than slower molecules. Such a speed should not be confused with the *root-mean-square* (rms) *molecular speed* of molecules within a gas as given by

$$\sqrt{\frac{3kT}{mm_u}} = 0.158\sqrt{\frac{T}{m}}\ \text{km/sec}$$

or the *most probable speed* given by

$$\sqrt{\frac{2kT}{mm_u}} = 0.129\sqrt{\frac{T}{m}}\ \text{km/sec.}$$

Mean solar day: the elapsed time between successive passages of the meridian of an observer past the mean Sun (amounts to 86,400 sec). The mean Sun being a fictitious Sun that moves along the celestial equator with the mean speed with which the true Sun apparently moves along the ecliptic throughout the year.

Measuring engine: a precision device in which a portion of a flat astronomical photographic plate is inserted; then cross hairs (mounted in a microscope) are brought into alignment with a stellar image on the plate (e.g., by the adjustment of precision screws attached to a plate holder) and the x, y, measured (or approximate) coordinate of the position of the star is read off from a scale.

Meridian: (1) Terrestrial meridians: great circles passing through the North and South Poles, e.g., the observer's local meridian passes through his local zenith and the North and South Poles. (2) Celestial meridian: a great circle on the celestial sphere in the plane of the observer's terrestrial meridian.

Mesometeorites: intermediate meteorites (having a characteristic dimension of the order of a fraction of an inch) that are stopped by the atmosphere, consumed, and are seen as common "meteors." The origin of these bodies appears to be related to that of comets.

Meteor swarms: a large collection of mesometeorites (probably the remains of an "old" comet) that enter the Earth's atmosphere and are seen as a swarm of meteors. The term is also often applied to the actual collection of mesometeorites on heliocentric orbits in space.

Michelson–Morley experiment: an experiment devised by Michelson and Morley to determine the motion of the Earth with respect to the privileged frame of reference (e.g., the "ether") in which the speed of light was assumed to be uniform, by comparing the apparent speed of light rays parallel and perpendicular to the direction in which the Earth was moving. See Fitzgerald–Lorentz contraction theory.

Micrometeorites: very small meteorites (having a characteristic dimension of a few microns) that are stopped by the atmosphere without being consumed in flight or without producing luminous phenomena visible at the Earth's surface.

Minor planets (or asteroids): small planets revolving about the Sun, estimated to number more than 40,000 with diameters more than 1 mile. The largest, Ceres, has a diameter of 488 miles.

Molecular scale temperature: the actual temperature of the atmosphere at any given height multiplied by the ratio of the mean molecular weight of the atmosphere at sea level divided by the mean molecular weight of the atmosphere at the given height.

Moon's celestial equator: a great circle on the celestial sphere in the plane of the Moon's equator, i.e., in a plane perpendicular to the Moon's axis of rotation.

Moon-watch station: station for the visual-optical observation of satellite vehicles.

N

Nadir: the downward plumb-bob direction or the point where the downward extension of the direction of a plumb-bob intersects the celestial sphere.

Navigation: the gathering and reduction of observational data to define the proper orbital alteration or redirection to be accomplished by a guidance system—in this sense navigation does not necessarily imply fixing the position of the space vehicle in space.

n-body problem: concerned with the gravitational interactions of masses

m_i, m_j, which are assumed homogeneous in spherical layers, under the Newtonian law.

Newton's laws: Law of gravitation: Every particle of matter in the universe attracts every other particle with a force proportional to the product of their masses and inversely as the square of the distance between them. Laws of motion: (1) Every body continues in its state of rest, or of uniform motion in a straight line, unless it is compelled to change that state by a force impressed upon it. (2) The rate of change of momentum is proportional to the force impressed, and takes place in the direction of the straight line in which the force acts. (3) To every action there is an equal and opposite reaction; or, the mutual actions of two bodies are always equal and oppositely directed.

Nodal passage, time of: the time T_Ω, when an object passes through the node from the southern hemisphere to the northern hemisphere. For a circular orbit

$$T_\Omega = t_0 - \cos^{-1}(\mathbf{U}_0 \cdot \mathbf{N})/n$$

where t_0 is the epoch when $\mathbf{U}_0$ and $\mathbf{V}_0$ are reckoned, $\mathbf{N}$ has the components

$$N_x = -W_y/\sqrt{W_x^2 + W_y^2},$$
$$N_y = W_x/\sqrt{W_x^2 + W_y^2},$$
$$N_z = 0$$

while $\mathbf{W} = \mathbf{U}_0 \times \mathbf{V}_0$.

Node: the points of intersection of the great circle on the celestial sphere cut by the orbit plane and a reference plane (e.g., the ecliptic or equator reference plane).

Node, longitude of ascending: see longitude of ascending node. For a circular orbit

$$\Omega = \cos^{-1}\{-W_y/\sqrt{W_x^2 + W_y^2}\}$$

or

$$= \sin^{-1}\{W_x/\sqrt{W_x^2 + W_y^2}\}.$$

Nominal orbit: is the true or ideal orbit that a space vehicle is expected to travel upon.

Normal places: formed, when several observations are available very close together in time, by smoothing observed coordinates.

Numerical differentiation: a process that allows for the numerical evaluation of the derivative of a quantity given tabular values of the quantity. As an example consider three tabular values and differences of a quantity X:

$$
\begin{array}{llllll}
 & & \delta X_{-1\frac{1}{2}} & & & \\
t_{-1} & X_{-1} & & \delta^2 X_{-1} & & \\
 & & \delta X_{-\frac{1}{2}} & & \delta^3 X_{-\frac{1}{2}} & \\
t_0 & X_0 & (\delta X_0) & \delta^2 X_0 & (\delta^3 X_0) & \\
 & & \delta X_{+\frac{1}{2}} & & \delta^3 X_{+\frac{1}{2}} & \\
t_{+1} & X_{+1} & & \delta^2 X_{+1} & & \\
 & & \delta X_{+1\frac{1}{2}} & & &
\end{array}
$$

where $\delta X_{-\frac{1}{2}} \triangleq X_0 - X_{-1}$,
$(\delta X_0) \triangleq \frac{1}{2}(\delta X_{-\frac{1}{2}} + \delta X_{+\frac{1}{2}})$
$\delta^2 X_0 \triangleq \delta X_{+\frac{1}{2}} - \delta X_{-\frac{1}{2}}$, etc.

and $t_0 - t_{-1} = t_{+1} - t_0 = w$.
If $s = \dfrac{t - t_0}{w}$ then by Bessel's formula the derivative at time t is

$$kw\dot{X} = \delta X_{+\frac{1}{2}} + \left(\frac{2s - 1}{2!}\right) \delta^2 X_{+\frac{1}{2}} + \cdots$$

$$k^2w^2\ddot{X} = \delta^2 X_{+\frac{1}{2}} + \left(\frac{2s - 1}{2!}\right) \delta^3 X_{+\frac{1}{2}} + \cdots$$

or by Stirling's formula

$$kw\dot{X} = \delta X_0 + s\delta^2 X_0 + \left(\frac{3s^2 - 1}{3!}\right) \delta^3 X_0 + \cdots$$

$$k^2w^2\ddot{X} = \delta^2 X_0 + s\delta^3 X_0 + \cdots$$

For a more complete discussion see reference 35.

Numerical integration: a process that allows for the numerical evaluation of a definite integral. As a very rudimentary example consider $a = a_0 + \int_{\tau_0}^{\tau} a' \, d\tau$, where a' is explicitly a function of time, τ, (e.g., caused by perturbations of a programmed tangential thrust). After a small time increment $\Delta\tau$ (or step) in which the integrand a' is not expected to vary greatly, $a_1 \cong a_0 + a_0'\Delta\tau$, where a_0' is evaluated at $\tau = \tau_0$. After another increment of time $\Delta\tau$ or step (throughout which a' is again not expected to significantly change) $a_2 \cong [a_0 + a_0'\Delta\tau] + a_1'\Delta$, where in this case a_1' is evaluated at time $\tau_1 = \tau_0 + \Delta\tau$. The summation proceeds step by step, e.g., $a_3 = [a_0 + a_0^{\backprime}\Delta\tau + a_1^{\backprime}\Delta\tau] + a_2^{\backprime}\Delta\tau$ at $\tau_3 = \tau_0 + 3\Delta\tau$ and so on, until the integral has been evaluated up to the desired time (in this example $a^{\backprime}$ is evaluated the $\Delta\tau$ step behind). In practice, much more sophisticated and accurate numerical integration techniques are employed than the one indicated here. (This explanation will be more meaningful after the reader has examined the sections on special perturbations.)

Nutation: short period terms in the precession (q.v.) arising from the obliquity, the eccentricity, and the inclination of the Moon's orbit and the regression of its nodes (approximately a 19-year period).

O

Obliquity of the ecliptic: the inclination of the ecliptic to the celestial equator; the angle of 23°27′ between the Earth's orbital plane and its equator.

Occultation: is the interruption of the light of one celestial body by the intervention of another.

Opposition: object's right ascention is 180° from Sun i.e., opposite to Sun.

Orientation angles: the classical orientation elements, i.e., the inclination, longitude of the ascending node, and longitude of perifocus.

Osculating orbit: an orbit tangent to the actual or disturbed trajectory, having the same coordinates and velocity.

P

Parallactic inequality: a secondary effect in the solar perturbations in the Moon's longitude due to the ellipticity of the Earth's orbit; useful for determining solar parallax since the principal coefficient $P = 14.2\pi_\odot$, assuming the Moon's mass relative to the Earth's is accurately known.

Parallax: (1) Geocentric parallax: the angle at an object subtended by the Earth's equatorial radius; applied to objects in the solar system. (2) Heliocentric parallax: the angle at a star, etc., subtended by the radius of the Earth's orbit; applied to objects outside the solar system.

Parameter: semi-latus rectum $= a(1 - e^2)$, not to be confused with the generic term "parameters."

Payload: the operating or mission accomplishing equipment, including associated telemetry, which is contained in the final stage of a space booster.

Perifocus: the point on an orbit nearest the dynamical center.

Perigee: the point on a geocentric orbit nearest the Earth's center.

Perihelion: the point on a heliocentric orbit nearest the Sun.

Perturbations: deviations from exact reference motion caused by the gravitational attractions of other bodies or other forces.

General perturbations: a method of calculating the perturbative effects by expanding and integrating in series.

Special perturbations: methods of deriving the disturbed orbit by numerically integrating the rectangular coordinates or the elements.

Piecewise continuous: a function that can be divided into a finite number of pieces such that the function is continuous on the interior of each piece and such that the function approaches a finite limit at the point of connection of one piece with another. In the context of the temperature profile discussion the term is used in a more restricted sense to imply a function that is divided into a finite number or series of connected linear pieces (straight line segments).

Planetocentric: referred to the center of a planet as dynamical center or origin of coordinates.

Planets: members of the solar system

(1) terrestrial planets:

Mercury	Mars	Venus
Earth	Pluto	

(2) major planets:

Jupiter	Uranus
Saturn	Neptune

(3) minor planets

Plasma: a collection of positive and negative ions that has no overall or gross charge per unit volume and is neutral.

Polar satellite: a satellite that passes over the north and south poles of the Earth, i.e., that has an inclination of 90° with respect to the Earth's equator.

Potential function: see *gravitational potential.*

Poynting-Robertson effect: the gradual decrease in the orbital semimajor axis and eccentricity of a micrometeorite caused by the re-emission of radiant energy from the micrometeorite. The theory was first announced by Poynting and later improved and brought into conformity with the theory of relativity by Robertson.

Precession of the equinoxes: the slow, 26,000 year period westward motion of the equinoxes (and equator) along the ecliptic, arising from solar and lunar perturbations on the Earth's equatorial bulge, which cause the Earth's axis to precess.

Pulsed radar system: a system in which pulses of electromagnetic radiation are transmitted, reflected by an object, and received again, by means of which the distance between the transmitter-receiver and the object can be computed by measuring the total transit time of the pulse.

R

Radiant: the vanishing point in the perspective of parallel meteor trails, i.e., it is located by extending the meteor trails backward until they intersect in the sky.

Radiation pressure: the pressure acting on a surface exposed to incident electromagnetic radiation caused by the momentum transferred to the surface by the absorption and reflection of the radiation. The momentum content of a photon of frequency ν is simply $h\nu/c$ where h is Planck's constant ($= 6.623 \times 10^{-34}$ joule-sec) and c is the speed of light.

Ratios of the triangles: In the orbit methods of Gauss, Olbers, *et al.* the ratios of the triangles formed by the radii and the chords are assumed in a first approximation to be ratios of the sectors, which are the ratios of the corresponding time intervals by Kepler's second law.

Raydis: a continuous wave, phase measurement system in which a mobile transmitter transmits continuously on an assigned frequency. A fixed ground transmitter transmits on a slightly different frequency. A measurement of the phase difference between these two signals allows for an accurate position fix.

Rectilinear orbit: A rectilinear orbit is a trajectory for which $q = 0$; $e = 1$.

Reference ellipsoid (or spheroid): oblate spheroid closely approximating the geoid.

Reference orbit: an orbit, usually but not exclusively, the best two-body orbit available, on the basis of which the perturbations are computed.

Refractive index (of a medium): the ratio of the speed of light in a vacuum to that in a medium, hence it is a measure of how greatly electromagnetic radiation rays are bent during their transit through a medium such as the Earth's atmosphere.

Regression of the Moon's nodes: the movement of the nodes of the Moon's orbit westward along the ecliptic, due to solar perturbations; with period $\cong 19$ years.

Red shift, gravitational: an effect predicted by the General Theory of Relativity in which the frequency of light emitted by atoms in stellar atmospheres is decreased by a factor proportional to the (mass/radius) quotient of the star; confirmed observationally by the spectra of white dwarfs.

Relativity effects: kinematic effects of the Lorentz transformations of the Special Theory of Relativity include: "Every clock appears to go at its fastest rate when it is at rest relatively to the observer. If it moves relatively to the observer with the velocity v, its rate appears slowed down by the factor $1 - v^2/c^2$. Every rigid body appears to be longest when at rest relatively to the observer. When it is not at rest, it appears contracted in the direction of its relative motion by the factor $1 - v^2/c^2$, whereas its dimensions perpendicular to the direction of motion are unaffected." Bergmann (131).

Representation: the computation of the position of a space vehicle given the orbital elements and the time.

Residuals $(O - C)$: small differences between the observed and computed coordinates in the sense observed minus computed.

Residuals $(O - I)$: small differences between the precomputed ideal observational data and the actual observed data on, for example, an interplanetary voyage.

Retrograde motion: westward or clockwise motion as seen from the North Pole, i.e., motion in an orbit in which $i > 90°$.

Retro-rocket: a rocket attached to a space vehicle whose thrust is directed antiparallel to the inertial velocity of the space vehicle.

Reynolds' number: the ratio of inertial forces to viscous forces—it is proportional to the Mach number, vehicle diameter, and the density, or in equivalent terms, proportional to the diameter of the space vehicle in mean free paths and the vehicle speed measured in terms of the average thermal speeds of gas molecules that constitute the oncoming flow.

Right ascension: angular distance from the vernal equinox measured counterclockwise along the equator to the foot of the hour circle through the object.

Root-solving technique: a numerical technique to determine by successive approximations a number which, when substituted for the unknown in an equation, reduces it to an identity, e.g., the root of the equation $2x^2 - 3x - 2 = 0$ is $x = 2$. See Newton's method, p. 134.

S

Scale height: the distance in which an isothermal atmosphere decreases in density from one to $1/e$.

Secular terms: expressions for perturbations that are proportional to the time; usually terms of extremely long period.

Selenocentric: referred to the center of the Moon; lunicentric.

Selenocentric equatorial coordinates: a right-handed coordinate system centered at the Moon with its three axes defined by the vernal equinox, north celestial pole (of the Earth), and a direction perpendicular to these two, i.e., an equatorial coordinate system translated to the Moon.

Selenographic coordinates: coordinates that are rigidly attached to the Moon (as geographic coordinates are attached to the Earth) defined by the Moon's equator and prime meridian. See *Mean center of Moon.*

Semimajor axis: the distance from the center of an ellipse to an apsis; one-half the longest diameter; one of the orbital elements.

Semiminor axis: one-half the shortest diameter of an ellipse.

Setting circles: a graduated scale that can be read visually and indicates the direction (e.g., altitude and azimuth or right ascension and declination) in which a telescope is pointed. Ordinarily they are employed to set or point a conventional astronomical telescope in the proper direction to make a given observation.

Shoran: a method for surveying in which the transit time for radio pulses to travel from an airplane are utilized to define the distance between two stations.

Sidereal time: the hour angle of the vernal equinox.

Sidereal year: the time required by the Earth to complete one revolution of its orbit; equal to 365.25636 mean solar days.

Sigma deviation: see *standard deviation.*

Slip flow: a flow regime in aerodynamics in which there is some departure from continuum flow and the layer of compressible fluid immediately adjacent to the surface of an object is no longer at rest but has a finite tangential "slipping" velocity.

Solar flares: short-lived areas of brilliance (covering areas of 10 million square miles or so) on the Sun's chromosphere that are associated with other solar activity. Often accompanied by bursts of emitted charged corpuscles and electromagnetic radiation. They reach several times normal brightness within one or two minutes and then subside slowly over 15 to 30 minutes.

Solar sailing: the use of radiation pressure for locomotion through space. Similar principal to ordinary sailing in which the wind pressure is utilized for locomotion through the water.

Solar wind: those low energy particles, i.e., corpuscular radiation (electrons and protons) emanating from the Sun. Typical flux rates are 10^8 to 10^{10} particles per cm^2 per second, and typical energies are 1000 to 100,000 ev for the protons and a few electron volts for the electrons.

Space range system: a system or network of observation stations, together with their associated communication links and computational facilities, that are utilized to observe and track space vehicles, e.g., the Pacific Missile Range, the National Space Surveillance System, etc.

Specular reflection: characterized by the relation that the angle of incidence equals the angle of reflection, in contrast to diffuse reflection.

Spheroid: an oblate ellipsoid which closely approximates the mean sea-level figure of the Earth or geoid.

Sputtering: the almost instantaneous ejection of surface atoms arising from collisions between the frontal surface of a vehicle and the oncoming molecules of air.

Standard atmosphere: a table of atmospheric density as a function of altitude that is accepted as a standard and used as a model to portray a typical average atmospheric density variation.

Standard deviation: the square root of the arithmetic mean of the squares of the deviations from the mean; also called root mean square error and sigma deviation.

Star tracker: an optical servo-mechanism device that automatically follows or tracks a celestial body such as a star. It is often utilized as a navigational aid to obtain angular measures of a star position relative to a planet or as a stabilization aid to perform a supervisory function in a gyro-stabilized inertial platform (the gyro nulls out the short term disturbances while star tracker(s) provide long term control of secular drifts).

Stationary points: points in the apparent path of a planet etc., where it appears to stand still, because it is moving only in the line of sight. Such a point occurs when a planet changes its motion from direct to retrograde and vice versa.

Station error: small differences, usually negligible, between the astronomical and geodetic latitudes, due to certain anomalies (such as a mountain) in the local gravitational field.

Surface-circular satellite: a hypothetical satellite on a circular orbit about the Earth having a semimajor axis equal to the Earth's equatorial radius. Hence, such a satellite would "skim the *surface* of the Earth" as it revolved on its orbit.

Synodic period of planet: the interval of time between two successive oppositions or conjunctions with the Sun, as observed from the Earth.

Synodic satellite: a hypothetical satellite, situated 0.84 of the distance to the Moon on a line joining the centers of the Earth and Moon and having the same period of revolution as the Moon, according to the Lagrangian "straight line solutions" of the three-body problem.

T

Telemetry: the radio link between a space vehicle and a ground station used to transmit information from the vehicle.

Tellurometer: an instrument similar to the "geodimeter;" but instead of utilizing a light beam, the tellurometer beams 3000 Mc radio waves, which upon reflection and phase measurement, allows for an accurate distance determination (between the instrument and the reflector) to about three parts in one million.

Thermal speed: see *mean molecular speed.*

Three-body problem: the problem of integrating the equations of motion of three bodies (e.g., Sun–Moon–Earth) moving under their mutual gravitational attractions; directly soluble only in particular cases. See Lagrangian solutions.

Thrust: the force exerted on a vehicle by the discharge of a gas or propellant.

Time dilatation: the apparent slowing-down of moving clocks, measured by Ives in the case of hydrogen "atomic clocks" in canal rays as a "relativistic Doppler effect."

Time of perifocal passage: the time when a space vehicle traveling upon an orbit passes by the nearer apsis or perifocal point. The date of the latest perifocal passage, T', is $T' = T + NP$ where N is the number of revolutions since the initial time of perifocal passage T and P is the orbital period.

Topocentric: referred to the position of the observer on the Earth, as origin.

Topocentric equatorial coordinates: a right-handed coordinate system centered at the observer with its three axes defined by the vernal equinox, north celestial pole, and a direction perpendicular to these two, i.e., an equatorial coordinate system translated to the topos.

Transitional flow: a flow regime in aerodynamics between the free-molecule flow and slip-flow regimes in which the molecules emitted from the surface of an object affect the flow of oncoming molecules, i.e., the mean-free path of the emitted molecules becomes comparable to a characteristic linear dimension of an object.

Transponder: an electronic device that receives a radio signal, amplifies it and immediately and automatically retransmits it.

Transverse axis: the distance between the apsides—identical to the semimajor axis for elliptical orbits.

Triaxial ellipsoid: a solid aspherical figure which when cut or sectioned in three orthogonal (normal or mutually perpendicular) directions exhibits three elliptical cross sections of differing semimajor axes and eccentricities.

An equation for the surface of the figure is given by $x^2/a^2 + y^2/b^2 + z^2/c^2 = 1$ where a, b, and c are constants and represent the extent of the figure along the three orthogonal directions.

Trojan asteroids: two groups of minor planets that librate in long-period orbits around the equilateral triangle points of the Sun and Jupiter; predicted by the "equilateral triangle solutions" of the three-body problem, discovered by Lagrange.

Tropical year: the time (365.2422 mean solar days) required by the Sun to make an apparent revolution of the ecliptic from vernal equinox to vernal equinox; shorter than the solar year owing to precession of the equinoxes. It is the civil year of the seasons.

Tropopause: the height (varying from about 9 km over the poles to 18 km over the equator) where the gradual decrease in temperature with elevation above sea-level ceases. Above this height, which marks the boundary of the troposphere or lower atmosphere, lies the stratosphere, a region in which the temperature remains constant up to a height of 30–35 km.

True anomaly: the angle at the focus between the line of apsides and the radius vector measured from perifocus in the direction of the motion.

True equinox of date: the actual position of the equinox including both precession and nutation.

Twenty four hour satellite: a satellite whose orbital period is exactly 24 hours. If such a satellite is on a circular equatorial orbit then it will remain fixed or "stationary" relative to the rotating Earth.

Two-body orbit: the motion of a body of negligible mass around a center of attraction.

U

Unit vector: a vector whose magnitude or length is unity—utilized to define directions in space.

Universal time (UT): mean solar time referred to the meridian of Greenwich; nonuniform owing to the irregular rotation of the Earth.

Universal variable: a variable denoted by the symbol $\tilde{X}$ that is equally applicable to the ellipse, parabola, and hyperbola; and is defined for these conics as equal to $\sqrt{a}\,E$, D, or $\sqrt{-a}\,F$ respectively.

V

Van Allen radiation belt: is comprised of two toroidal-shaped zones or belts of charged particles roughly situated in the plane of Earth's equator.

The inner belt commences at about one fifth of an Earth's radius above the equator and extends out to a little less than one Earth's radius. The outer belt is located at about two and one half Earth radii from the Earth at the equator and is about one Earth's radius thick. Actually the outer belt has a cross section that is shaped somewhat like a banana and extends north and south of the equatorial plane two Earth radii. The northern and southern extremes of the belt's cross section (at about 45° latitude) approach the Earth one half of an Earth radius closer than at the equator.

Variant orbits: computed orbits in which one of the initial conditions (or parameters) is varied slightly from those of the nominal trajectory—such orbits are utilized to compute numerical partial derivatives (Eq. (199)) or to determine the effects of errors in launch conditions.

Variation of latitude: small periodic changes in the position of the Earth's poles due to a "wobbling" of the axis of rotation about the geometrical axis (the shortest diameter) of the Earth.

Vector component: the projection of a vector on a given axis in space, e.g., if it is the x axis then the component of the vector $\mathbf{A}$ on this axis is denoted by A_x.

Vector equation: an equation, whose terms include vectors, that can be resolved into three component equations e.g., $\ddot{\mathbf{r}} = -\mu\mathbf{r}/r^3$ actually represents the three component equations

$$\ddot{x} = -\mu x/r^3$$
$$\ddot{y} = -\mu y/r^3$$
$$\ddot{z} = -\mu z/r^3$$

where $\ddot{\mathbf{r}}$ has been replaced by its three components $\ddot{x}$, $\ddot{y}$, and $\ddot{z}$ and $\mathbf{r}$ by its three components x, y, and z.

Vernal Equinox: that point of intersection of the ecliptic and celestial equator where the Sun crosses the equator from south to north in its apparent annual motion along the ecliptic.

Vis-viva *integral:* an important integral of the two-body problem giving the orbital velocity:

$$\left(\frac{ds}{dt}\right)^2 = k^2(m_1 + m_2)(2/r - 1/a).$$

Z

Zedir technique: the use of two cameras on a satellite whose optical axes are parallel, one of which photographs the sky (zenith) while the other simultaneously photographs the ground (nadir). Upon development and measurement the photographs can be utilized to find the attitude of the camera's optical axis at the time of photograph.

Zenith: the point where the upward extension of the plumb-bob direction intersects the celestial sphere.

GLOSSARY OF SYMBOLS MORE FREQUENTLY USED

If a symbol is utilized infrequently in a single chapter, then ordinarily it will not be listed.

The reader's attention is called to the not-infrequent ambiguity in notation. Unfortunately, because of the extent to which astrodynamics cuts across the lines of other scientific disciplines, such ambiguity cannot be avoided.

Superscripts

d	days
h	hours
m	magnitude
m	minutes of time
s	seconds of time
y	years
$''$	seconds of arc
$'$	minutes of arc
$'$	"quote derivative," denotes a perturbative derivative with y_ω as independent variable or the coordinates of position and velocity relative to a selenocentric equatorial coordinate system
.	"dot derivative," denotes a derivative with respect to time exclusive of perturbations
\`	"grave derivative," denotes a derivative with respect to time that involves only perturbations
*	units include geopotential meters
$\sim$	universal variable

Subscripts

A	astronomical
B	barycenter
b	base altitude
c	computed, corrected, required to complete the mission, or measured to the surface of the Earth in a meridian plane of a reference spheroid
D	drag, Deimos
E	east
e	equatorial value, Earth, emitted molecules, and Encke reference orbit
g	Greenwich
h	hyperbola, heliocentric, or horizon
I	ideal orbit
i, j, k	running indices, e.g., indicates that the quantity is evaluated at the ith or jth time (i.e., t_i or t_j)
L	lift
m	molecular scale
0	reference, initial, sea-level, observed, or epoch value
o	oncoming molecules
p	parabola or planet
r	retrograde
s	Sun (Gaussian) value, surface, or secular
T	equatorial coordinates of the topos or transfer orbit
x, y, z	components along the x, y, and z axes
ω	orbit-plane system or referred to orbital axes
$\odot$	Sun
☿	Mercury
♀	Venus
$\oplus$	Earth
☾	Moon
♂	Mars
♃	Jupiter
∞	limit as $r \rightarrow \infty$
Δ	object or space vehicle
ϵ	ecliptic

Equivalence signs

$\equiv$	identically equal to

Equivalence signs

$\cong$	approximately equal to
$\propto$	proportional to
$\triangleq$	equal to by definition

Special symbols

0	order of
Υ	vernal equinox (Ram's horns or the first point of Aries)
Υ'	inertial direction in space (located at an angle Ω from the line of nodes measured in the orbit plane)
∞	infinity
$\vert\ \vert$	absolute value (magnitude)
$x \rightarrow y, z$	two other equations can be obtained by replacing x by y and then by z or "yields"
$A \rightarrow B$	A approaches B
$a\ (b, c, \ldots)$	denotes that a is a function of b, c, etc.
$x \rightarrow y$ $\nwarrow z \swarrow$	two other equations can be obtained by cyclical replacement of x by z, y by x, and z by y, etc.
$>, <$	greater than, less than
$\angle\mathbf{A}, \mathbf{B}$	the angle between any two typical vectors **A** and **B**

English symbols

A	the azimuth measured from the north point eastward along the horizon; the term in μ for the Earth due to the mass of the atmosphere; or the effective or average projected frontal area of a space vehicle (also stands for certain miscellaneous constants)
a	the semimajor axis of an elliptical orbit or the semitransverse axis of a hyperbolic orbit (also stands for certain miscellaneous constants)
$\mathbf{a}$	$e\mathbf{P} = (\dot{D}\mathbf{r} - D\dot{\mathbf{r}})/\sqrt{\mu}$
a_e	the equatorial radius of the Earth
B	the transitional parameter $= d/L_{eo}$ i.e., the ratio of a characteristic length of a space vehicle to the mean free path of an emitted molecule with respect to an oncoming molecule (also stands for certain miscellaneous constants)
b	an angle measured normal to the orbit plane; the semimajor axis of an elliptical orbit ($= a\sqrt{1 - e^2}$); the semiconjugate axis of a hyperbola; and the collision parameter or radius

English symbols

of the effective gravitational cross-section (also stands for certain miscellaneous constants)

b $e\sqrt{p}\mathbf{Q} = (\dot{H}\mathbf{r} - H\dot{\mathbf{r}})/\sqrt{\mu}$

C an auxiliary quantity tabulated in the almanacs that is used for finding the geocentric coordinates of a station referred to a reference spheroid or $= \mathbf{r}_1 \cdot \mathbf{r}_3$ (also stands for certain miscellaneous constants)

C_i the constants obtained by a fit of $\sigma\gamma(\sigma)$ to $\sum_{i=0}^{n} C_i r^i$ over limited levels in the atmosphere

C_D the drag coefficient $\triangleq$ Drag Force$/\frac{1}{2}\rho A v^2$

c the distance measured from the center of an ellipse to a focus ($= ae$); the shortest axis of a triaxial ellipsoid; the speed of light; the local speed of sound; or the exhaust speed (also stands for certain miscellaneous constants)

D $\frac{r\dot{r}}{\sqrt{\mu}}$ (for a parabola $= \sqrt{2q}\tan[v/2]$) or a determinant

D_0^2 $C_{D_0} A_0 \rho_0 V_{c0}^2/2g_0 m_0$

d the angular distance, e.g., traveled by an ICBM over the Earth's surface or a lunar vehicle between injection and impact or the effective or average diameter of the projected frontal area of a space vehicle (also stands for certain miscellaneous constants)

E the eccentric anomaly (also stands for certain miscellaneous constants)

e the eccentricity ($= \sqrt{1 - b^2/a^2}$)

F $-iE$ which is a variable related to hyperbolic orbit that corresponds to the eccentric anomaly in the ellipse (also stands for certain miscellaneous constants)

f the flattening of the reference spheroid of the Earth; force; or frequency (also stands for certain miscellaneous constants)

$\mathbf{f}_{ij}$ the vector force exerted on mass m_i by mass m_j

G the universal constant of gravitation given in the cgs (or other "laboratory") units (also stands for certain miscellaneous constants)

g the terrestrial gravitational acceleration (also stands for other miscellaneous constants)

English symbols

H the coefficient of the third-order zonal harmonic in the Earth's gravitational potential; the altitude above a surface in characteristic units such as Earth radii or in geometric meters; or $= r - p$ or $-\mathbf{r} \cdot \mathbf{a}$ (also stands for certain miscellaneous constants)

H^* the geopotential altitude measured in "geopotential meters"

$\mathbf{h}$ the angular momentum vector ($= \sqrt{p}\mathbf{W}$), i.e., its magnitude is twice the area velocity

h the "altitude" or angular distance above the horizon or the interval between two successive data points

$\mathbf{I}$ a unit vector in the direction of the vernal equinox, ♈

i the inclination of an orbit plane to a fundamental plane (e.g., the angle between a geocentric satellite orbit plane and the Earth's equator plane), or $+\sqrt{-1}$

J the coefficient of the second order zonal harmonic in the Earth's gravitational potential

$\mathbf{J}$ a unit vector perpendicular to $\mathbf{I}$ and $\mathbf{K}$

K the coefficient of the fourth-order zonal harmonic in the Earth's gravitational potential

$\mathbf{K}$ a unit vector in the direction of the north celestial pole

Kn the Knudsen number $= L_{oo}/d$

k the gravitational constant $k = k'$ herein

k' a constant whose definition determines the units of τ and μ. Four definitions of k' are employed: $k' = k$, $k' = k\sqrt{m_1 + m_2}$, $k' = 1/w$ (where w is the interval for numerical integration), and $k' = 1$ (see Herrick[1])

L the mean longitude $= M + \pi = L_0 + n(t - t_0)$

$\mathbf{L}$ the unit vector from an observing station to a space vehicle

L_{ij} the mean free path of molecules i with respect to molecules j

l the true longitude $= \Omega + \omega + v$

M the mean anomaly ($= n(t - T) = E - e \sin E = M_0 + n(t - t_0)$) or the Mach number ($= \nu/c$) (also stands for certain miscellaneous constant numbers)

$\mathbf{M}$ the unit vector perpendicular to $\mathbf{N}$ and $\mathbf{W}$

m the mass of, e.g., the Sun, planets, space vehicle, etc.; the molecular weight (also stands for certain miscellaneous constant numbers), m = meter

English symbols

N the number of atmospheric molecules or charges per unit volume (also stands for certain miscellaneous constant numbers)

$\mathbf{N}$ a unit vector in the direction of the ascending node

n the mean motion ($= k\sqrt{\mu}/a^{3/2}$ for elliptic orbits) and the refractive index (also stands for certain miscellaneous constants numbers)

P the orbital period of revolution ($= 2\pi/n$), the parallactic inequality; the pressure; or perturbative acceleration (also stands for certain miscellaneous constants)

$\mathbf{P}$ a unit vector in the direction of the perifocus

p the parameter or semilatus rectum of a conic section ($= r(1 + e \cos v) = a(1 - e^2)$) or a typical parameter

$\mathbf{Q}$ a unit vector perpendicular to $\mathbf{P}$ and $\mathbf{W}$

q the perifocal distance from the principal focus to the nearer apsis ($= a(1 - e)$), the speed of the cross wind measured in a frame-work rotating at the Earth's angular rate; or a series utilized in Encke's method and defined by Eq. (179)

q_2 the apofocal distance from the principal focus to the farther apsis ($= a(1 + e)$)

R the perturbative function

$\mathbf{R}$ the radius vector from the observatory to the center of coordinates

R^* the universal gas constant

Re the Reynolds' number $\propto Md\rho$

$\mathbf{r}$ a radius vector from the principal focus to a space vehicle

r_0 a radius to the surface or to an atmospheric level from the center of a planet; equal to the perifocal distance in a grazing orbit

r_1 a radius to some reference altitude from the center of a planet

$\mathbf{r}_2$ a radius vector from the secondary or empty focus to a point on a conic section

S an auxiliary quantity tabulated in almanacs used for finding geocentric coordinates referred to a reference spheroid (also stands for certain miscellaneous constants) or $= |\mathbf{r}_1 \times \mathbf{r}_3|$

$\dot{s}$ the tangential velocity ($\dot{s} = |\dot{\mathbf{r}}|$)

$\dot{s}_\infty$ the hyperbolic residual or "excess" speed as $r \to \infty$

English symbols

T the time of perifocal passage; the absolute temperature in degrees Kelvin; or the thrust force per unit mass (thrust to mass ratio)

t the time as measured in conventional units (e.g., hours, minutes, and seconds)

U the mean argument of latitude ($= M + \omega$)

$\mathbf{U}$ a unit vector in the direction of an object ($\mathbf{U} = \mathbf{r}/r$) that makes an angle of $u = v + \omega$ with the line of nodes

u the argument of latitude ($u = v + \omega$)

$\mathbf{V}$ a unit vector perpendicular to **U** and **W**

$\bar{V}_e$ the average thermal speed of the emitted molecules

V_{c0} the circular-satellite speed at unit distance

v the true anomaly, i.e., the angle between the perifocal direction (**P**) and the radial direction to the object (**U**), or the speed with which a reference frame moves

$\mathbf{W}$ a unit vector perpendicular to the orbit plane, it is common to all orbital coordinate systems

w the time interval for numerical integration (i.e., the step size)

$\tilde{X}$ the universal variable $= \sqrt{-a}\, E$ or D or $\sqrt{a}\, F$

x, y, z coordinates measured along three orthogonal axes

$\mathbf{Z}$ a unit vector in the direction of the zenith

Greek symbols

α the right ascension of an object, accommodation coefficient, or the ratio A/A_0 (also stands for certain miscellaneous constants)

β $1/\sqrt{1 - (v/c)^2}$, celestial latitude, phase angle, or a constant in the gravity formula (also stands for certain miscellaneous constants)

γ a constant in the gravity formula (also stands for other miscellaneous constants)

$\gamma(\nu)$ the drag-coefficient variation with Mach number ($= C_D(\nu/c)/C_{D0}$

$\gamma(\sigma)$ the drag-coefficient variation in the transitional regime ($= C_D(\sigma)/C_{D0}$)

Δ a small increment, error, or residual

δ declination, difference, or small increment

Greek symbols

ϵ	the mean square error of a quantity
ξ, η, ζ	the components of $\boldsymbol{\varrho}$ or departures from a reference orbit in Encke's method
ζ	the entry angle or the bank angle
θ	the sidereal time or the elevation angle
λ	the longitude in a geographic coordinate system
μ	$[k^2/(k')^2](m_1 + m_2)$ or the ratio m_0/m with $k = k'$ herein
$\boldsymbol{\nu}$	the velocity of a space vehicle relative to a moving atmosphere
π	the longitude of perifocus ($= \Omega + \omega$), the parallax, or the ratio of the circumference of a circle to the diameter
ρ	the atmospheric density
$\boldsymbol{\varrho}$	a vector from an observatory to an object or, in general, a vector from one point to another
σ	the density ratio ($= \rho/\rho_0$)
τ	a characteristic unit of time ($= k\ (t - t_0)$)
Φ	the gravitational potential
ϕ	the geodetic latitude
ϕ'	the geocentric latitude
ϕ_a	the astronomical latitude
ψ	the angle of elongation between the direction to an object and to the center of the coordinate system reckoned at the observer
Ω	the longitude of the ascending node, i.e., the angle between the principal direction (e.g., vernal equinox) and the line of nodes
ω	the argument of perifocus, i.e., the angle between the line of nodes and the perifocus direction or the angular rotation rate of the Earth

REFERENCES

1. Herrick, Samuel. (1961). "Astrodynamics." Van Nostrand, New York. In Press.
2. Baker, R. M. L., Jr. (1960). Astrodynamics. *In* "Space Trajectories." Academic Press, New York.
3. Smart, W. M. (1953). "Celestial Mechanics." Longmans, New York.
4. Vinti, J. P. (1959). A new method of solution for unretarded satellite orbits. *Nat. Bur. Stand. Rept.* **6449.**
5. Gauss, K. F. (1857). "Theoria Motus Corporum Coelestium." (C. H. Davis, trans.) Little, Brown, Boston.
6. Williams, K. P. (1934). "The Calculation of the Orbits of Asteroids and Comets." Principia Press, Bloomington.
7. Garfinkel, Boris. (1957). On the motion of a satellite of an oblate planet. *Ballistic Research Lab Rept. No.* **1018.** Aberdeen Proving Ground, Md.
8. Sterne, T. E. (1958). The gravitational orbit of a satellite of an oblate planet. *Astron. J.* **63,** 28–40.
9. Baker, R. M. L., Jr. (1959). Application of astronomical perturbation techniques to the return of space vehicles, *ARS Journal* **29,** 207–211. Also, Three-Dimensional Drag Perturbation Technique *ARS Journal* August 1960 (in press).
10. Benedikt, E. T. (1959). Scientific significance of deep space exploration, *Am. Astronaut. Soc. Preprint No.* **59–8.**
11. Bode, John E. and Piazzi, G. (1929). The Titus-Bode Law of Planetary Distances and the Discovery of Ceres. *In* "A Source Book in Astronomy" (H. Shapley and H. E. Howarth, eds.), 180–182. McGraw-Hill, New York.
12. Herschel, Sir W. (1929). The discovery of Uranus. *In* "A Source Book in Astronomy" (H. Shapley and H. E. Howarth, eds.), 140–142. McGraw-Hill, New York.
13. Moulton, F. R. (1914). "Celestial Mechanics." 324–354. Macmillan, New York.
14. Leuschner, A. O., and Thiele, H., (1935). Research surveys of the orbits and perturbations of minor planets 1 to 1091 from 1801.0 to 1929.5. *Publications of the Lick Observatory,* **XIX.**
15. Kirkwood, Daniel. (1929). Gaps in the asteroid belt. *In* "A Source Book in Astronomy" (H. Shapley and H. E. Howarth, eds.), 305–307. McGraw-Hill, New York.
16. Brouwer, D. (1950). Families of minor planets and related distributional problems. *Astron. J.* **55,** 162–163.
17. Herrick, Samuel. (1953). Icarus and the variation of parameters. *Astron. J.* **58,** 156–164.

18. Brouwer, D., and Ashbrook, J. (1951). Minor planet 619 Triberga and the mass of the moon. *Astron. J.* **56,** 57.
19. Baker, R. M. L., Jr. (1959). Sputtering as it is related to hyperbolic meteorites. *J. Appl. Phys.* **30,** 550–555.
20. Halley, Edmond. (1929). A Discussion of elliptical orbits of comets. *In* "A Source Book in Astronomy" (H. Shapley and H. E. Howarth eds.), 94–96. McGraw-Hill, New York.
21. Mebane, A. D. (1956). Observations of the Great Fireball Procession of 1913, February 9, made in the United States. *Meteoritics* **1,** 405.
22. Baker, R. M. L., Jr. (1958). Ephemeral natural satellites of the earth. *Science* **128,** 1211–1213.
23. O'Keefe, J. A. (1959). A probable natural satellite: the meteor procession of February 9, 1913. *J. Roy. Astron. Soc. Can.* **53,** 59–65.
24. Robey, D. H. (1959). Hypothesis on the slow moving fireballs. *Convair Astronautics Rept. No.* **AZM-079.**
25. Robey, D. H. (1958). Cold re-entry of space vehicles at meteor speeds. *Convair Astronautics Rept. No.* **ASM-15.**
26. Olivier, C. P. (1930). "Comets." Williams and Wilkins, Baltimore.
27. Bredikhine, Theodor (1929). On comets and meteors. *In* "A Source Book in Astronomy" (H. Shapley and H. E. Howarth, eds.), 358–361. McGraw-Hill, New York.
28. Lyttleton, R. A. (1953). "The Comets and Their Origin." Cambridge Univ. Press, Cambridge.
29. Sundman, K. F. (1913). Memoire sur le problème des trois corps. *Acta Math.* **36,** 105–179.
30. Koskela, Paul (1959). Selenocentric and selenographic coordinate systems. *Aeronutronic Pub. No.* **C-365.**
31. Klemperer, W. B. and Baker, R. M. L., Jr. (1957). Satellite librations. *Astronaut. Acta* **3,** 16–27.
32. Baker, R. M. L., Jr., (1960). Libration of a prolate ellipsoidal shell. *ARS Journal* **30,** 124–125.
33. Baker, R. M. L., Jr., (1960). Librations in a slightly eccentric orbit. *ARS Journal* **30,** 126–128.
34. Hilton, C. G. (1959). A study of planetary position data requirements for space vehicle trajectory computations. *Aeronutronic Pub. No.* **U-397.**
35. "Interpolation and Allied Tables." (1936). H. M. Stationery Office, London.
36. Herrick, S., Westrom, G. B., and Makemson, M. W. (1959). Solar Parallax and Astronomical Unit. University of California at Los Angeles. *Astrodynamical Report No.* **5.**
37. Herrick, S., Baker, R. M. L., Jr., and Hilton, C. G. (1957). Gravitational and related constants for accurate space navigation, *U.C.L.A. Astron. Papers No.* **24.**
38. Wolaver, Lynn E. (1958). Factors in precision space flight trajectories. *WCLJEY Internal Memo* **58-57.** Wright Air Development Command Aeronautical Research Laboratories, Ohio.
39. Adams, W. S. (1940). Some results with the Coudé spectrograph of the Mount Wilson Observatory. *Astrophys. J.* **93,** 11–23.
40. Münch, G. (1958). Fundamental astronomical constants. *Space Technology Lab. Rept. No.* **GM-TM-0165-00234.**

41. Lilley, A. E. and Brouwer, Dirk. (1959). The solar parallax and the hydrogen line. *Am. Astron. Soc. Meeting Toronto, Paper No.* **42.**
42. Spencer Jones, Sir Harold (1941). The solar parallax and the mass of the Moon from observations of Eros at the opposition of 1931. *Mem. Roy. Astron. Soc.* **66,** Pt. 2, 55.
43. Rabe, Eugene. (1949). Derivation of fundamental astronomical constants from the observations of Eros during 1926–45. *Astron. J.* **55,** 112–125.
44. Price, R., and Green, P. E., (1959). Radar echoes from Venus. *Science* **129,** 751–753.
45. Cohen, E. R., Crowe, K. M., and DuMond, J. W. M. (1957). "Fundamental Constants of Physics." Vol. I., Interscience, New York.
46. Brouwer, Dirk. (1950). A new determination of the solar parallax from the parallactic inequality in the Moon's longitude; comments on the masses of the inner planets; notes on investigations in progress. *Bull. Astron.* **15,** 165–180.
47. O'Keefe, J. A., Eckels, A., and Squires, R. K. (1959). *Astron. J. 64,* No. 7, 245.
48. Yaplee, B. S., Bruton, R. H., Craig, K. J., and Roman, H. G. (1958). Radar echoes from the Moon at a wavelength of ten centimeters. *Proc. I.R.E.* **46,** 293.
49. O'Keefe, J. A. and Anderson, J. P. (1952). The earth's equatorial radius and the distance of the Moon. *Astron. J.* **57,** 108–121.
50. Delano, Erwin. (1950). The lunar equation from observations of Eros, 1930–31. *Astron. J.* **55,** 129–132.
51. Alexandrov, Igor. (1958). Constants related to the lunar mission. *Aeronutronic Pub. No.* **U-240.**
52. Jeffreys, H. (1948). The figures of the earth and the moon. *Monthly Notices Roy. Astron. Soc. Geophys. Suppl.* **5,** 219–247.
53. Yakovkin, A. A. (1952). General characteristics of the contour of the Moon. The free libration of the Moon. *In* "Transactions of the International Astronomical Union, VIII" (P. T. Oosterhoff, ed.) 218–233. Cambridge Univ. Press.
54. Urey, H. C., Elsasser, W. M., and Rochester, M. G. (1959). Note on the internal structure of the Moon. *Astrophys J.* **129,** 842–848.
55. MacCullagh, James (1855). On the attraction of ellipsoids with a new demonstration of Clairaut's Theorem. *Trans. Roy. Irish Acad.* **22,** (part 2) Dublin.
56. Westrom, G. B. (1958). High precision orbit determination. *Aeronutronic Pub. No.* **U-583.**
57. Leveau, M. G. (1896). Tables de mouvement de Vesta. *Ann. Observatoire de Paris* **22,** 1–317.
58. Burton, H. E. (1929). Elements of the orbits of the satellites of Mars. *Astron. J.* **39,** 155–164.
59. Campbell, W. W. (1895). A determination of the polar diameter of Mars. *Astron. J.* **15,** 145–149.
60. Kallmann, H. K. (1959). A preliminary model atmosphere based on rocket and satellite data. *RAND Report No.* **P-1591.**
61. Kallmann, H. K., White, W. B., and Newell, H. E. (1956). Physical properties of the atmosphere from 90 to 300 kilometers. *J. Geophys. Research* **61,** 513–524.
62. Minzner, R. A. and Ripley, W. S. (1956). The *ARDC* model atmosphere. *ASTIA Doc. No.* 110233. *AFCRC* **TN-56-204.**
63. Champion, K. S. W. and Minzner, R. A. (1959). Atmospheric densities from satellite and rocket observation. *AFCRC,* May, 1959.

64. Jacchia, L. G. (1959). The diurnal effect in the orbital acceleration of satellite 1957 β One. *Smithsonian Inst. Astrophys. Observatory, Spec. Rept. No.* **20,** Cambridge; Atmospheric fluctuations of solar origin revealed by artificial satellites. *Astron. J.* **64,** 129–130.
65. Whitney, C. A. (1959). Atmospheric conditions at high altitudes from satellite observations. *ARS Preprint No.* **779-59.**
66. Jacchia, L. G. (1959). Solar effects on the acceleration of artificial satellites. *Smithsonian Inst. Astrophys. Observatory Spec. Rep. No.* **29** Cambridge.
67. Baker, R. M. L., Jr., Koskela, P., Hilton, C. G., and Sokol, J. (1959). Interim report covering task five, range planning study for project Mercury. *Aeronutronic Pub. No.* **U-538.**
68. Herrick, Samuel. (1940). The Laplacian and Gaussian orbit methods. *Univ. of Calif. Pub., Contributions of Los Angeles Astronomy Dept.*, **I,** 1–56.
69. Van Sant, C. T., Walters, L. G., and Nicola, L. (1959). Interim report covering task three, range planning study for project Mercury. *Aeronutronic Pub. No.* **U-536,** 44–46.
70. Baker, R. M. L., Jr. (1960). Orbit determination from range and range-rate observations. *ARS Preprint No.* **1220–60.**
71. Crout, P. D. (1941). A short method for evaluating determinants and solving systems of linear equations with real or complex coefficients. *Trans. Am. Inst. Elec. Engrs.* **60,** 1235–1241.
72. Herrick, Samuel and Liu, A. (1959). Two-body orbit determination from two positions and time of flight. *Appendix A. Aeronutronic Pub. No.* **C-365.**
73. Herget, Paul. (1948). "The Computation of Orbits." Published privately by the author, Ann Arbor, Mich.
74. Brown, R. S., Dindley, L. D., Patton, P. C., Smith, W. P., and Wimp, J. J. (1959). Research in surveying mapping and geodesy. *Midwest Research Inst. 1st Interim Tech. Report. MRI Proj. No.* **2235-E.**
75. Herrick, Samuel, and Walters, L. G. (1959). Project Mercury task one report. *Aeronutronic Pub. No.* **U-468.**
76. Lagrange, J. L. (1772). Essai d'une nouvelle méthode pour résoudre le problème des trois corps. *In* "Prix de l'Académie, IX."
77. Klemperer, W. B. and Benedikt, E. T. (1957). Selenoid satellites. *Proc. VIII Intern. Astronaut. Federation Congr., Barcelona.* 563–568.
78. Baker, R. M. L., Jr., Westrom, G. B., Hilton, C. G., Arsenault, J. L., Gersten, R. H., and Browne, E. (1959). Efficient precision orbit computation techniques. *ARS Preprint No.* **869-59** and *ARS Journal* August 1960 (in press).
79. Finlay-Freundlich, E. (1958). "Celestial Mechanics." Pergamon Press, New York.
80. Whittaker, E. T. (1944). "A Treatise on the Analytical Dynamics of Particles and Rigid Bodies, with an Introduction to the Problem of Three Bodies." Dover, New York.
81. Rabe, Eugene. (1954). The Trojans as escaped satellites of Jupiter. *Astron. J.* **59,** 433–439.
82. Sissenwine, N. (1954). Wind speed profiles . . . for vertically rising vehicles. *Air Force Surveys in Geophysics, No.* **57.**
83. "Planetary Coordinates for the Years 1960–1980." Her Majesty's Stationery Office, London.

84. Hansen, P. A. (1852, 1854). Uber die Berechnung der Störung durch mechanische Quadraturen. *Astron. Nachr.* **34,** cols. 101–142; **37,** cols. 301–307.
85. Vienop, E. and Brady, J. L. (1958). The Themis Code; and astronomical numerical integration program for the IBM 704. *Univ. of Calif. Radiation Lab. Report No.* **5242.**
86. Herget, Paul. (1946). Numerical integration with punched cards. *Astron. J.* **52,** 115–117.
87. Tross, Carl. (1959). Lunar vehicle orbit determination. *Aeronutronic Publication No.* **U-703.**
88. Herrick, Samuel. (1948). A modification of the variation of constants' method for special perturbations. *Publs. Astron. Soc. Pacific* **60,** 321–323.
89. Samoilova-Iakhontova. (1959). Remark on the computation of special perturbations of the elements. *Soviet Astronomy-AJ*, 147.
90. Stracke, G. (1929). "Bahnbestimmung der Planeten und Kometen." Springer, Berlin.
91. Musen, Peter. (1954). Special perturbations of the vectorial elements. *Astron. J.* **59,** 262–267.
92. Hoelker, R. L., Sterling, H. J., and Miner, W. (1959). Barycentric method of space flight calculation with introduction of ephemerides. *ABMA Report No.* **DA TN 9359.**
93. Brown, E. W. (1896). "Lunar Theory." Ch. 9. Cambridge Univ. Press.
94. Kovalevsky, Jean. (1959). Méthode numérique de calcul des perturbations générales. Application au VIIIe satellite de Jupiter. Thèse de l'Université de Paris.
95. Herrick, Samuel and Walters, L. G. (1959). Influence of the earth's potential field on a nearly circular satellite. *Aeronutronic Pub. No.* **U-326.**
96. Sterne, T. E. (1958). An atmospheric model, and some remarks on the inference of density from the orbit of a close earth satellite. *Astron. J.* **63,** 81–87.
97. Nonweiler, T. R. F. (1958). Perturbation of elliptic orbits by atmospheric contact. *J. Brit. Interplanet. Soc.* **16,** 368–379.
98. Rowell, L. N. and Smith, M. C. (1958). Secular variation in the inclination of the orbit of earth satellite (1957) and air drag. *RAND Report No.* **P-1611.**
99. Vinti, J. P. (1959). Theory of the effect of drag on the orbital inclination of an earth satellite. *J. Research Natl. Bur. Standards* **62,** 79–88.
100. O'Keefe, J. A. and Eckels, A. (1958). Announcement of the third harmonic for the Earth. *Harvard College Observ. Announcement Card No.* **1420.**
101. Sterne, T. E. (1959). Effects of the rotation of a planetary atmosphere upon the orbit of a close satellite. *J. Am. Rocket Soc.* **29,** 777–782.
102. Kozai, Yoshihide. (1959). On the effects of the Sun and the Moon upon the motion of a close Earth satellite. *Smithsonian Inst. Astrophys. Observatory Research in Space Sciences Spec. Rept. No.* **22,** 7–10.
103. Kozai, Yoshihide and Whitney, C. A. (1959). Anticipated orbital perturbations of satellite 1959 Delta Two. *Smithsonian Inst. Astrophys. Observatory, Spec. Rept. No.* **30,** Cambridge, 1–8.
104. Baker, R. M. L., Jr. (1959). Accuracy required for a return from interplanetary voyages. *J. Brit. Interplanet. Soc.* **17,** No. 5.
105. Charwat, A. F. (1959). Lift and pitching moment in near-free-molecule flow. *RAND Report No.* **R-339,** 15-1 to 15-43.

106. Baker, R. M. L., Jr. and Charwat, A. F. (1958). Transitional correction to the drag of a sphere in free molecule flow. *Phys. Fluids* **1,** 73–81.
107. Łunc, M., and Luboński, J. (1957). La perturbation de l'écoulement moléculaire libre produite par un obstacle. *Bull. Acad. Polom. Sci.* **5,** No. 147–57.
108. Whitney, C. A. (1959). The structure of the high atmosphere-I. linear models. *Smithsonian Contr. to Astrophys., Spec. Rept. No.* **21,** 1–12.
109. Baker, R. M. L., Jr. (1959). The transitional aerodynamic drag of meteorites. *Astrophys. J.* **129,** 826–841.
110. Baker, R. M. L., Jr. (1959). The effect of accommodation on the transitional aerodynamic drag of meteorites. *Astrophys. J.* **130,** 1024–1026.
111. Jahnke, E. and Emde, F. (1943). "Tables of Functions" Dover (New York).
112. Stuhlinger, E. (1957). Flight path of an ion-propelled space ship. *Jet propulsion* **27,** 410–414.
113. Tsien, H. S. (1953). Take-off from a satellite orbit. *Jet Propulsion* **23,** 233.
114. Levin, E. (1959). Low thrust transfer between circular orbits, *A.S.M.E. Paper* **59-AV-2.**
115. Copeland, J. (1959). Interplanetary trajectories under low thrust radial acceleration. *ARS Journal* **29,** 267.
116. Irving, J. H. and Blum, E. K. (1958). Comparative performance of ballistic and low-thrust vehicles for flight to Mars. *Space Technology Labs. Report No.* **59-263.**
117. Perkins, F. M. (1959). Flight mechanics of low-thrust spacecraft. *J. Aero/Space Sci.* **26,** 291.
118. Jastrow, R. and Pearse, C. A. (1957). Atmospheric drag on the satellite. *J. Geophys. Research* **62,** 413.
119. Gringauz, K. I. and Zelikman, M. X. (1957). Measurement of the concentration of positive ions in the orbit of the artificial earth satellite. *Uspekhi Fizichesk Nauk* **63,** 239–252.
120. Kraus, L., and Watson, K. M. (1958). Plasma motions induced by satellites in the ionosphere. *Phys. Fluids* **1,** 480–488.
121. Chopra, K. P. and Singer, S. F. (1958). Drag of a sphere moving in a conducting fluid. *Univ. of Maryland, Phys. Dept. Tech. Report No.* **97,** 1–12.
122. Jefimenko, O. (1959). Effect of the Earth's magnetic field on the motion of an artificial satellite. *Am. J. Phys.* **27,** 344–8.
123. Roberson, R. E. (1959). A review of the current status of satellite attitude control. *J. Astronaut. Sci.* **6,** 25–30.
124. Baker, R. M. L., Jr. (1958). Passive stability of a satellite vehicle. *Navigation* **6,** 66–67.
125. Robinson, A. C. (1958). On the three-dimensional librations of a dumbbell-shaped satellite over an oblate Earth. *WCLJY Internal Memo* **58-54,** Wright Patterson Air Force Base, Ohio.
126. Poynting, J. H. (1920). "Collected Scientific Papers." Cambridge Univ. Press.
127. Robertson, H. P. (1937). Dynamical effects of radiation in the solar system. *Monthly Notices Roy. Astron. Soc.* **97,** 423–438.
128. Wyatt, S. P. and Whipple, F. L. (1950). The Poynting–Robertson effect on meteor orbits. *Astrophys. J.* **111,** 134–141.
129. Garwin, L. I. (1958). Solar sailing—a practical method of propulsion within the solar system. *Jet Propulsion* **28,** 188–190.
130. Tsu, T. C. (1959). Interplanetary travel by solar sail. *ARS Journal* **29,** 422.

131. Bergmann, P. G. (1944). "Introduction to the Theory of Relativity." Prentice-Hall, New York.
132. Gilvarry, J. J. (1953). Relativity advances of the perihelia of minor planets. *Publs. Astron. Soc. Pacific* **65,** 173–178.
133. La Paz, Lincoln. (1954). Advances of the perigees of Earth-satellites predicted by general relativity. *Publs. Astron. Soc. Pacific* **66,** 13–18.
134. Baker, R. M. L., Jr. (1959). Astrodynamics. *IRE Student Quarterly,* May, 6–9.
135. Bock, C. D. and Mundo, J. M. (1959). Guidance techniques for interplanetary travel. *ARS Journal* **29,** 931–940.
136. Larmore, L. (1959). Celestial observations for space navigation. *Aero/Space Engng.* **18,** 37.
137. "The American Ephemeris and Nautical Almanac, 1960." U.S.G.P.O., Washington, 1958.
138. Van der Waerden, B. L. (1959). The irregular rotation of the earth. *Astron. J.* **64,** 96–115.
139. Spencer Jones, Sir H. (1939). The rotation of the Earth and the secular accelerations of the Sun, Moon and Planets. *Monthly Notices Roy. Astron. Soc.* **99,** 541–558.
140. Spencer Jones, Sir H. (1950). The system of astronomical constants. *Bull. Astron.* **15,** 247–263.
141. Brouwer, D. (1952). A study of the changes in the rate of rotation of the Earth. *Astron. J.* **57,** 125–146.
142. Herrick, Samuel. (1959). Precision orbits and observation reduction. *UCLA Contribution to Astrodynamics, No.* **1.**
143. Bouwers, A. (1950). "Achievements in Optics." Elsevier, New York.
144. Henize, K. G. (1957). The Baker-Nunn satellite tracking camera. *Sky and Telescope* **16,** 108–111.
145. Smart, W. M. (1956). "Spherical Astronomy." 3rd ed. Cambridge Univ. Press.
146. Andersen, N. Y., Packer, L. S., and Ford, J. W. (1959). A scientific investigation into photographic reconnaissance from space vehicles. *Cornell Aeronautical Laboratory Inc. Report No.* **VF-1260-P-3.**
147. Tuve, M. A., Ford, W. K., Jr., Hall, J. S., and Bain, W. A. (1959). Results of preliminary tests of cascade image converters. *Publs. Astron. Soc. Pacific* **70,** 592.
148. Bowen, E. G. (1954). "A Textbook of Radar." Cambridge Univ. Press.
149. Mengel, J. T. (1957). Minitrack system design criteria. *Elec. Engn.* **76,** 666–677.
150. Mengel, J. T. and Herget, P. (1958). Tracking satellites by radio. *Sci. American* **198,** 23–29.
151. Fishman, M. (1958). Satellite tracking techniques. *Vistas in Astronautics* **1,** 67–70.
152. Schroeder, C. A., Looney, C. H., and Carpenter, H. E., Jr. (1957). Project Vanguard Report No. 18: Minitrack Report No. 1—Phase Measurement. *Naval Research Lab. Rept. No.* **4995.**
153. Simas, V. R. (1958). Project Vanguard Report No. 24, Minitrack Report No. 4N—Satellite Telemetry Receiver System, *Naval Research Lab. Rept.* **5065.**
154. Nielson, C. L. (1958). Principals and applications of phase-lock detection in phase-coherent systems. *Jet Propulsion* **28,** 541–547.
155. Richter, H. L., Jr., Sampson, W. F., and Stevens, R. (1958). Microlock: a minimum weight radio instrumentation system for a satellite. *Jet Propulsion* **28,** 523–531.
156. Crooks, J. W. (1959). A simplified high precision 200-million-mile tracking, guidance

and communication system. *4th Symposium on Ballistic Missile and Space Technology, UCLA.*
157. Sternke, E. C. (1959). Doppler velocity and position study. *Aeronutronic Report No.* **U-356.**
158. Guier, W. H. and Weiffenbach, G. C. (1958). Theoretical analysis of doppler radio signals from earth satellites. Johns Hopkins Univ. Applied Phys. Lab. *Bumblebee Report No.* **276,** April.
159. Breakwell, J. V., Gillespie, R. W., and Stanley, R. (1959). Researches in interplanetary transfer. Paper presented to the ARS Washington meeting.
160. Karrenberg, H. K. and Arthur, P. D. (1959). Interplanetary ballistic orbits. *ARS Reprint No.* **870–59.**
161. Hohmann, W. (1925). "Die Erreich barkeit der Himmels Korper." R. Oldenbourg, Munich.
162. Baker, R. M. L., Jr. (1958). Practical limitations on orbit determination. *Inst. of Aero. Sci. Nat. Meeting, Los Angeles.*
163. Baker, R. M. L., Jr. (1958). Note on interplanetary navigation. *Jet Propulsion* **28,** 834–835.
164. Bock, C. D. (1959). High-precision stellar navigator for interplanetary guidance. Paper presented to the *4th Symposium on Ballistic Missiles and Space Technology, UCLA.*
165. Parkinson, R. S., Jones, H. M., and Shapiro, I. I. 1960. Effects of solar radiation pressure on earth satellite orbits. *Science,* **131,** No. 3404, 920–921.
166. Musen, P., Bryant, R., and Bailie, A. 1960. Perturbations in perigee height of Vanguard I. *Science,* **131,** No. 3404, 935–936.
167. Charlier, C. V. L., *Medd. Lunds Obs.* No. 46.
168. Crommelin, A. C. D. (1927) *J. Brit. Astron. Assoc.* Circ. No. 55.
169. Makemson, M. W. (1930). The Orbit of Comet f1927 (Gale) with Special Reference to the Question of Double Solutions. *Lick Observatory Bull.* No. 426.
170. Leuschner, A. O. (1913). *Lick Observatory Publ.,* **7.**
171. Beard, D. B., and Johnson, F. S. (1960). Charge and magnetic field interaction with satellites. *J. Geophys. Research* **65,** No. 1, 1–7.
172. King-Hele, D. G., Cook, G. E., and Walker, D. M. C. (1959). The contraction of satellite orbits under the influence of air drag. *Royal Aircraft Establishment Technical Note G-W* **533,** Ministry of Aviation, London, November, 1959.
173. Miele, A. (1960). Theorem of image trajectories in the earth-moon space. Paper presented at the *XI Intern. Astronaut. Federation Congr., Stockholm, 1960.*
174. Tolman, R. C. (1938). "The Principles of Statistical Mechanics." Oxford Univ. Press, London and New York.
175. Markowitz, W. (1954). Photographic determination of the moon's position and applications to the measure of time, rotation of the earth, and geodesy. *Astron. J.* **59,** 69.

EXERCISES

FUNDAMENTALS AND BACKGROUND

1. Compute the semimajor axis of a "24-hour" geocentric satellite given that the period of a geocentric surface circular satellite is 84.490 minutes. Should the "hours" be sidereal or solar, i.e., should they be defined as $\frac{1}{24}$ of the time that the Earth rotates 360° relative to the stars or to the Sun? What is the speed of the "24-hour" satellite in terms of surface-circular satellite speed if it is on a circular orbit?

2. Sketch an Intercontinental Ballistic Missile orbit as it would appear if the Earth were reduced to a mass point. Identify perigee and apogee and indicate the **P** and **Q** directions.

3. A space vehicle orbit from a massless Earth to a massless Venus has a semimajor axis of 0.8617 a.u. (astronomical units). Determine the transit time in years if the vehicle left the Earth at aphelion and reached Venus at perihelion. Is this a Hohmann transfer orbit? (Neglect all non two-body perturbations.)

4. What does "Bode's Law" predict for the semimajor axis of Pluto ($N = 7$) and how does this compare with its true value of 39.5 a.u.?

5. Some Martians are planning a trip to one of their Moons, Deimos, which is about 7 Martian radii away from Mars' center traveling on an (assumed) circular orbit. What impulsive takeoff speed would their Moon ship require to reach Deimos on a rectilinear transfer orbit at its apareon, if the surface circular satellite speed for Mars is 3.6 km/sec. Assume that the mass of Deimos is negligible and that Mars is spherical.

6. Given that the escape or "parabolic" speed at the Earth's equator is 11.180 km/sec and that the speed of a rocket "very far" from the Earth is 5 km/sec (i.e., $r \gg a_e$), what is the impulsive takeoff speed of the rocket at the equator? Suppose that the vehicle burned out in a horizontal attitude headed due East, what would be the burnout speed if the Earth's rotation is considered? (Neglect the atmosphere and asphericity of the Earth.)

7. Given that the eccentric anomaly is $\pi/4$ at 7:57 p.m., when was the last perigee passage of a geocentric satellite having $a = 4$ Earth radii and $e = \pi/4\sqrt{2}$ (note that $k_e = 0.07436$)?

8. Show from the *vis-viva* integral that the ratio of the orbital speed at the perifocus to that at the apofocus is $(1 + e)/(1 - e)$.

9. Mars is at a distance of 1.52 a.u. from the Sun. Suppose one launches from an assumed massless Earth at the proper time to achieve an impact with (an assumed massless) Mars. Furthermore, let us choose that specific heliocentric space-vehicle orbit to Mars whose perihelion is at the Earth at launch and whose aphelion is at Mars at impact. What would be the *relative* velocity between the Earth and the space vehicle at launch and how long would the trip take? (Assume a circular Martian orbit and no perturbative forces.)

10. What is the longest possible transit time to the *distance* of the Moon (assumed to be at a distance of 60 Earth radii)? What initial speed is required at the Earth's equator for an Eastward launch? (Neglect all non two-body perturbative forces including the attraction of the Moon.)

11. The mean motions n of the minor planets Ceres and Medusa are $711''.2414$ and $1105''.8897$ per day, respectively. What are their semi-major axes in a.u.'s and their periods in years? Note that the mean motion of a circular heliocentric satellite 1 a.u. from the Sun (e.g., the Earth) has a mean motion of 2π radians or 360° per year or 0.985,607° per day.

12. Find the time-average length and the angle-average length of the radius vector of an elliptical orbit. See Moulton[13] p. 154.

13. The Vth satellite of Jupiter has approximately a 12-hour period and is 112,600 miles from the jovicenter. If Jupiter has a diameter of 87,000 miles, what is the speed of a surface circular satellite? Assume that the Vth satellite's orbit is circular. Suppose that you were traveling from the satellite (Moon) of Jupiter called Ganymede (which is larger than Mercury) situated at a distance of 664,200 miles from the jovicenter. What would be the vehicle's landing speed on the Vth satellite assuming it to be essentially massless, i.e., what would be the vehicle's relative velocity with respect to the Vth satellite? Assume a Hohmann transfer orbit.

14. Given a range of total speeds available to launch a space vehicle from burnout at a horizontal attitude at a distance r_1 from the geocenter and to restart it at apogee and inject it onto a final circular orbit with radius a_c, set up an equation that can be employed to compute the values for the radius of the circular orbit as a function of the *total* speed available (initial launch plus final injection).

15. A space vehicle containing two astronauts is proceeding to the Moon on a rectilinear orbit with $a = 50$ Earth radii. Exactly halfway to the Moon one of the astronauts decided that he forgot his TV guide and wants to return to Earth. What minimum impulsive speed would be required to just reverse the motion and how fast would they enter the Earth's atmosphere? How long would it take them to return to Earth if the mean motion, n, of a surface circular satellite was 2π radians or $360°$ per 84.490 minutes? (Neglect all non two-body perturbative forces.)

16. The minor planet Eros exhibits an eccentric angle ($\sin^{-1} e$) amounting to $12°52'48''.2$ and a mean motion n of $2015''.12740$ per day. Find its distance from the Sun 80 days after perihelion by solving Kepler's equation.

17. Two satellites are on the same circular orbit but are separated by $\pi/2$ radians. What incremental decrease in the semimajor axis of the trailing satellite would be necessary in order for it to catch up to the leading satellite in four revolutions?

18. Consider a more sophisticated orbital transfer manuever in which a transfer is accomplished by means of two doubly tangent or Hohmann orbits. The first phase of the transfer is from a circular orbit of radius r_1 to an intermediary circular orbit of radius r_3 and finally to the desired circular orbit of radius r_2. If $r_1 < r_2 < r_3$ what is a general expression for the total speed required? (Neglect all non two-body perturbative forces and assume all velocity increments are added impulsively.)

19. Determine four bands of commensurability between the orbits of Mars and Jupiter (Kirkwood's gaps).

20. Compare the time interval that Halley's comet remains within 1 a.u. of the Sun to the same interval in the case of Encke's comet (for Halley's comet $a = 17.947$ a.u. and $e = 0.967281$ while for Encke's comet $a = 2.219$ a.u. and $e = 0.8458$).

21. In 1858 the osculating two-body elements of the comet Pons-Winnecke were $a = 0.764$ a.u., $e = 0.755$, and $i = 10.8°$; while in 1886 they were $a = 0.886$, $e = 0.726$, and $i = 14.5°$. Utilize Tisserand's criterion to see if the two sets of elements could be correlated to the same comet. In 1945 the osculating elements were $a = 1.160$, $e = 0.655$, and $i = 21.7°$. How well does the 1945 value of Tisserand's criterion fit the older values?

22. The right ascension of Sirius in 1927 was $\alpha = 6^h41^m55\overset{s}{.}87$ and $\delta = -16°36'53\overset{''}{.}7$. What was the rate of change of α and δ due to precession?

23. Sketch approximately the conic for the following cases, showing specifically the perifocus and parameter distance to the same scale in each sketch: $e = 0$, $a = 1$; $e = \frac{1}{2}$, $a = 1$; $e = 1$, $a = 1$; $e = 1$, $a = \infty$, $q = 1$; $e = 1$, $a = -1$, $q = 0$; and $e = 1\frac{1}{2}$, $a = -1$.

24. Given that $p = r^4\dot{v}^2/\mu$ and $D \triangleq r\dot{r}/\sqrt{\mu}$, verify Eqs. (16).

25. Substitute $iF = E$ in Eqs. (15) and thereby derive Eqs. (18).

26. Substitute $\tilde{X} = \sqrt{a}E$ into Eqs. (15) and $\tilde{X} = \sqrt{-a}F$ into Eqs. (18), expand in a power series and thereby generate the universal variable equations found on p. 56. Clearly, convergence can be improved by expanding about some epoch ($t_0 \neq T$), i.e., $\tilde{X} = \sqrt{a}(E - E_o) \triangleq \widehat{X}$. Establish the formula for r in terms of $\widehat{X}$ for this case. See Herrick,[1] Chap. 6.

27. Express the flattening, f, in terms of the eccentricity, e.

28. Given that for the Jodrell Bank radio telescope $f = 1/298.34$, $H = 70/6{,}378{,}145$, $\phi = 53°20'32''$, and $\theta = 6$ hours, compute C, S, X, Y, Z, and $\dot{X}$, $\dot{Y}$, $\dot{Z}$.

29. If the equatorial coordinates of a satellite are $x = 1.5$, $y = 2$, and $z = 0.5$, represent α, δ, h, A, and ρ from Jodrell Bank at the local sidereal time $\theta = 8$ hours.

30. If a space vehicle is observed from Jodrell Bank at $h = 30°$, $A = 60°$ East of North, $\rho = 0.5$ Earth radii, and the local sidereal time is $\theta = 12$ hours, what are the geocentric equatorial coordinates of the vehicle?

31. Prove that

$$\begin{aligned}\mathbf{N} &= \mathbf{I}\cos\Omega + \mathbf{J}\sin\Omega,\\ \mathbf{M} &= \mathbf{H}\cos i + \mathbf{K}\sin i, \text{ and}\\ \mathbf{W} &= -\mathbf{H}\sin i + \mathbf{K}\cos i, \text{ if}\\ \mathbf{H} &\triangleq -\mathbf{I}\sin\Omega + \mathbf{J}\cos\Omega.\end{aligned}$$

and that

$$\begin{aligned}\mathbf{P} &= \mathbf{N}\cos\omega + \mathbf{M}\sin\omega \text{ and}\\ \mathbf{Q} &= -\mathbf{N}\sin\omega + \mathbf{M}\cos\omega.\end{aligned}$$

32. Verify that

$$\begin{aligned}N_x &= \cos\Omega,\ M_x = -\sin\Omega\cos i,\\ N_y &= \sin\Omega,\ M_y = +\cos\Omega\cos i,\\ N_z &= 0, \qquad M_z = \sin i,\\ P_x &= \cos\omega\cos\Omega - \sin\omega\sin\Omega\cos i,\\ P_y &= \cos\omega\sin\Omega + \sin\omega\cos\Omega\cos i,\\ P_z &= \sin\omega\sin i,\\ Q_x &= -\sin\omega\cos\Omega - \cos\omega\sin\Omega\cos i,\\ Q_y &= -\sin\omega\sin\Omega + \cos\omega\cos\Omega\cos i,\\ Q_z &= \cos\omega\sin i,\\ W_x &= \sin\Omega\sin i,\\ W_y &= -\cos\Omega\sin i, \text{ and}\\ W_z &= \cos i.\end{aligned}$$

33. Express i, Ω, and ω as functions of the equatorial components of the unit vectors **P**, **Q**, and **W**.

34. If the Earth were homogeneous in spherically symmetric shells and if we lived on a satellite describing a nearly circular orbit about the Earth, what would be the logical choice for the units of time and distance? What, basically, would limit the accuracy, e.g., for the distance to the Moon in terms of our unit of distance, if the Moon's mass was negligibly small?

35. Substitute $r = a(1 - \cos E)$ into the rectilinear form of the *vis-viva* integral $\dot{r}^2 = \mu(2/r - 1/a)$ and obtain Kepler's equation in its simplified rectilinear form.

36. Explain how, if you were on the Moon, you would determine the latitude of your Moon base, e.g., carefully explain the significance of selenodetic, selenocentric, and astronomical latitude and discuss how they might be obtained. On the lunar hemisphere facing the Earth, how might you utilize the Earth for longitude determination? What special provisions should you make in this regard?

37. What is the difference between geometric and geopotential altitude at 100 km?

38. Suppose that as our Sun moved through interstellar space with an average relative velocity with respect to the neighboring stars of 20 km/sec, it attracted to itself a mesometeorite that originated in interstellar space. Furthermore, suppose that this mesometeorite took up a retrograde hyperbolic orbit about the Sun in the plane of the ecliptic with a perihelion distance of 1 a.u. and impacted the Earth. Assuming the Earth's attraction to be a negligible effect, what is the speed with which the mesometeorite enters the Earth's atmosphere? Could the situation be modified so that this entry speed would be greater still assuming an approach speed to the solar system, $\dot{s}_\infty$, of 20 km/sec? Suppose the mesometeorite were instead on a very elongated heliocentric orbit (e.g., $a = 1000$ a.u.) and not from interstellar space, what would its maximum entry speed be in this case?

39. Spurred on by recent spectrographic studies, which showed that Halley's Comet is completely smog-free, a group of space experts from Los Angeles have planned an expedition there during the Comet's next passage around the Sun. They wish to leave the Earth at the point where it crosses the major axes of Halley's Comet's orbit and arrive at the Comet as it passes closest to the Sun. Sketch a transfer orbit that is tangent to the Earth's orbit at launch and Halley's comet's orbit at landing (all of the orbits assumed to be coplanar). If a vertical ascent from the Earth were utilized, what time of day would the launch ing take place and what total speed would be required for a "soft" landing on Halley's Comet? How far from the Sun is Halley's Comet at the time of the launch from the Earth? See Exercise **20**.

40. Utilizing the fact that the acceleration of gravity is proportional to the mass and inversely proportional to the square of the distance, compute the acceleration of gravity in Earth "g's" at the surfaces of Venus, Moon, Mars, and Jupiter. Recognizing that $k_s/k_{\text{planet}} = m_\odot/m_{\text{planet}}$, compute k for each of these objects.

MORE DETAILED ANALYSES

1. By substituting $\tilde{X} = \sqrt{a}E$ into Kepler's equation, expanding, and by identifying $\tilde{M}$ with $a^{3/2}M$, derive the universal variable formulation of Kepler's equation found on p. 118.

2. Given the equatorial coordinates and velocities of a space vehicle: $x = 1$, $y = 2$, $z = 3$ Earth radii and $\dot{x} = 0.5$, $\dot{y} = 1.5$, $\dot{z} = 2$ Earth's surface circular satellite speeds, determine orbital elements a, e, M_o, P_x, P_y, P_z, Q_x, Q_y, and Q_z. What are the values of the space vehicle's equatorial coordinates two hours later?

3. Given the following set of heliocentric satellite coordinates in a.u.'s:

	t_1	t_2	t_3
x	2.24752	2.33583	2.40744
y	−0.64645	−0.37110	0.00279
z	−0.24502	−0.20856	−0.15590

Compute the orbital elements as in **2** by means of the Gibbsian procedure.

4. If $t_1 = 0$, $t_2 = 24^d$, and $t_3 = 56$ in Exercise **3** compute the orbital elements by means of the Herrick-Gibbs formulas.

5. Assume that observations of a geocentric circular satellite are obtained from on board another geocentric circular satellite designed as an observatory. In this case the radius vector from the observatory to the geocenter at the jth time can be expressed by

$$\mathbf{R}_j = -a_1(c_{1j} \cdot \mathbf{U}_{01} + s_{1j} \cdot \mathbf{V}_{01})$$

where a_1 is the semimajor axis of the circular orbit; $c_{1j} \triangleq \cos n_1(t_j - t_0)$ $s_{1j} \triangleq \sin n_1(t_j - t_0)$ (where n_1 is the mean motion $= k_e \sqrt{\mu}/a_1^{3/2}$ and t_0 is the epoch); and $\mathbf{U}_{01}$ and $\mathbf{V}_{01}$ are unit vectors that define the position of the observatory at the epoch, i.e., $\mathbf{U}_{01} = \mathbf{R}_0/a_1$ and $\mathbf{V}_{01} = \dot{\mathbf{R}}_s/\dot{s}_1$. By algebraically eliminating the four unknowns $\mathbf{U}_0 \cdot \mathbf{U}_{01}$, $\mathbf{U}_0 \cdot \mathbf{V}_{01}$, $\mathbf{V}_0 \cdot \mathbf{U}_{01}$, $\mathbf{V}_0 \cdot \mathbf{V}_{01}$, set up an equation similar to Eq. (113) and show how it can be solved for the semimajor axis of the observed satellite by means of range measurements alone. See reference 70. Could the unit vector interrelationships $\mathbf{V}_0 \cdot \mathbf{U}_0 = 0$, $\mathbf{U}_0 \cdot \mathbf{U}_0 = 1$, and $\mathbf{V}_0 \cdot \mathbf{V}_0 = 1$ be utilized in order to decrease the required number of observations? Since for trigonometric relationships there are an infinite number of roots, what limits on a could be established to narrow down the search for roots?

6. Consider a geocentric satellite whose direction cosines and derivatives are measured from Palomar Mountain Observatory ($r_c \sin \phi' = 0.54685$ and $r_c \cos \phi' = 0.83635$) and found to be

$$\begin{aligned} L_x &= +0.9225, & \dot{L}_x &= +0.0474, & \ddot{L}_x &= -0.0783 \\ L_y &= +0.0519, & \dot{L}_y &= +0.0205, & \ddot{L}_y &= +0.2913 \\ L_z &= +0.3826, & \dot{L}_z &= -0.1158, & \ddot{L}_z &= +0.1003. \end{aligned}$$

Determine the orbit by the Laplacian procedure.

7. Establish a range-rate (and higher order derivatives) Laplacian procedure for determining the orbit of a rectilinear parabolic probe orbit. Generalize the method to the case where the probe is illuminated by a radar transmitter at station $\mathbf{R}_1$ and picked up by a receiver at station $\mathbf{R}_2$. In this case the range-rate measurement will be $\dot{\rho} = \boldsymbol{\varrho}_{1\Delta} \cdot \dot{\boldsymbol{\varrho}}_{1\Delta}/\rho_{1\Delta} + \boldsymbol{\varrho}_{2\Delta} \cdot \dot{\boldsymbol{\varrho}}_{2\Delta}/\rho_{2\Delta}$.

8. On a lunar probe orbit let the takeoff point be at $x = 1$, $y = 0$, $z = 0$ Earth radii and the landing point (center of an assumed massless Moon) be at $x = -60$, $y = -12$, and $z = 1$ Earth radii. If the total transit time is to be 80 hr what are the orbital elements of the lunar probe orbit?

9. For nearly-rectilinear orbits it is difficult, if not impossible, to differentially correct from ellipses over to hyperbolas. If, however, one utilizes as elements $\tilde{M}_0$, $1/a$, $c^* \triangleq \sqrt{p} \cos \phi^*$, $s^* \triangleq \sqrt{p} \sin \phi^*$, and the right ascention, α_0, and the declination, δ_0, of the preliminary rectilinear orbit, then it is possible to carry out a differential correction. With the definition that ϕ^* is the angle between the $\mathbf{W}$ of the orbit plane and the equatorial system meridian plane that includes $\mathbf{U}_0$ of the rectilinear orbit, establish the appropriate analytical partial derivations for the differential correction. See reference 70.

10. Utilizing Eq. (155) verify that the position of a synodic satellite of Jupiter is about 4.84 a.u. if ϵ/λ = Jupiter Mass/Sun Mass = 1/1046.

11. If the subscript B denotes the barycenter, derive the following equation of motion in the barycentric form (see Herrick,[1] Chapter 15):

$$\frac{d^2x_B}{dt^2} = -k^2\left(\sum_{j=1}^{n} m_j\right)\frac{x_{B2}}{x_{B2}{}^3} + k^2 \sum_{\substack{j=1\\ j\neq 2}}^{n} m_j x_{j2}\left(\frac{1}{r_{B2}{}^3} - \frac{1}{r_{j2}{}^3}\right)$$

$$x \rightarrow y,\ z.$$

12. If the wind is 176 miles per hour (10^{-2} surface circular satellite speed) due North at the equator during the vertical re-entry of a space vehicle exhibiting the position and velocity components $x = 1.1$, $y = 1.1$, $z = 0$, $\dot{x} = 0.5$, $\dot{y} = 0.5$, $\dot{z} = 0$, what are the vehicle's velocity components relative to the atmosphere?

13. Verify Eq. (179).

14. Prove that $\dot{v} = \sqrt{\mu p}/r^2$, $\dot{E} = \sqrt{\mu/a}/r$, $\dot{M} = n/k$, and $M' = v'\sqrt{1-e^2} - 2r\dot{r}'/\sqrt{\mu a}$.

15. Establish the gravity-free drag orbit formulas in a rotating coordinate system.

16. Extend section 9.2.3.1 to include also the perturbative variation of ω.

17. How might a rotation Earth's atmosphere be included in the drag general perturbations analysis?

18. Consider a flat plate moving in free molecule flow at an angle θ between the plate and its atmospheric velocity $\mathbf{v}$, if $T = 300°K$ and the accommodation coefficient equals zero, prove that the lift-to-drag ratio is $\sin 2\theta/(1 - \cos 2\theta)$. What would the ratio be if $T = 0°K$ and the accommodation coefficient equals unity?

19. What is the ratio of C_D to C_{D0} for a meteorite for which $\mathbf{v} = 9.8$, $m_e/m_0 = 2$, $\bar{\epsilon} = 0.13$, $\beta = 1 \times 10^{-13}$, $V_{c0} = 7.905 \times 10^5$ cm/sec, and $\mathbf{v}_t = 2$? (See reference 19.)

20. What is the charge on a space vehicle passing through a plasma having a temperature $T = 1000°K$ at a speed $\mathbf{v} = 11$ km/sec?

21. What is the relativistic difference in rate between a clock on the Earth's equator and one on a circular geocentric satellite orbit at an altitude of 0.1 Earth radii?

22. Compute the local sidereal time at the Steward Observatory at the University of Arizona (west longitude $7^h23^m47^s.68$) at 8:05 p.m. (MST) August 30, 1956. What was the E.T.?

23. Given the measurements of the images of a space vehicle and three stars on a photographic plate, and the ideal coordinates of the three stars from a star catalog, algebraically eliminate the plate constants from Eq. (276) and solve for the true or standard plate coordinates of the space vehicle. How could a star's ξ,η be obtained from its α,δ?

24. Consider a specularly reflecting spherical balloon satellite having a diameter of 100 meters and a reflectivity of 90% observed at a distance of 200 km and at an altitude h of 60°. What would be its magnitude?

25. Assuming only the attraction of Jupiter and the Sun, what would be Jupiter's "tidal radius"? For simplicity consider only one object in conjunction with Jupiter and the Sun. Jupiter's mass is 1/1046 solar masses. What would be the Moon's tidal radius?

26. Given the two apsidal positions on a Hohmann orbit to Mars, determine the orbital elements a and e for transfer from an assumed circular Earth orbit to the perihelion and to the aphelion of the Martian orbit ($e_{♂} = 0.09335$ and $a_{♂} = 1.5237$). What are the relative velocities of the interplanetary vehicle with respect to the Earth at the beginning and Mars at termination? How long will the two different voyages take? Using elliptic integrals of the second kind how far will the two vehicles travel?

27. In order to insure a rendezvous with Venus it is necessary to specify a proper launch date. Prove that the proper launch date for a Venusian voyage lasting N days on a transfer orbit having an angle between the heliocentric radius vector to the vehicle at launch and the heliocentric radius vector to the vehicle at landing of $d°$ is Δt days *after some epoch*, where

$$\Delta t = [d° - (L_{♀} + Nn_{♀}) + L_{\oplus}]/(n_{♀} - n_{\oplus}).$$

In this formula $n_{♀}$ and $n_{\oplus}$ are the mean motions of Venus and Earth, respectively, in degrees per day (assume that both bodies move on coplaner circular orbits), $L_{♀}$ is the mean longitude of Venus at the epoch and $L_{\oplus}$ is the mean longitude of the Earth at the same epoch. As an example, take $N = 146$ days, $d° = 180°$, and the epoch as June 15, 1960 (where from p. 169 of the 1960 *American Ephemeris* $L_{♀} \cong 75\overset{\circ}{.}8$ and from p. 50 $L_{\oplus}$ (180° plus the Sun's mean longitude) $\cong 263\overset{\circ}{.}3$), and compute Δt (see Chap. 9 of Herrick[1]).

28. Compute the three injection speeds at $r = 1.1$ Earth radii for an interplanetary space vehicle launched from an equatorial launch site into the plane of the ecliptic bound for Venus and for Mars (both at Mars' perihelion and aphelion) on a doubly tangent or Hohmann transfer orbit. Assume that the last booster stage burns out at a horizontal attitude directly above the equator and neglect the Earth's atmosphere and asphericity. How could you accomplish the same missions by launching due north? Sketch these polar launches and indicate the time of day and season of the year. What would be the new launch speeds?

29. Given a dumbbell-shaped satellite on a circular geocentric orbit with a separation between the dumbs of $2e$. For small angle displacement about a position of vertical stable equilibrium prove that the periodicity of the libration is $\sqrt{3}$ times the orbital period. If the orbit were elliptical prove that the motion follows Mathieu's equation. (See references 31, 32, and 33.)

30. One rather interesting simple application of Hamiltonian mechanics to astrodynamics that yields succinct results is the application to *dynamical reversibility*. Those familiar with Lagrange's equations will remember that L does not contain time explicitly and that the Lagrangian function for conservative mechanical systems is known to be a quadratic or, in any event, an even function of the velocity components and position components in inertial coordinates. Under these circumstances verify the results of A. Miele[173] who showed that any Earth-to-Moon orbit (circular unperturbed Moon orbit assumed) has a corresponding Moon-to-Earth orbit that is identical in all respects except that time is run "backwards," i.e., impact on the forward hemisphere of the Moon is replaced by takeoff from the trailing hemisphere when the motion of all three bodies is reversed. What problems would be encountered if solar perturbations were included? For an elliptical lunar orbit can the principle be applied to perigee and apogee lunar landing and takeoff? Can this principle also be extended to interplanetary orbits? Another interesting principle is that of *dynamical reflectivity* (which can also be proved on the basis of Lagrange's equations; see Tolman[174] pp. 102–105), i.e., that any motion of a dynamical system and any mirror image of that motion would be equally possible—the position and orientation of the reflecting plane being chosen arbitrarily. How does this principle relate to lunar and interplanetary trajectories? In the above it is tacitly assumed that all three bodies are of finite mass, but that the perturbations of the lunar vehicle on the Earth and Moon are negligibly small. Suppose that the vehicle is assumed to be completely massless, i.e., assume the *restricted three-body problem*. Is the system still conservative? Is there any effect on the above-stated principles in this case?

AUTHOR INDEX

Numbers in parentheses are reference numbers and are inserted to enable the reader to locate a reference when the author's name is not mentioned at the point of reference in the text. Numbers in italics show the page on which the reference is listed.

T

U

V

W

Y

Z

SUBJECT INDEX

D

E

N

S

W

Z

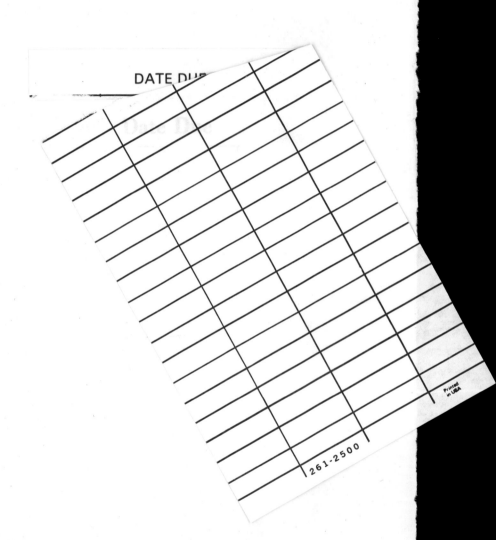